McGraw-Hill Astronomical Series

EDWARD ARTHUR FATH, *Consulting Editor*

FATH · Elements of Astronomy

HYNEK · Astrophysics

NASSAU · Practical Astronomy

THE ELEMENTS OF ASTRONOMY

The Hale 200-inch telescope of the Palomar Observatory. (*Mt. Wilson and Palomar Observatories.*)

THE ELEMENTS OF ASTRONOMY

*A Nonmathematical Textbook for Use as an Introduction
to the Subject in Colleges, Universities, etc.,
and for the General Reader*

EDWARD ARTHUR FATH

Former Professor of Astronomy in Carleton College

FIFTH EDITION

McGRAW-HILL BOOK COMPANY, INC.

New York   Toronto   London

1955

THE ELEMENTS OF ASTRONOMY

THE MAPLE PRESS COMPANY, YORK, PA.

PREFACE

This book is the result of attempting to present the subject matter of astronomy to many classes of college students, over half of whom had had no mathematics beyond one year of algebra and one year of plane geometry in high school. In consequence, very little is presented in mathematical form, but an effort has been made to develop the necessary physical concepts so that at the close of the course the student would be in possession of the main facts of the subject as well as have an elementary understanding of the principles and methods involved in modern astronomical investigation.

The increasing use of the metric system has led the author to believe that the time has come to adopt it in a textbook of this character. The equivalents in the English system of units are given in parentheses after the metric values for those who do not care to make the change of systems.

Whenever possible, credit is given to the person originating an idea or beginning a new line of investigation. In many cases, however, it seemed impossible to trace matters to their sources, as so much is now common knowledge and the names of originators appear to be lost.

Permission to use photographic material or drawings was freely given by many and is hereby gratefully acknowledged. The source of each illustration is given in the appropriate place.

In the years that have elapsed since the fourth edition was issued much new observational material has been obtained and many new ideas have been developed. The changes in viewpoint arising from the shifting of the zero point of the period-luminosity law for the classical cepheids are far-reaching. It is hoped that no important discovery published up to the time of going to press has been omitted.

Special acknowledgments are due Dr. Walter O. Roberts for many fruitful suggestions for the chapters on the sun and stars; to Dr. Albert W. Recht for permission to use the library of the Chamberlin Observatory; and to Dr. W. F. G. Swann for the statement of the Einstein theory of relativity in Sec. 173.

Edward Arthur Fath

CONTENTS

CHAPTER 1

INTRODUCTION

Astronomy is the science of the heavenly bodies. These include the sun, moon, planets and satellites, comets, stars, and nebulae. The pursuit of astronomy implies not only a study of these bodies with relation to their distances, dimensions, movements, physical characteristics, and the laws which govern them, but also the attempt to determine both their past and future.

1. Early Astronomy. When man was nothing more than a savage, it was necessary for him to pay some attention to astronomical occurrences, even if only to the extent of recognizing the daily return of the sun or the connection between the growth of vegetation and the seasons.

At a later stage of development he used the day, month, and year as units of time, and many religious observances were timed by the position of sun or moon in the sky. There is some evidence that at least certain of the Egyptian pyramids were used in making astronomical observations and that ancient temples and other places of worship were frequently oriented with respect to sun or stars.

So far as can be determined, astronomy was the first of the sciences to be developed by the ancients, and its study, without doubt, played an important part in the intellectual development of ancient peoples. Old records of the Chinese, writings on Babylonian tablets, and remnants from the chronicles of the early Egyptians all show evidence of the cultivation of astronomy. They contain records of eclipses of sun and moon, the appearance of bright comets, the conjunctions of planets, etc.

Ancient navigators used the stars to guide them when they made their voyages, caravans crossing the deserts did likewise, and the old-time shepherd or farmer was aided in his pursuits by paying attention to sun and stars.

2. Place of Astronomy among the Sciences. Astronomy is the only one of the sciences which gives man some knowledge of the entire visible universe. Other sciences devote their attention to some one phase of the universe and play their part in getting an understanding of some of the fundamental laws governing matter and energy, but they restrict them-

1

selves, almost exclusively, to those phases of nature which are in evidence upon the earth, which is only an insignificant part of the whole.   Astronomy, however, strives to unravel the secrets of nature, not only upon the earth but also throughout all space within reach of the most powerful instruments, and thus acquaints man with his immediate surroundings as well as with what is going on in regions far removed from ordinary, everyday experience and contacts.   One of the goals of astronomy may be said to be to make man feel "at home" in the universe.

3. Relation of Astronomy to Other Sciences. In pursuing as its aim the understanding of the universe, astronomy is indebted to other sciences for much of its progress.   It utilizes the information gathered by the students of physics, chemistry, geology, and biology as well as all the resources of mathematics.   It repays the debt by unfolding to these sciences the vast laboratories in sun, stars, and nebulae, where matter is met with in a variety of forms and under conditions which cannot as yet be duplicated on the earth.

The solution of some astronomical problems has been the direct cause of some of the greatest developments in mathematics.   Newton's "Principia" stands as one of the greatest products of the human intellect. It was the desire to solve the problem of the motions of the members of the solar system which led its author to produce it.

4. Practical Aspects of Astronomy. Accurate time, land surveys, international boundaries, map making, and navigation are directly dependent upon astronomical observations.

Accurate time is one of the necessities of modern civilization.   The astronomer sets his clocks by means of observations of the stars, and the official time of all civilized countries is obtained from the clocks in the astronomical observatories.

Land surveys depend upon a knowledge of true north-and-south lines. These are determined by astronomical observations and are the prime meridians upon which accurate surveys depend.

When the 49th parallel of latitude was decided upon as part of the boundary line between the United States and Canada, the international commission appointed to mark this line included eminent astronomers from both countries, by whose observations of the stars the exact location was determined.

Map making depends upon an exact knowledge of the shape and the size of the earth and the locations of the meridians and parallels.   This knowledge is directly dependent upon observations of the stars whose exact positions in the heavens have been determined by generations of astronomers.

The *location of a ship at sea* is obtained by astronomical observations and the errors of the compass are found by comparing it with known directions in the sky.   Without such knowledge modern commerce would

be greatly handicapped and it is doubtful if it could be carried on successfully if this information were lacking.

Long-distance flying, particularly over the ocean, requires careful
navigation of the plane. This is accomplished by observations of the
heavenly bodies in much the same way as a mariner navigates his ship
at sea.

It is thus evident that the modern world is greatly indebted to astronomy, which supplies it with time, directions, positions on the earth, and
their relationships.

Another phase of astronomy is being developed at the present time which
presages vast possibilities of service to mankind. The weather and the climate
of any region on the earth are largely dependent, in the last analysis, upon the
heat which comes from the sun. A careful study of the heat received from this
body shows that the amount undergoes minute changes from day to day and
larger variations in longer periods of time. A correlation has been shown to
exist between the amount of heat received at any time and the mean temperatures,
several days later, at certain selected stations. This correlation is so close that
it is used to forecast temperatures with considerable success. It seems possible,
therefore, that in time such forecasts can be made for any place on the earth.
It also seems possible that the law of variation of the sun's heat will ultimately be
discovered and the heat to be received in a month or a year thus rendered predict-
able. When this shall be accomplished, long-range weather forecasts will almost
certainly follow. The immense value to agriculture of the previous knowledge
that a certain summer will be hot, cold, wet, or dry can hardly be overestimated
if the world's food supply continues to come from the land. Such a development
of astronomy is as yet little more than a dream, but it does not seem wholly
outside the realm of possibility.

5. Place of Astronomy in Education. The greatest value of astronomy
to the average individual at the present time lies in its appeal to the
intellect. The contemplation of great worlds outside the earth; the
study of the stars individually, in clusters, or in vast systems; the realization that the universe is a universe of order and subject to law; the gradual
discovery of the laws in accordance with which it operates and the thoughts
aroused as to its origin, purpose, and future development will more than
repay the investment of time and effort necessary to make them possible.

To the great majority the universe is practically a sealed book. We exert
ourselves through great educational systems, maintained at enormous expense,
to make the student acquainted with his city, state, and nation as well as with
foreign lands, and we endeavor to acquaint him with the laws of nature as they
operate on this small earth, so that he shall feel in touch with his environment,
but, thus far, we have done very little to make him acquainted with the vast
universe in which he finds himself, and we allow him to spend his entire life in
ignorance of the wonderful realms outside the earth. It is important that he be

acquainted with the earth and what it contains, but it seems a great mistake to keep his thoughts forever centered on this globe and not allow them to go out to the stars.

6. Subdivisions of Astronomy. According to purpose and method, astronomy may be divided into four main branches: astrometry, practical astronomy, theoretical astronomy, and astrophysics.

Astrometry deals primarily with the measurement of the positions, distances, dimensions, and apparent motions of the heavenly bodies; *practical astronomy* deals with such matters as the determination of time, latitude, and longitude; *theoretical astronomy* devotes itself to the mathematical study of the motions of the heavenly bodies under the influence of gravitation; and *astrophysics* deals with their physical and chemical characteristics, such as brightness, temperature, composition, magnetic properties, and motion in the line of sight as determined by the spectrograph. There is, however, no sharp distinction between these various parts of the subject, each being more or less connected with or dependent upon the others.

CHAPTER 2

THE CELESTIAL SPHERE

7. Celestial Sphere. When we look at the sky at night, the stars seem to be fixed on the inside of a spherical surface and we appear to be at the center. This spherical surface is called the *celestial sphere*, but the term includes not only the hemisphere above the horizon but also the hemisphere below. The stars are so far away that we can assume the radius of the sphere to be practically infinite. This implies that any two parallel lines a measurable distance apart, if extended until they reach the celestial sphere, will appear to intersect it at the same point, the "vanishing point" of the two lines.

The celestial sphere is only *apparent*, however, for some of the stars are relatively near and others are far away.

8. Position and Distance on the Celestial Sphere. When two stars are said to have practically the same position in the sky, we mean that they have practically the same direction as seen by the observer. Thus in Fig. 1 stars a and b would be said to be in about the same position in the sky even though b might be 2 or 200 times as far from the observer as a. Two stars are said to be close together when lines drawn to them make only a small angle with each other, and they are said to be far apart when these lines make large angles.

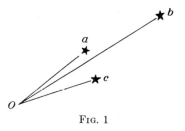

Fig. 1

The observer at O would thus say that star a is closer to star b than to star c, even though in reality a might be many times farther away in space from b than from c. The reason for this is that the real distances to most stars are not known with any degree of accuracy, and we are therefore compelled to resort to direction alone. Hence, distances in the sky must be given in angular measure, in degrees, minutes, and seconds.

Persons who have had no experience in observing sometimes say that two stars look to be a foot apart. This, of course, is misleading unless they also state how far from the eye the foot rule is to be held.   If this information is added, the angular distance can be determined.

Until the student has become accustomed to estimating angles, the following values will be helpful.   A rough measure for an angle of 1° is the apparent diameter of a dime held at arm's length from the eye.   The apparent diameter of sun or moon is about half a degree, while the longest dimension of the bowl of the Big Dipper is about 10°.

9. Coordinate Systems. In the study of elementary algebra we learn something of graphs and the representation of points on a plane.   Thus, if we draw the lines OX and OY (Fig. 2) perpendicular to each other, the

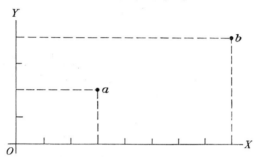

Fig. 2. A rectangular coordinate system.

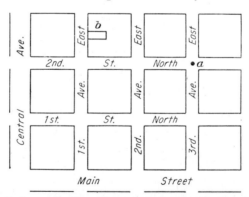

Fig. 3. An application of a rectangular coordinate system.

point a is said to have the *coordinates* 3,2, which means that it is 3 units to the right of the origin O and 2 units above it.   Similarly, the coordinates of point b are 8,4.   Such a method of representing position is often of great convenience.

This principle is often applied to the numbering of streets and houses in a city.   In Fig. 3, a is at the intersection of Avenue 3 East and Second Street North, while a house at b might be located as No. 250 First Avenue Northeast.   Coordinate systems of this kind are known as *rectangular coordinate systems* because the two axes are at right angles to each other. Rectangular coordinate systems are used only on plane surfaces or those so nearly plane that no appreciable errors result.

On a sphere we cannot use a system of rectangular coordinates because of the curvature of the surface of the sphere. We are therefore compelled to adopt what are known as *spherical coordinates* to indicate the position of a body on a sphere.

The principle involved in a spherical-coordinate system may be illustrated by the well-known system of latitudes and longitudes used on the earth. The earth's rotation axis cuts the surface at two opposite points called the poles. Halfway between the poles is the great circle of the equator. The meridians are circles which pass through the poles and intersect the equator at right angles (Fig. 12). The parallels of latitude are secondary circles whose planes are parallel to the plane of the equator.

In this system the equator is known as the *fundamental circle*, the North and South Poles are the *poles of the fundamental circle*, and the meridians and parallels are the two sets of *secondary circles*.

Angular distance north or south of the fundamental circle is called *latitude*. After selecting one of the meridians, such as the meridian through Greenwich, as a *zero circle*, the angle at the pole which this circle makes with the meridian through any other place is called *longitude*. *Latitude* and *longitude* are called the *coordinates* of a point on the earth.

On the celestial sphere various systems of spherical coordinates are used depending upon the choice of the fundamental circle.

THE HORIZON SYSTEM

10. Zenith, Nadir, Horizon. The plumb line indicates the direction of gravity at any point. The point of the celestial sphere where the plumb line extended cuts the sphere overhead is called the *zenith* and the opposite point the *nadir*. The circle of the sphere halfway between zenith and nadir is called the *astronomical horizon*. It might also be defined as the intersection of the celestial sphere by a plane tangent to a level surface at any point on the earth where the observer is located. The plumb line is always perpendicular to a level surface and is therefore perpendicular to the plane of the horizon.

The *visible horizon*, determined by trees, buildings, or elevations of land, must not be confused with the astronomical horizon as defined above.

11. The Horizon System of Circles. The horizon system uses the astronomical horizon as its fundamental circle with its poles at zenith and nadir. Through the zenith and nadir are passed the *vertical circles*, which will be perpendicular to the horizon. A second set of circles, the *parallels of altitude*, are arranged so as to be parallel to the horizon.

In Fig. 4, Z and X are zenith and nadir, respectively, of the observer at O. The horizon circle $NWSE$ lies halfway between them, N being the north point, W the west point, etc. Circles like $ZBXT$ are the vertical circles and those like $CDFG$ are the parallels of altitude.

The vertical circle NZS is called the *celestial meridian* and the vertical circle EZW, which cuts NZS at right angles, is called the *prime vertical*. The celestial meridian and prime vertical intersect at right angles at zenith and nadir.

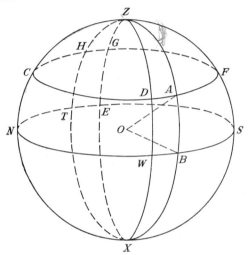

Fig. 4. The horizon system of circles.

12. Altitude and Azimuth. If an observer at O sees a star in the direction OA, then the line OA makes an angle BOA with the plane of the horizon. This angle (in degrees) measures the height of the star above the horizon and is equal to the arc AB, of the vertical circle through A. This angle is called the *altitude* of the star above the horizon. If a star is below the horizon the altitude is given a minus sign. *Altitude is the angular distance from the astronomical horizon measured along a vertical circle.*

The arc AZ measures the angular distance of a star at A from the zenith. It is called the *zenith distance* of A. Zenith distance plus altitude equal 90°.

Altitude alone, however, will not define the star's position, for all points on the parallel of altitude $AFGC$ have the same altitude. The vertical circle ZSX, accordingly, is used as the zero circle, and the angle SZB at the zenith, or its equivalent in degrees, the arc SB, measures the direction from the circle ZSX. This angle SZB is called the *azimuth* of the star A. *Azimuth is the angle at the zenith between the vertical circle through the south point and the vertical circle through the celestial object measured from south through west.*

Azimuth is reckoned all the way around the horizon up to 360°, beginning from the south point and going through the west. Thus, a star H, seen in the ENE, would have an altitude HT and an azimuth SZH equal to 247°.5.

The azimuth as thus defined may be called the *astronomical azimuth*. The navigator usually measures the azimuth from the north point of the horizon, the direction of measurement, clockwise, remaining the same. In this case a star at H would have an azimuth of 67°.5.

The two quantities, *altitude* and *azimuth*, are called the *coordinates* of a celestial body in the horizon system.

13. Disadvantages of Horizon System. The horizon system is of value in locating an object in the sky with reference to the horizon, but it is useful only for a single location, for it is evident that, since each observer has a different zenith from every other observer, no two observers have the same horizon. The altitude and the azimuth of a heavenly body, while being nearly the same if two observers are near each other, will differ greatly if the observers are far apart. Furthermore, since the earth rotates, the altitudes and the azimuths of the heavenly bodies are constantly changing. It is, therefore, desirable to have a system of circles whose positions are referred to the stars themselves. Such a system is the equator system.

THE EQUATOR SYSTEM

14. Relation to the Earth. If we extend the earth's rotation axis until it intersects the celestial sphere, the two points thus determined are called the *celestial poles*. The one in the northern sky is known as the *north celestial pole* and the one in the southern sky the *south celestial pole*. Except for a very slow motion to be considered later, they may be considered fixed among the stars.

The earth's equator lies midway between the terrestrial poles, and its plane is perpendicular to the earth's rotation axis. Accordingly, if we consider the plane of the earth's equator as extending outward indefinitely until it intersects the celestial sphere, this intersection will be a circle, called the *celestial equator*, which will be just halfway between the celestial poles.

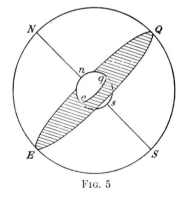

FIG. 5

Figure 5 illustrates this. We are thus presented with a fundamental circle EQ and its poles N and S, and can draw secondary circles just as in the horizon system.

15. Hour Circles and Parallels of Declination. The secondary circles drawn through the celestial poles and perpendicular to the celestial equator are called *hour circles*, while the secondary circles drawn parallel to the celestial equator are called *parallels of declination* (Fig. 6).

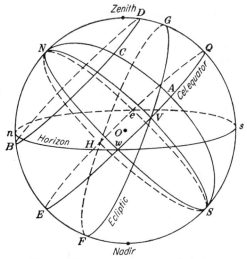

FIG. 6. The equator system of circles.

The *north* and *south points* of the horizon are actually determined by the vertical circle passing through the celestial poles. The hour circle passing through the zenith will, therefore, pass through the north and south points and coincide with the celestial meridian as defined in Sec. 11. We thus have a second way of defining the celestial meridian. A third way would be to say that the celestial meridian is the intersection of the plane of the observer's terrestrial meridian with the celestial sphere.

16. The Equinoxes and Solstices. Because of the earth's annual revolution about the sun the latter appears to move eastward among the stars. This apparent path of the sun around the celestial sphere is known as the *ecliptic*. The plane of the ecliptic makes an angle[1] of approximately 23°.5 with the celestial equator. In Fig. 6 the circle *FG* represents the ecliptic and the circle *EQ* the celestial equator. These intersect at two points *V* and *H*. The point *V*, where the sun crosses the celestial equator from south to north, is called the *vernal equinox*.[2] When the sun is at this point, spring commences in the Northern Hemisphere. The other point *H*, where the sun crosses the celestial equator from north to south, is called the *autumnal equinox*, and the instant of crossing marks the beginning of the northern autumn.

[1] This angle is called the *obliquity of the ecliptic*.
[2] This point is also called the *first of Aries*.

The two points on the ecliptic halfway between the equinoxes are called the *solstices*. The one north of the celestial equator is called the *summer solstice* and the one south of the equator the *winter solstice*, since the sun is at these two points at the beginning of summer and winter, respectively, in the Northern Hemisphere.

17. Right Ascension and Declination. The hour circle *NVS*, passing through the vernal equinox, is used as the zero hour circle, and angles are measured from this circle eastward up to 360°. This coordinate is known as *right ascension*. Thus a star at *C* will have a right ascension of about 15°.

The right ascension of a star is the angle at the celestial pole between the hour circle through the vernal equinox and the hour circle through the star, measured eastward. It could also be defined as the arc of the celestial equator measured eastward from the vernal equinox to the intersection of the hour circle passing through the star with the celestial equator.

The other coordinate in this system is *declination*. It is defined as *the angular distance of a star from the celestial equator measured along the hour circle through the star.* The star at *C* has a declination of about +40°, the plus sign indicating north declination. South declination is indicated by a minus sign. A star at *F* would have a right ascension of about 250° and a declination of −23°.5.

Right ascension is usually measured by means of a clock and it is therefore more convenient, in general, to express this coordinate in time rather than in degrees of arc. For this purpose 1 hr of time is equivalent to 15° of arc. Hence the position of a star at *C* would be given as R.A. 1^h, Dec. +40°, while the position of a star at *F* would be R.A. 16^{h}40^m, Dec. −23°.5.

18. Hour Angle. It is often convenient to use an angle known as *hour angle*. *It is the angle at the pole which any given hour circle makes with the celestial meridian and is measured westward from the meridian.* If the sun is on the celestial equator and just rising, its hour angle is 18^h. Four hours later its hour angle is 22^h, and when it is on the meridian, the hour angle is 0^h.

Sometimes it is convenient to say that an object is a certain number of hours east or west of the meridian, meaning either that it will be on the meridian in that number of hours or that it was on the meridian that many hours ago. This form of expression must not be confused with the term "hour angle" as defined above.

19. Sidereal Hour Angle. There has recently come into use, particularly in air navigation, a term called *sidereal hour angle*. It is defined as *the angle at the pole between the hour circle through the vernal equinox and the hour circle through the star measured westward from the vernal equinox.* The sidereal hour angle of a star is thus equal to 360° minus the right ascension of the star. The use of this angle simplifies certain calculations in navigation.

20. The Ecliptic System. For some purposes another system of coordinates is used. This is called the *ecliptic system* because the ecliptic is taken as the fundamental circle and the poles of the ecliptic, two opposite points 90° from the ecliptic, are used as poles. The poles of the ecliptic are about 23°.5 from the corresponding celestial poles.

The secondary circles passing through the poles of the ecliptic and perpendicular to the ecliptic are called *circles of latitude,* while those drawn parallel to the ecliptic are called *parallels of latitude.*

The coordinates in this system are known as *celestial longitude* and *latitude.* The longitude is measured eastward from the vernal equinox all the way around the sphere, while the latitude is the angular distance north or south of the ecliptic.

The ecliptic system is used when we wish to refer the motions or positions of planets to the sun, which is always in the ecliptic. It is not possible to observe celestial longitude and latitude directly. If they are employed, the right ascension and the declination are determined by observation and then converted into celestial longitude and latitude by calculation.

21. Summary. Table I on page 13 shows the similarity between the various systems considered.

22. Angular Measurement—the Radian. The circumference of a circle is usually divided into 360 equal parts, called *degrees;* the degree is divided into 60 equal parts, called *minutes of arc;* and the minute of arc into 60 equal parts, called *seconds of arc.* These various arcs subtend corresponding angles at the center of the circle which are measured in degrees, minutes, and seconds of angle. Where no ambiguity exists the phrases "of arc" and "of angle" are usually omitted.

If an arc of a circle is laid off equal to the radius, it subtends an angle at the center known as a *radian.* The value of the radian is evidently 360°/2π. In the various units a radian is equal to 57°.3, 3437'.7, and 206,264''.8 when values to the nearest tenth of each unit are used.

23. Relation between Angular Diameter and Distance. If an object subtends an angle of 1°, its diameter is practically equal in length to 1° of

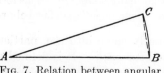

FIG. 7. Relation between angular diameter and distance.

arc of the circle whose center is at the eye of the observer. Thus, in Fig. 7, if the object whose diameter is the chord *CB* subtends an angle equal to 1° at the point *A*, the diameter *CB* will be very nearly equal to the arc *CB* whose center is at *A*.

Since the arc *CB* is 1/57.3 of radius *AB*, the diameter *CB* will be very nearly equal to the same fractional part of *AB*.

The smaller the angle subtended at *A*, the nearer will the chord *CB*

TABLE I

	The earth	The celestial sphere		
		Horizon system	Equator system	Ecliptic system
Fundamental circle.............	Equator	Horizon	Celestial equator	Ecliptic
Poles.........................	North and south terrestrial poles	Zenith and nadir	North and south celestial poles	North and south poles of ecliptic
Secondary circles.............	Meridians and parallels of latitude	Vertical circles and parallels of altitude	Hour circles and parallels of declination	Latitude circles and parallels of latitude
Coordinates..................	Longitude and latitude	Azimuth and altitude	Right ascension and declination	Celestial longitude and latitude
Zero circle...................	Meridian through Greenwich	Vertical circle through south point	Hour circle through vernal equinox	Latitude circle through vernal equinox
Direction of first coordinate......	Eastward and westward	Through west	Eastward	Eastward

13

equal the arc CB in length. We may, therefore, say that if a body subtends an angle of 1°, its diameter is approximately equal to $\frac{1}{57}$ of its distance; if the body subtends an angle of 1′, its diameter is equal to 1/3438 of its distance, while if it subtends an angle of 1″, its diameter is equal to 1/206,265 of its distance.

This relation between angular diameter and distance is of great importance, for if either diameter or distance is known in linear units, such as miles or kilometers, the other may be immediately determined.

24. Parallax. The word *parallax* means the apparent displacement of a heavenly body depending upon a change in the position of the observer (Fig. 8).

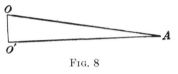

Fig. 8

An observer at O would see a body at A in the direction OA, while if he shifted his position to O', the direction would be $O'A$. The difference in direction of OA and $O'A$ is measured by the angle A. The angle A would be the parallax of a body at the point A. The parallax of a body at A decreases as the distance $O'A$ is increased.

To be of value the length OO' must have a definite value. For bodies comparatively near the earth this length is taken as the equatorial radius of the earth. The moon's parallax is about 57′ while that of the sun is only 8″.8. This means that the sun is nearly 390 times as far away as the moon.

For distant bodies like the stars the radius of the earth would be too small. Accordingly the radius of the earth's orbit is used for the distance OO'. Even with this great increase in the length of OO' no star is known whose parallax is as large as 1″.

To illustrate the methods of determining parallax and distance we shall consider the determination of the parallaxes of moon and sun.

25. Measurement of Moon's Distance and Parallax. The principle involved in determining the distance of the moon is illustrated in Fig. 9.

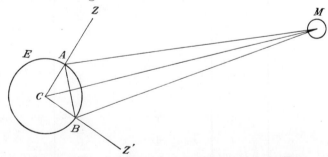

Fig. 9. Determination of moon's distance and parallax.

Let E be the earth, M the moon, A and B two observing stations on the earth as far apart as possible and located on the same meridian. Let AZ

be the direction of the zenith for A and BZ' the direction of the zenith for B.

In the triangle ABC we know the angle ACB, the difference in latitude of the two stations, and the lengths of AC and BC; hence AB and the angles CAB and CBA can be computed. Then assume the moon to be on the meridian of A and B and that observers at that instant measure the zenith distance of the moon. Angle $BAM = 180° - CAB - ZAM$ and angle $ABM = 180° - CBA - Z'BM$. In the triangle AMB we now know AB and the angles at A and B; hence we can compute AM and BM. From the triangles ACM and BCM we can now compute CM. The mean of the two values will give the distance from earth to moon. The mean value for this distance is 384,000 km (238,860 miles).

Since we now know the moon's distance and the value of the earth's equatorial radius, we can apply Sec. 24 and obtain the moon's mean parallax, which is $57'2''.7$.

We have introduced certain simplifications in order not to complicate the problem, such as having the two observatories on the same meridian, etc. The actual observations are not so simple and the computations are far more complex, but the principle is unchanged.

26. Measurement of Sun's Distance and Parallax. The sun is a large body and there are no permanent markings on its surface as in the case of the moon. It is therefore difficult to observe its position accurately, and we are compelled to determine its distance by an indirect method. From observations extending over centuries it has been possible to determine the *relative distances* of the planets from the sun with great accuracy. If therefore any distance in the system can be measured exactly in terms of kilometers or miles, it can be applied proportionally to any distance, such as the earth's distance from the sun.[1] The object best adapted for such measures is an asteroid or minor planet (Sec. 283) which comes close to the earth.

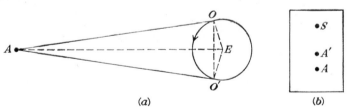

(a)   (b)

FIG. 10. Asteroid method of determining the earth's distance from the sun.

In Fig. 10a, let the circle represent the earth whose center is at E; O and O' two positions of an observer at the equator who is carried around by the earth's rotation in the direction of the arrow; and A an asteroid. Let us assume, for the sake of simplicity, that the asteroid and the earth are

[1] This distance is called the *astronomical unit*.

stationary in space and that the angles AOE and $AO'E$ are right angles. Let S be a star in the sky near the position of the asteroid. When the observer is at O, asteroid and star would be photographed at S and A (Fig. 10b). Later, when the observer is at O', star and asteroid would be photographed at S and A'. By measuring on the photographic plate the angular distances SA and SA', the value of AA' and hence the angle $O'AO$ are obtained. This is the amount by which the asteroid is displaced in the sky when the observer changes his position from O to O' because of the earth's rotation. Knowing the dimensions of the earth, the length OO' can be determined, the triangle AOO' solved and, finally, the distance AE determined. Knowing the value of AE in astronomical units from the elements of the orbits of the asteroid and the earth (Sec. 248), the value of the astronomical unit in kilometers is obtained.

The angle OAO' is small at best and it is therefore evident that the closer the asteroid the larger the angle, while the larger the angle the more accurately can it be measured. Hence Eros, an asteroid which comes near the earth, is especially important for the purpose of determining the sun's distance. The starlike appearance of the asteroid is also of great importance, as its small image on the photographic plate permits very accurate measures of the distances SA and SA'.

The ideal conditions assumed are not realized. The asteroid and the earth are both moving in their orbits about the sun; with one exception observatories are not located at the equator and the asteroid cannot be observed on the horizon, so that the angles AOE and $AO'E$ are not right angles. These conditions introduce additional work in the computations but the principle outlined is the same.

The determination of the sun's distance is affected not only by any errors which may be inherent in the accurate measurement of the angle OAO' but also by any errors in the determination of the earth's equatorial radius. Since this is the only measured length involved, it is evident that the highest degree of accuracy in its determination is desirable.

The most recent value of the sun's distance is 149,670,000 km (93,000,-000 miles). This value is probably correct to within 10,000 km.

With this value of the distance the *equatorial parallax* of the sun is 8″.79. Most astronomical almanacs, by international agreement, still use the value 8″.80, which had been adopted at an international conference at Paris in 1911. This slightly larger, older value corresponds to a distance of 149,500,000 km (92,900,000 miles).

EXERCISES

1. What are the azimuths of the usual 4, 8, 16, and 32 points of the compass?
2. Compare the altitudes and azimuths of the same star for observers at the north and south terrestrial poles.

3. Where does the celestial equator cut the horizon?

4. Under what conditions does the ecliptic pass through the east and west points of the horizon?

5. Under what conditions will two stars have equal azimuths? Equal right ascensions? Equal sidereal hour angles?

6. What are the right ascensions and declinations of the equinoxes? Of the solstices?

7. If Venus has an angular diameter of 1′ and a linear diameter of 12,200 km (7600 miles), what is its distance from the observer in kilometers? In miles?

Ans. 41,943,600 km; 26,128,800 miles.

8. Mars may come within 56,000,000 km (35,000,000 miles) of the earth. If its angular diameter at the time is 25″, what is its diameter in kilometers? In miles?

Ans. 6790 km; 4240 miles.

9. The sun's mean parallax is 8″.79. If the earth's equatorial diameter is 12,760 km (7930 miles), what is the sun's mean distance?

Ans. 149,700,000 km or 93,040,000 miles.

10. The crater of the formation Copernicus on the moon has an angular diameter of 40″. If the moon's distance is 386,000 km (240,000 miles), what is the linear diameter of the crater?   *Ans.* 75 km or 46.5 miles.

CHAPTER 3

THE EARTH

All astronomical observations must be made at the earth's surface and through the earth's atmosphere. These circumstances determine, to a large extent, not only what we can learn concerning the heavens, but also the methods which must be employed in studying them. It is therefore necessary to learn something about the earth before we can study the rest of the universe to the best advantage.

FIG. 11. Partial phases of a lunar eclipse showing boundary of earth's shadow to be an arc of a circle. (*Yerkes Observatory*.)

27. The Earth's Shape. Mankind, with few exceptions, seems always to have held the belief that the earth is approximately flat, and it was not until Magellan's ships actually sailed around it that the agelong belief was shattered and the rotundity of the earth generally accepted as a fact.

Another of the elementary proofs that the earth is at least approximately spherical can be obtained by observing eclipses of the moon. No matter how the moon moves into or out of the shadow of the earth, the edge of the shadow is always seen to be bounded by an arc of a circle (Fig. 11).

Another proof of its approximate shape is that when a vessel is observed going out to sea the hull vanishes first, the superstructure next, and the smoke from its fires last.

The exact shape and size are determined by the principles described in Secs. 31 and 32.

28. Plumb Lines and Level Lines. If a plumb line is hanging freely, its position with respect to the earth is determined by the direction of gravity. The direction of the plumb line is usually determined by first leveling an instrument by means of delicate spirit levels and then turning off an angle of 90° in a vertical plane. *A level surface is perpendicular to the direction of the plumb line at any point.*

If the surface of the ocean were not disturbed by waves and tides, it would be a level surface. A level surface therefore is not a plane but a curved surface. Similarly, a level line is not a straight line but a curved line which follows the curvature of a level surface.

29. Longitude. From a study of geography we are familiar with the terms *longitude* and *latitude*. We say that if we assume a series of imaginary lines, meridians, drawn from the North to the South Pole of the earth (Fig. 12), and designate a certain meridian, such as *NGS*, as the zero meridian, then *the longitude of a point P is the angle which the meridian through P makes with the zero meridian,* namely, the angle *PNG*. We also know from the geometry of the problem that the angle *PNG* is equal to the angle *ACB* subtended at the center of the earth by that part of the equator between the two meridians. Longitude is measured eastward and westward from the meridian through Greenwich, England, to 180°.

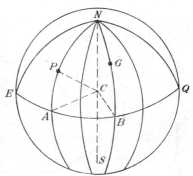

Fɪɢ. 12. Diagram illustrating longitude and geocentric latitude.

30. Latitude. There are three kinds of latitude: astronomical, geographic, and geocentric.

1. *Astronomical latitude* is defined as the angle between the direction of the plumb line and the plane of the earth's equator. If the earth were a homogeneous sphere without rotation, the plumb line would point toward its center, but, as we shall see later on, the earth is not an exact sphere.

It is evident to everyone that matter is not uniformly distributed at the surface at any rate, for in some places we have a water surface and in others there are mountains. This lack of uniformity in the distribution of matter at the earth's surface, as well as any lack of uniformity within the body of the earth, will make the direction of the plumb line slightly different on the rotating earth from what it would be if these inequalities of surface, etc., were not present. This effect on the plumb line is called the *station error*. In Hawaii station errors up to 67″ have been noted. The method of determining station error is somewhat beyond the scope of this book.

2. *Geographic latitude* is the astronomical latitude corrected for station error. It is the latitude used in the drawing of maps.

3. *Geocentric latitude* is the angle at the center of the earth between the line drawn from the center to the point on the surface and the plane of the equator. Thus, in Fig. 12 the angle *PCA* is the geocentric latitude of the point *P*. Geocentric latitude is used when results calculated for the earth's center must be changed to a point of observation at the surface, and vice versa.

The greatest difference between geographic and geocentric latitude occurs at 45°, where it amounts to 11′.6.

31. Measuring the Earth. The exact dimensions of the earth are obtained by measurement. The process is termed *triangulation* because it depends upon a network of triangles. It is indicated in principle in Fig. 13.

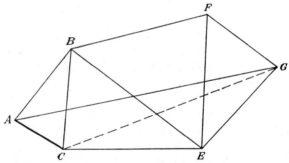

Fig. 13. The principle of determining the distance between two points, *A* and *G*, by triangulation.

Suppose it is desired to determine the distance between two points, *A* and *G*, so far apart that one cannot be seen from the other nor both from a single intermediate point. First a distance *AC* is measured with great exactness. This is termed a *base line*. Then, after selecting a point *B*, the angles *A*, *C*, and *B* in the triangle are measured by a surveyor's transit or similar instrument. In the triangle *ACB* one side, *AC*, and the three angles are known, so that the two other sides can be computed by trigonometry. Another point, *E*, is then selected which is visible from *B* and *C*. Having computed *CB* and measured the angles at *C*, *B*, and *E* in the triangle *CBE*, it is, in turn, possible to compute the length *EB*. This process is continued until the final triangle *EFG* is solved. In the triangle *CEG* we now know *CE*, *EG*, and the angle *CEG*, so that *CG* can be computed. Then in the triangle CGA we know CG, CA, and the angle ACG, so that we are in a position to compute AG, the distance required.

In this statement it has been assumed that all the triangles lie in the same plane. Because of the curvature of the earth's surface it is evident that this is not actually the case, although each triangle may be considered a plane triangle unless very large. This complicates the problem, but the principle used is the same.

Many such lines have been measured in this manner in various countries. It is evident that such a network of lines of known length, used in connection with the known longitudes and latitudes of the places connected, enables us to know the dimensions of the earth with great accuracy.

The measurement of the base line is carried out with tapes of invar whose lengths have been most carefully determined. The actual error of base-line measurements is believed to be never greater than 1 part in 300,000, and some special base lines have been measured whose error is probably less than 1 part in 1,000,000.

In a comparatively flat region steel towers about 100 ft high are used to elevate the lines of sight above buildings and trees. The sides of the triangles may then become as much as 30 km (20 miles) in length. In mountainous regions much longer sides may be used. In the southwestern part of the United States the U.S. Coast and Geodetic Survey has used triangles whose sides were up to 180 km (120 miles) in length.

The accuracy of first-class triangulation work is remarkable. The closing error of the series of triangles around the western half of the United States was only 33 ft in a circuit of 5300 miles, or 1 part in 848,000.

32. Length of a Degree of Astronomical Latitude.

In traveling along a meridian from the equator toward a pole it is found that it is necessary to travel a little farther for each change of 1° in latitude. This means that the curvature of the earth's surface is greatest at the equator and that it becomes less the nearer we approach the poles. This is illustrated in Fig. 14. Each line drawn toward the interior is perpendicular to the tangent at the point of the curve from which it is drawn, and is therefore the direction of the plumb line at the surface. The angles between adjacent lines are all equal. It is therefore evident that the arc of the meridian between adjacent lines at the pole is greater than at the equator, or that a degree of latitude increases in length as one goes away from the equator. Measurements of arcs of meridians by triangulation in various parts of the earth have shown the following values for the length of 1° of astronomical latitude:

	Kilometers	Miles
At equator	110.55	68.71
At 45°	111.12	69.06
At 90°	111.68	69.41

Arcs of longitude along parallels have also been measured, and it is found that these are essentially uniformly curved at any particular latitude.

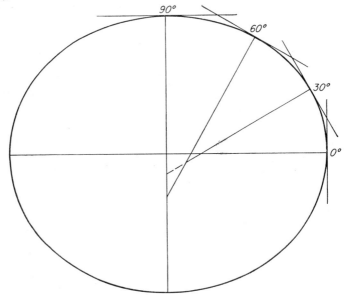

Fig. 14. Cross section of the earth through the rotation axis (the oblateness greatly exaggerated). The tangents represent the horizon planes at different latitudes. The perpendiculars to the tangents show the directions of the plumb lines. Each tangent drawn makes an angle of 30° with the next and therefore the plumb lines do likewise. Note how the length of the arc increases for the equal differences of astronomical latitude from equator to pole.

33. Results of Earth Measurement.

By means of triangulation the lengths of many meridian arcs as well as arcs of parallels of latitude have been measured. Furthermore the latitudes and longitudes of many points on these arcs have been determined by astronomical observations.

When reduced to sea level, each meridian gives the same value for the distance from pole to equator and uniform values for the lengths of arcs between the same parallels of latitude whether the arcs are in Africa, America, Asia, or Europe. Each arc likewise shows the same increase in the lengths of the degrees of latitude in going from equator to pole.

Similarly a given number of degrees of longitude at a given latitude have the same length, whether the longitude arc is measured in the Eastern or Western Hemisphere or north or south of the equator.

Neglecting certain slight irregularities still under investigation, we may conclude that

1. All cross sections of the earth which pass through the poles are of the same size and shape at sea level.

2. All cross sections of the earth perpendicular to the axis are circles at sea level.

3. The curvature of the meridians is progressively less in going from equator to either pole. Accordingly the earth is an oblate spheroid whose shortest axis is the rotation axis.

The best results of earth measurements at present available are those obtained by Hayford. These are 12,713.82 km (7899.98 miles) and 12,756.78 km (7926.68 miles) for the polar and equatorial diameters, respectively. This deviation of the earth from a spherical form is frequently called the *earth's equatorial bulge* and is caused by the earth's rotation.

34. An Early Measure. Some of the ancients were satisfied that the earth is approximately spherical and Eratosthenes of Alexandria, about 250 B.C., attempted to measure the circumference by measuring an arc. The two stations marking the length of the arc were Alexandria and Syene in upper Egypt. He was told that on the longest day of the year the sun was in the zenith at Syene while at Alexandria he noted that the gnomon cast a shadow which showed the sun to have a zenith distance of $7°.2$. Since this is $\frac{1}{50}$ of a circumference and he assumed the distance between the two stations to be 5000 stadia, a circumference of 250,000 stadia resulted.

If we knew the length of the stadium used, we could determine how accurate his value was. Unfortunately this value is unknown so that there can be no direct check against modern values. However, on a recent map the difference in latitude between Assuan (the ancient Syene) and Alexandria is found to be $7°.1$ so that Eratosthenes must be given great credit for the accuracy attained in measuring this quantity which is the essential one in the problem.

35. Relation between Astronomical Latitude and Altitude of Pole. In Fig. 15 let NS be the earth's axis, EQ the plane of the equator, O the observer, ZOD the direction of the plumb line, BO the plane of the horizon, NP the direction of the celestial pole and OP' a line parallel to NP.

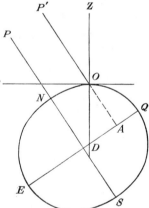

Fig. 15. The relation between astronomical latitude and the altitude of the celestial pole.

Since the line OP' is parallel to NP, the prolongation of the earth's axis, the two lines will meet when extended to the celestial sphere. Accordingly, the angle BOP' will be the altitude of the celestial pole above the observer's horizon. The angle ODQ, the angle between the observer's plumb line and the plane of the equator, will be his astronomical latitude. The point D, in general, is not at the earth's center (see Sec. 32).

By elementary geometry it can be shown that angle $P'OB$ is equal to angle ODQ, or *the altitude of the celestial pole is equal to the astronomical latitude of the observer.*

36. The Parallel Sphere. If an observer were located at one of the poles of the earth, the celestial pole would be located in the zenith. The stars would then all revolve around the zenith in circles which would be parallel to the horizon, and hence the name of *parallel sphere.* For such an observer no stars would ever rise or set (Fig. 16).

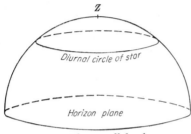 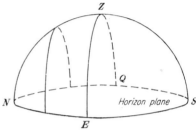

FIG. 16. The parallel sphere. FIG. 17. The right sphere.

37. The Right Sphere. For an observer at the equator the celestial poles would lie in the north and south points of the horizon, and the celestial equator would pass through the zenith. For such an observer all stars would rise and set at right angles to the horizon, their visible paths being semicircles parallel to the celestial equator as shown in Fig. 17.

38. The Oblique Sphere. For an observer anywhere between equator and either pole, the celestial pole would be at an altitude equal to his latitude. In consequence, stars near the elevated pole would move around the latter in circles, the stars near the pole below the horizon would never be seen, while the remaining stars would be at times above and at other times below the horizon and would move in circles oblique to the horizon (Fig. 6).

39. The Variation of Latitude and Longitude. Many years ago the question was raised whether the possible shifting of masses within the earth, the denudation of the continents, and even seasonal changes might not produce a sufficient change in the position of matter within or on the earth to have an appreciable effect on the position of the axis of rotation with respect to the body of the earth. This change in the axis of rotation would show itself in changes in the latitudes and longitudes of places on the earth.

In 1888, Küstner published a series of observations made in 1884 and 1885 at Berlin, in which he showed that variation in the latitude of the Berlin Observatory had occurred in the course of the observations. During the same period Chandler at Cambridge, Mass., had shown that a variation existed in the measures of the latitude of the Harvard Observatory. Küstner's results led to special test observations at Berlin, Potsdam, Prague, and Strassburg in 1889, which showed such accordant results that the problem was attacked by the International Geodetic Institute and for a long series of years observations were made at selected stations, mostly in the Northern Hemisphere. Some of these stations are still in operation. The results obtained show clearly that the rotation

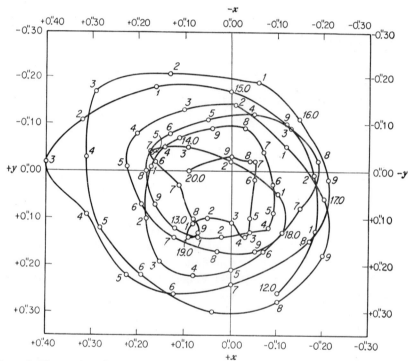

FIG. 18. The motion of the North Pole of the earth from 1912 to 1920. (*According to Wanach.*)

axis is not fixed with respect to the earth but is moving about a mean position. Another way of expressing this fact is to say that the poles wander about within a small area on the surface of the earth. Figure 18 shows the motion of the North Pole of the earth from 1912 to 1920. The figure is taken from the report of Wanach in *Astronomische Nachrichten.*

It is evident that if the poles change their positions, the meridians which join the poles must also be in motion. In consequence, there will be slight changes in the longitudes of places on the earth as well as changes in the latitudes.

Kimuro has found a correlation to exist between earthquakes and the movement of the poles. Some of his conclusions are: (1) great earthquakes change the course of pole shift and mostly form angular points on the curve; and (2) the velocity of the pole shift changes before and after great earthquakes.

40. The Mass of the Earth. The earth's mass can be determined in a number of ways which give results in good agreement considering the difficulty of the problem. The value adopted at present is 6×10^{21} metric tons (6.6×10^{21} short tons). Methods employed in determining this value will be considered in Chap. 8.

41. The Earth's Density. Applying the well-known equation in physics, $D = M/V$, where D is the density, M the mass, and V the volume expressed in the proper units, we obtain the mean density of the earth. The mean value derived from various determinations is about 5.5 times the density of water.

Since the density of continental rocks is approximately 2.7, it is evident that the material near the center must have a density considerably greater than the mean density in order to produce an average of 5.5. It is thought by many that the central parts of the earth are either composed almost wholly of iron or are at least very rich in iron and heavy elements.

42. Rotation. The earth's rotation may be proved in a number of ways. We shall consider two of them, the Foucault pendulum method and the change in the value of gravity as we go from pole to equator.

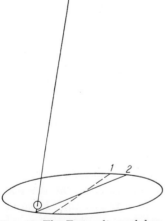

The Pendulum Method. This experiment was first performed by the French physicist Foucault in 1851. He suspended a heavy iron ball about 30 cm (1 ft) in diameter by means of a wire about 60 m (200 ft) in length. After the pendulum had been drawn aside and allowed to come to rest, it was started swinging and a pin fastened to the bottom of the iron ball was allowed to cut a ring of sand. It soon became evident that the plane in which the pendulum vibrated deviated toward the right with reference to the floor; that is, in reality the floor was turning under the pendulum, or the earth was rotating. Figure 19 illustrates this.

FIG. 19. The Foucault pendulum method of showing the rotation of the earth.

It is evident that, if a pendulum which is free to move in any direction could be set up at the pole, the earth would turn around under it once in 24 hr. At the equator, on the other hand, the plane of the pendulum would continuously cut the earth's surface at the same angle and no shift would occur. In intermediate latitudes, therefore, the time of rotation would lie between the 24 hr at the pole and the infinitely long time at the equator. In latitude 45° the rate of rotation would be one complete rotation of the plane of the pendulum in about 34 hr.

The experiment has been repeated many times since Foucault's day. In order to be successful, great care must be taken to see that the support is so designed that the pendulum is actually free to move in any direction, that the ball is smooth and symmetrical with respect to the wire, and that it is at rest before starting to swing. A recently designed pendulum only 3 m (10 ft) long has proved successful.

The Gravity Method. The second proof depends upon the fact that the force of gravity at the equator is less than at the poles. After allowing for the decrease in the force caused by the equatorial radius being 21.5 km (13.4 miles) greater than the polar radius, it is found that there is a difference which is exactly equal to the effect of the centrifugal force developed by the earth's rotation. This experiment is performed by means of a specially devised pendulum. It will be remembered that the vibration time of a pendulum is given by the equation

$$ T = 2\pi \sqrt{\frac{l}{g}} $$

where l is the length of the pendulum and g is the force of gravity. By timing the swing of the pendulum, the only unknown in the equation is g, and the value of this can therefore be determined wherever the pendulum can be set up and the means of accurate timing are available.

Other proofs are the eastward deviation of falling bodies; the trade winds and the direction of revolution of the winds in cyclones, which is counterclockwise in the Northern Hemisphere and clockwise in the Southern.

43. Constancy of the Earth's Rotation Period. The question of the constancy of the earth's rotation is of the greatest importance in astronomy, because the day is the fundamental unit of time. Various natural processes must affect the period of rotation. If the earth's diameter were shrinking, the period would decrease, while if expanding, it would increase, provided the mass remains constant. If meteoritic matter is being added to the mass while other things remain unchanged, the period must be increasing. The friction of the tides will act like a brake on the rotating earth and lengthen the period. Jeffreys estimates that the day has increased in length by 1 sec in the last 120,000 years because of tidal friction.

At times some of the heavenly bodies, notably the moon, are not found in the exact positions calculated for them. It has been shown by Brown,

Innes, Jones, and others that these discrepancies can be most easily accounted for by assuming a small variation in the earth's rotation period, that is, the apparent lack of punctuality of the heavenly body really means irregularity of the timekeeper (the rotating earth). According to Brown:

"The maximum change for which the observational evidence is good took place about 1898. This made the day longer by about $0^s.003$. A change in the opposite direction of smaller amount took place about 1918. These changes are quite sudden, that is, they occupied a year or two only at most. Other and more gradual changes have taken place in the past, some increasing and others diminishing the length of the day."

The variations observed can be divided into three classes: the slow secular lengthening of the rotation period, irregular changes, and annual changes. The first and second can be measured by astronomical observations, but the third has become evident only since highly accurate quartz-crystal clocks have been available.

One of the causes of the secular lengthening of the day seems to be tidal friction, especially in shallow seas; the cause of the irregular fluctuations is uncertain; the causes for the annual change may possibly lie in changes in atmospheric pressure, wind velocities, and precipitation which depend on the seasons.

44. The Diurnal Rotation of the Heavens. If we stand in a room and slowly turn around, we see that all the objects about us appear to be going around in a direction opposite to that in which we turn. We have a similar experience if we place ourselves on a rotating platform, such as a merry-go-round. In the first case we could also note, by looking directly upward, that the ceiling would appear to be turning about a point directly overhead, and, in the second case, we could see that the sky would appear to be turning about a point directly above the center of rotation of the merry-go-round. These points in ceiling or sky we shall call the rotation poles—they are the points where the axes around which our rotation takes place reach the boundary of our surroundings. We should also find a similar pole directly opposite the first, around which floor or ground, respectively, would appear to rotate.

The earth is a globe rotating about an axis. If at night we observe the position of the stars for several hours, we see that there is a point in the sky about which the stars appear to turn. In the Northern Hemisphere this point will be above the north point of the horizon, and in the Southern Hemisphere it will be above the south point. These two points are called the north and south *celestial poles* and are the points where the earth's axis prolonged in opposite directions appears to pierce the sky. The stars near these poles appear to move around them in circles, and cameras with reasonably large lenses can be used to photograph them. Figure 20 is such a photograph, made at the Goodsell Observatory with an exposure of about 10 hr, of the star trails around the north celestial pole. If the sky were clear and dark for 24 hr, the trails would form complete circles.

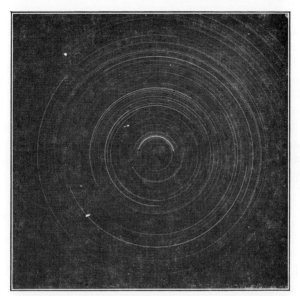

Fig. 20. Star trails around the north celestial pole. (*Goodsell Observatory.*)

The period of rotation with respect to the stars is 24 sidereal hours (Sec. 121), or $23^h56^m4^s.1$ mean time.

The apparent rotation of the heavens may be considered another proof of the rotation of the earth.

THE EARTH'S ATMOSPHERE

45. Atmospheric Pressure. The gases of the atmosphere are bound to the earth by its gravitation. The lowest layer must therefore support the weight of all other layers. In consequence, the air at sea level is compressed most and is therefore densest, while the higher we go above sea level, the less air remains above, the pressure decreases, and the density diminishes.

The instrument used to measure air pressure is the barometer. At sea level the pressure is equal to 1100 g per cm^2 (15 lb per $in.^2$) and will support a column of mercury 76 cm (30 in.) high. The barometric pressure diminishes about one-half for each 5.5 km (3.5 miles) of elevation, that is, the pressure at 5.5 km is 38 cm, at 11 km it is 19 cm, etc.

The decrease in pressure is accompanied by a corresponding decrease in density, since the density of a gas is directly proportional to its pressure provided the temperature remains constant. The density of the atmosphere at sea level is approximately 0.0012 that of water.

46. The Height of the Atmosphere. Theoretically, there is almost no limit to the height of the atmosphere, but practically a limit can be found. On the basis of 50 per cent decrease in density for each 5.5-km elevation, a brief calculation shows that at an elevation of 55 km the density has decreased to less than 0.001 of the density at sea level and at 72 km the density is only about 0.0001. It is therefore evident that at no very great elevation the density is less than that of the highest vacuum attainable in the laboratory.

A second method of determining a limit is by means of meteors (Sec. 364). These are small particles, entering the atmosphere at high velocities, which are rendered incandescent by the friction of the air. Meteors seldom appear at heights exceeding 150 km (100 miles).

A third method is the determination of the height of the aurora, a luminosity of the upper atmosphere apparently caused by electric discharges from the sun (Sec. 213). Norwegian observers, especially Störmer, have made many observations on this point, and they find only occasional streamers to exceed a height of 300 km. One of these reached a height of 1100 km (680 miles). We may, therefore, take this value as the approximate limit of an appreciable atmosphere for the earth.

47. Astronomical Refraction. When a ray of light passes from a rarer to a denser medium, it is bent toward a line perpendicular to the surface separating them (Sec. 66). A ray of light passing from the practically absolute vacuum of interstellar space into the earth's atmosphere suffers a

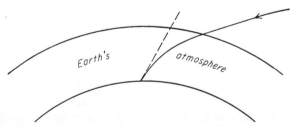

Fig. 21. Refraction in the earth's atmosphere. The observer sees the star in the direction of the broken line whereas its real direction is outward along the full line. The figure greatly exaggerates the effect.

similar deviation, and the deeper it penetrates, the denser the air becomes and hence the greater the deviation until it reaches the earth's surface. Figure 21 illustrates this, although the bending of the ray of light in the figure is greatly exaggerated. This bending of the ray is called *astronomical refraction*.

A ray which enters the atmosphere so as just to graze the earth's surface will be compelled to pass through the air at a larger angle of incidence than one coming in more nearly perpendicular to it, and in consequence the refraction is greater. On the other hand, a ray entering exactly perpendicularly is not affected at all. The refraction accordingly varies with the altitude of the source of light above the horizon. At the horizon the refraction amounts to 35′; at an altitude of 10° it is reduced to 5′; at 45° to 1′ and at the zenith it becomes 0. These are mean values for average observing conditions. Refraction increases with increase in barometric pressure and decrease in temperature, and vice versa.

In consequence of refraction a heavenly body is never exactly in the direction we see it unless in the zenith. When accurate observations for position are made, it is necessary to correct these for refraction, and in observatories where such observations are made there are usually rather extensive tables already calculated, so that the corrections may be determined quickly.

The sun and moon have apparent diameters of about 32′ and 31′, respectively. When the lower edge of one of these bodies is just seen above the horizon, that edge is in reality 35′ below the horizon, but refraction elevates it by that amount. Hence we see the entire body when its zenith distance is over 90° and therefore below the horizon plane.

When the sun is just rising or setting, it often assumes an elliptical shape with the longer diameter parallel to the horizon. This is caused by the refraction raising the lower edge more than the upper and therefore apparently shortening the diameter perpendicular to the horizon.

48. Twinkling of the Stars. On a hot summer day distant objects near the horizon appear to be trembling. Similar effects can be seen by looking at an object if the line of sight passes near a heated surface, such as a stove. This trembling is caused by the unequally heated air masses, which produce a varying refraction as they move across the line of vision.

In the earth's atmosphere there are found various air currents, the air of which is at different temperatures. At the boundary between any two currents there is a mixing of the two air masses, which thus gives rise to irregular motions in a beam of light coming from a star. This irregularity is called *twinkling* or *scintillation*.

The twinkling of a star in the telescope appears as a rapid motion of the image, and this motion is magnified by the eyepiece. The larger the telescope, the greater the number of irregularities in the line of sight. On some perfectly clear nights large telescopes cannot be used because the image is too unsteady to permit anything to be seen properly. Steadiness of the image is essential to good observing. The quality of the steadiness is usually termed the *seeing*.

49. Why Planets Do Not Twinkle. The brighter planets visible to the naked eye in general do not twinkle like the stars. At the earth's distance from them they have appreciable angular diameters; hence many rays of light may come from them along slightly different paths. These various rays traverse sufficiently different paths through our atmosphere so that, under normal conditions, only a portion is deviated at any one time by atmospheric disturbances. In consequence the unaided eye does not perceive a twinkling effect.

50. Twilight. The sun continues to illuminate the earth's atmosphere long after sunset and this light in turn reaches the observer. This illumination is known as *twilight* (Fig. 22). Twilight is visible until the sun is about 18° below the horizon.

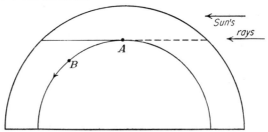

FIG. 22. Twilight. The observer at *A* sees the sun on his horizon. The observer at *B* is in the shadow of the earth but still receives some light from the atmosphere by reflection and scattering by dust particles.

The duration of twilight depends on the length of time required for the sun to go from the horizon to 18° below it. In the tropics this requires only a little over an hour at any time of year, but in the summer in latitudes of 40° or more the angle at which the sun moves is such that a much longer time is required before it has reached the necessary distance below the horizon. This accounts for the long summer twilight in regions beyond ±40° latitude.

51. The Earth as a Magnet. The fact that the earth has magnetic properties has been known for many centuries. The magnetic compass appears to have been known to the Chinese as early as the twelfth century B.C.

The simplest magnet is a short magnetized bar of steel. If iron filings are scattered about it, they will arrange themselves in a well-known pattern. The ends where the lines of filings converge are called the *poles* of the magnet, the lines along which they arrange themselves are called the *magnetic lines of force*, and the region about the magnet is called its *magnetic field*.

If a magnetized needle is placed in a magnetic field, the needle will set itself parallel to the lines of force at the point *as nearly as the mounting of the needle will permit*. In accordance with this principle, if a delicately balanced magnetic needle is set in the earth's magnetic field, it will set itself parallel to the vertical plane through the lines of force of the earth's field, one end pointing more or less toward the north and the other end toward the south.   The pole at the north end of the needle is called its *north-seeking pole* and the other its *south-seeking pole.*

The earth's magnetic poles are over 1000 miles from the geographic poles.   Each magnetic pole is approximately 2300 km (1400 miles) from a point diametrically opposite the other pole.   If we assume the magnetic axis to be a straight line joining the magnetic poles, it misses the earth's center by approximately 1100 km (700 miles).

The earth's magnetic field is a complicated phenomenon.   There is evidence that while most of it is due to causes inside the earth, there are also causes external to the body of the earth.   What the actual causes are has not yet been determined.

The earth's magnetic poles are not fixed in position.   In 1831 Ross located the north magnetic pole in latitude 70°.1N, longitude 96°.9W, while in 1946–1948 Canadian observers located it at 70°N, 100°W.   The south magnetic pole was located by the First British Antarctic Expedition in 1903 at 72°.7S, 156°.4E, while the Second British Antarctic Expedition in 1909 found it to be at 72°.4S, 154°.0E.   The range of the wandering of the magnetic poles is not known.

52. Magnetic Declination and Dip. The lines of force of the earth's magnetic field run from one magnetic pole to the other, but local conditions affect the exact direction at any one place.   The angle which the compass needle makes with the meridian at any point is called the *magnetic declination* or the *magnetic variation* at the point.   At present (1954) the range of magnetic declination in the United States is from 21°W in Maine to 24°E in the state of Washington.   In polar regions the declination may reach 180°.

The magnetic declination is not constant at any particular place. London has recorded declinations ranging from 11°E in 1580 to 24°W in 1820.   Since 1820 the declination at London has been decreasing and is now about 13°W.

If a magnetic needle is mounted so that it can move in a vertical plane around a horizontal axis, it will, like the compass needle, set itself parallel to the lines of force of the earth's field.   The angle which such a needle makes with the horizontal is called the *dip* of the needle.   At the magnetic poles the dip is 90°, while at the magnetic equator the dip is 0°.

THE EARTH AND ITS ORBIT

53. The Earth's Orbit and Motion around the Sun. If we observe the stars near the setting sun for a few weeks, we shall see that they appear a little lower in the sky each evening. This shows that the sun appears to be moving eastward among the stars. If we continue our observations for an entire year, we shall find that at the end of the period the sun has made a complete circuit among the stars and is again at the starting point. This apparent motion of the sun is explained by the earth's revolution about it in a year.

The apparent path of the sun among the stars is called the *ecliptic*. When marked on a celestial globe it proves to be a great circle. This means that the earth's path about the sun lies in a plane. The plane of the earth's orbit is termed the *plane of the ecliptic*.

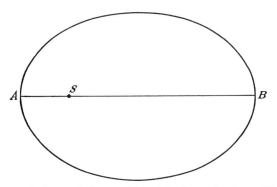

FIG. 23. The general shape of the earth's orbit about the sun. The ellipticity is greatly exaggerated in the figure.

The shape of the earth's orbit is that of an ellipse (Fig. 23), with the sun at one focus. The longest diameter of the ellipse is called the *major axis*. The point A of the orbit at the end of the major axis which is nearest the sun is called *perihelion* and the point B, farthest from the sun, is called *aphelion*.

The half length of the major axis, or semimajor axis, is called the *mean distance* from earth to sun. It is approximately 150,000,000 km (93,000,000 miles) in length.

As the earth's orbit is nearly circular, we may assume, without serious error, that its radius is equal to the semimajor axis. Multiplying this length by 2π and dividing by the number of seconds in a year will give the velocity of the earth in its orbit. This amounts to 30 km (18.5 miles) per sec, approximately.

The curvature of the earth's orbit is very slight. While the earth is traveling 30 km (18.5 miles), it deviates from a straight line only about 3 mm (0.12 in.).

54. Aberration. If rain is falling vertically, the drops will fall directly through a vertical tube, but, if the tube is moved horizontally, it is necessary to tip the upper end forward in order to allow the drops to fall freely through the tube without striking the side (Fig. 24). If the tube is moved in the direction of the arrow and is in the position *ac* when a drop is just entering, then, if it moves at such a velocity that it reaches

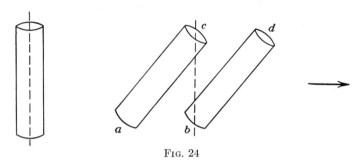

Fig. 24

the position *bd* by the time the drop has fallen through the distance *cb*, the drop will have passed along the tube without touching the sides. The angle *cbd* through which the tube is tilted will depend upon the velocities of drop and tube and is called the *angle of aberration*. The tube must always be tilted in the direction of its own motion.

If a star at the pole of the ecliptic were observed from a stationary earth, the telescope would be pointed directly at the star,[1] but since the earth's orbital velocity is 30 km per sec, the telescope must be tilted forward in the direction of the earth's motion by a small angle in order to allow the rays of light from the star to pass through the instrument (Fig. 25).

A star at the pole of the ecliptic will therefore appear to move around in a small orbit of exactly the shape of the earth's orbit. The angle of aberration is about 20″.5; hence the major axis of the aberrational orbit

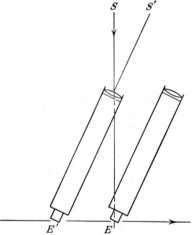

Fig. 25. Aberration of light. *SE* is the actual path of light while *S'E'* is the apparent path for observer at *E'*.

will be 41″. For a star in the plane of the ecliptic there will be no aberration when the earth is moving directly toward or away from it, but the maximum effect will be found when the earth is moving perpendicularly to the star's direction. The star will therefore appear to move

[1] It must be remembered that the stars are so far away that their rays are practically parallel, and for a star at one of the poles of the ecliptic these rays are perpendicular to the plane of the earth's orbit.

back and forth along a straight line 41″ in length. For a star between
the plane of the ecliptic and its pole the aberrational orbit will be an
ellipse of greater or less eccentricity, depending on its distance from the
pole of the ecliptic.

This displacement in the apparent position of a star caused by the
earth's revolution about the sun is called the *annual aberra-*

FIG. 26

tion. There is also a slight aberration caused by the earth's
axial rotation which is known as the *diurnal aberration.* The
diurnal aberration is very small and need be considered only
in refined observations.

The aberration of light was discovered by Bradley in 1726.
It is a definite proof that the earth revolves about the
sun.

55. The Sun's Distance by Aberration. In Fig. 26 let CA
represent the velocity of light and AB the velocity of the
earth in its orbit. If we can measure accurately the angle
of aberration C, we can compute the velocity of the earth in
its orbit. Knowing the velocity of light, we can write

$$AB = 299{,}774 \text{ km per sec} \times \tan 20''.5 = 30 \text{ km per sec}$$

Multiplying this value by the number of seconds in a year, the circumference of the earth's orbit is obtained. Dividing this value by 2π, we
obtain the radius of the orbit or the sun's distance from the earth.

56. The Seasons. If the axis of the earth were perpendicular to the
plane of the ecliptic, the sun would always be on the celestial equator
and hence the days and nights always equal in length. Under such
conditions there could be no change of seasons as is now the case.

Since the axis of the earth is tipped about 23°.5 from the perpendicular
to the plane of its orbit, it is evident that, when the earth is at A (Fig. 27)

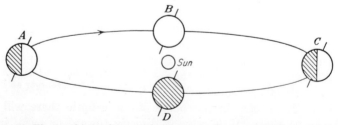

FIG. 27. The earth's position with respect to the sun at different seasons.

in its orbit, the sun shines perpendicularly on a point 23°.5 north of the
equator, shines past the North Pole 23°.5, and fails by a like amount of
shining on the South Pole. Three months later, when the earth is at B,
the sunlight just reaches both poles and falls perpendicularly at the

equator.   Three months later still, when the earth is at C, conditions are just opposite to what they were at A, while after another interval of three months, when the earth is at D, the sunlight again just reaches both poles.   During the time the earth is near A, the Northern Hemisphere has its summer and the Southern its winter, while, when the earth is near C, the opposite condition prevails.   When the earth is at B, we have the autumnal equinox, and when at D, the spring or vernal equinox.

At the time of the winter solstice, the sun is in the zenith at *noon* for any place on the Tropic of Capricorn, the parallel of latitude at 23°.5S latitude, and is on the horizon at *noon* for any place on the arctic circle at 66°.5N latitude.   At the time of the summer solstice the sun is in the zenith at *noon* for places on the Tropic of Cancer at 23°.5N latitude and is on the horizon at *noon* for places on the Antarctic Circle at latitude 66°.5S.   At the time of the equinoxes the sun is in the zenith at *noon* for places on the equator and on the horizon throughout the 24 hr at both poles.

57. The Length of Day and Night. The duration of day and night depends on the declination of the sun and on the latitude of the observer. Figure 28 illustrates the conditions for an observer at latitude 45°N. P

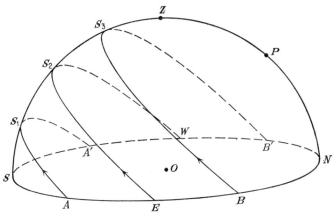

FIG. 28. Diurnal paths of the sun at the equinoxes and solstices for an observer at latitude 45°N.

represents the north celestial pole, $SENW$ the plane of the horizon for the observer at O, Z his zenith, ES_2W the diurnal circle of the sun when on the celestial equator, and AS_1A' and BS_3B' the diurnal circles of the sun at the times of the winter and summer solstices, respectively.

For the assumed latitude of 45°N the arcs NP, PZ, ZS_2, and S_2S are each equal to 45°.   The arcs S_1S_2 and S_2S_3 are each equal to 23°.5.

At the time of the summer solstice, when the sun's diurnal circle is BS_3B', it will rise about 35° north of east, set 35° north of west, and cross

the meridian at an altitude of 68°.5.   At the time of the equinoxes the
sun's diurnal circle is ES_2W; it rises at the east point, sets at the west
point, and has a noon altitude of 45°.   At the time of the winter solstice
the sun rises about 32° south of east, sets about 32° south of west, and
crosses the meridian at an altitude of only 21°.5.   It is obvious from the
figure that the sun is above the horizon the longest time at the time of
the summer solstice and the shortest time at the time of the winter
solstice.   The days are therefore much longer in summer than in winter.
At the latitude chosen, 45°, the sun is above the horizon about 15.6 hr
at the time of the summer solstice, about 8.8 hr at the time of the winter

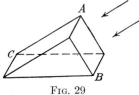

Fig. 29

solstice, and 12 hr at the equinoxes.

58. The Lag of the Seasons. The season at
any point on the earth depends upon the amount
of sunlight that region receives; the more sunlight, the warmer the season.   The daily amount
of sunshine per unit of area depends upon two
factors, the elevation of the sun above the

horizon and the duration of the daylight.   It is evident, from Fig. 29,
that if the incoming rays fall on a surface AB which is perpendicular to
them, each unit of area of AB will receive more heat than a unit of area
of a surface CB which is not perpendicular to them.   Even a low sun,
however, if it shines through a long day, may furnish more heat in the
course of such a day than a high sun shining for a shorter time.   Thus,
neglecting atmospheric absorption, during the long days of summer the
North Pole actually receives more heat from the sun in the course of
24 hr than does a region near the equator.

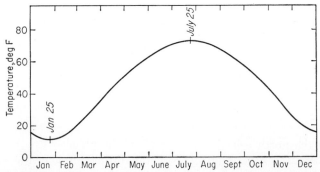

Fig. 30. Mean temperature curve, 1912–1941, at the Goodsell Observatory.

Another factor which affects the mean temperature is the relation
between the heat received from the sun during the day and the heat
radiated at night.   So long as more heat is received during the day than
is lost at night, the mean temperature must rise.   In consequence of this

accumulation of heat the warmest weather usually occurs during late July and early August, and not at the time of the summer solstice. Similarly, the mean temperature will continue to drop during the winter until there again is a balance between the heat received and heat radiated. This usually occurs late in January or early in February (Fig. 30).

EXERCISES

1. What level lines are often drawn on maps?

2. Does the length of a degree of geocentric latitude change in the same way as for astronomical latitude?

3. Give a geometric demonstration proving that the astronomical latitude of the observer is equal to the altitude of the pole.

4. At the North Pole, do the stars move from left to right or vice versa? At the South Pole?

5. Assuming one degree equal to 111.7 km (69.4 miles), what are the approximate dimensions of the large rectangle in Fig. 16? *Ans.* 20.2 × 21.7 m or 66.2 × 71.3 ft.

6. If the earth's rotation period increases, how will it affect the timing of astronomical events, i.e., will they occur earlier or later by the clock?

7. What is the approximate weight of the earth's atmosphere?

Ans. 6×10^{15} tons.

8. If the earth's rotation axis were in the plane of its orbit, how would this affect the length of day (sun above horizon) at different points on the earth's surface at various times of the year? What would be the effect on the seasons?

CHAPTER 4

LIGHT

Practically all the information on the heavenly bodies is obtained by means of the light they send us through space. It is therefore desirable that some of the elementary considerations concerning light be taken up.

59. The Nature of Light. For many years following Sir Isaac Newton it was generally held that light consisted of streams of particles (corpuscles) which passed outward from a body emitting light. If they reached the eye, these corpuscles impinged on the retina and produced the sensation of light. This theory is called the *corpuscular theory of light*.

The experiments in the first half of the last century, however, produced results which could not be explained by the corpuscular theory but could be explained if light consisted of waves instead of particles. These experiments seemed conclusively to establish the *wave theory of light*, and for a century no other theory was seriously considered.

Soon after the beginning of the present century, new conceptions and experiments have again raised the question of the nature of light, and certain experiments seem most readily explained on the corpuscular theory, while others cannot be explained except by the wave theory. It may be, therefore, that under certain conditions light behaves as a particle, and under other conditions it acts like a wave. For the present we shall hold to the wave theory.

60. The Ether. If light is a wave motion, it seems necessary to assume that there must be some medium to transmit this motion. This medium is called the *ether*. The necessity for such an assumption is partly philosophic and partly scientific.

The ether is assumed to fill all space, to penetrate all bodies, and to be highly elastic. Much has been written about the ether, but, as a matter of fact, its existence has never been proved conclusively. It seems necessary, however, to assume its existence in order to account for the transmission of light, for magnetic and electric fields, etc. Some scientists hold that an ether is not essential to the explanation of physical phenomena, but the scientific world in general holds to the ether theory.

In this book we shall follow the majority and assume the existence of the ether.

61. Wavelength, Vibration Frequency, and Velocity of Light. In a water wave the distance between two successive crests or troughs, such as *bf* or *dh* (Fig. 31), is called the *length* of the wave. The distance which a wave will travel in a unit of time, such as 1 sec, is the *velocity* of the

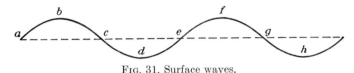

Fig. 31. Surface waves.

wave. When a train of waves passes a given point, a water particle at that point will make one upward and one downward motion for each wave of the train. The upward and downward motions together are called one complete vibration, and it is evident that a particle of water will make as many vibrations in 1 sec as there are waves passing per second. The number of vibrations per second is called the *vibration frequency*. The relation between wavelength, frequency, and velocity is given by the equation

$$v = n\lambda$$

where *v* is the velocity of the wave train, *n* the vibration frequency, and λ the wavelength.

In an analogous manner we may speak of the velocity, vibration frequency, and wavelength of light in the ether or other transparent medium.

The velocity of light can be determined in a number of ways, but different methods give slightly different results. The values range from 299,774 km (186,271 miles) per sec (Michelson, 1933) to 299,794 km (186,284 miles) per sec (Aslakson, 1951) if we consider only those of the last quarter of a century.

Just as water waves differ in length, so ether waves differ. The unit of length for the ether wave used in radio communication is the meter, and the length of these waves varies from a few meters to many thousands. When we consider the wavelength of light, a much smaller unit is desirable; the one now in general use is the one ten-billionth ($1/10^{10}$) of 1 m and is called the angstrom, which is abbreviated to A. Deep-red light has a wavelength of about 7800 A, yellow light about 5900 A, and violet light about 3900 A. The Greek letter lambda, λ, is usually used as a symbol for wavelength.

Owing to the extremely high velocity of light and the exceedingly short wavelength, the vibration frequency is expressible only by very large numbers. Thus the frequency for deep-red light is of the order of

400,000000,000000 or 4×10^{14}, while the frequency for violet light is of the order of 8×10^{14}.

62. Polarized Light. In a ray of ordinary light the vibrations occur at

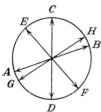

FIG. 32. Unpolarized light. A beam of unpolarized light moving perpendicular to the plane of the figure will have vibrations in any plane perpendicular to its path.

any and all angles. Thus, in Fig. 32, let us assume that we are looking along a ray of light. At one instant the vibration may occur along the plane AB, at another along the plane of CD, etc. Such a ray is said to be *unpolarized*.

If an unpolarized ray of light is repeatedly reflected from a polished surface at a suitable angle, or if it is passed through certain crystals, the vibrations are no longer haphazard but are confined to a definite plane or planes. Such a ray of light is said to be *plane-polarized*. The polarization of light can be detected by suitable means such as a Nicol prism. The presence or absence of polarization in light coming from a heavenly body may give a clue to its physical condition.

63. The Atomic Theory. The unit of matter usually dealt with by the chemist is called the *atom*. There are at present 100 different kinds of atoms known which distinguish the various chemical elements. Thus we have atoms of hydrogen, helium, sodium, iron, silver, gold, etc. It has been possible to determine the relative weights of the various atoms beginning with the lightest, hydrogen, which is arbitrarily said to have an atomic weight of 1. On this basis helium has an atomic weight of 4, sodium 23, iron 56, etc. The heaviest atom known in nature is that of uranium, with an atomic weight of 238.

In recent years it has been found that the atom is not the ultimate unit, but that the structure of the atom, in general, is rather complicated. The nucleus of the atom consists of one or more of a very small number of ultimate particles. This nucleus is very small and very dense. Outside the nucleus and revolving around it are one or more electrons.

The simplest atom known is that of hydrogen, which consists of one proton as a nucleus and one electron revolving about it. In the heavier atoms there are numerous electrons revolving about the nucleus in certain stable configurations.

64. The Atom the Source of Light. The ultimate source of light must lie in the atom. The means by which the atom transfers its energy to the ether and causes it to vibrate is not known. Various atomic models have been proposed and various theories put forth to explain the connection between the atom and the ether, but thus far none has proved entirely satisfactory. We feel reasonably certain that there is some sort of motion of the constituent parts of the atom, probably the outer electrons, and that by some means some of this energy of motion is released at times and shows itself as a series of vibrations in the ether. This is called *radiation*.

But atoms not only give off energy in the form of ether vibrations; they may also absorb energy from such vibrations and thus add to their own store. The method of absorption of energy is no doubt closely allied to the method of emission but is likewise unknown. We must wait as patiently as possible until further information is available.

65. Reflection of Light. When a ray of light strikes a plane polished surface, then, neglecting absorption and refraction (Sec. 66), the ray is reflected as shown in Fig. 33. If AB is the incident ray, BD the reflected ray, and CB a perpendicular to the reflecting surface, then the angle ABC is equal to the angle CBD. The angle of ABC is called the *angle of incidence* and the angle CBD the *angle of reflection*. The law of reflection from a plane surface may then be stated: *The angle of incidence is equal to the angle of reflection.*

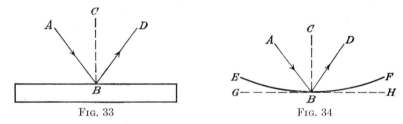

FIG. 33   FIG. 34

If reflection takes place from a curved surface, the result is as shown in Fig. 34. Let EBF be a curved surface and AB the incident ray falling on the surface at the point B. Draw GH tangent to the curve at B. Erect the perpendicular BC. The reflected ray BD will then take such a position that the angles ABC and CBD are equal.

We might have reached the result in another way. If we consider a very minute portion of the surface about the point B, it will be essentially a plane coincident with the tangent GH. We can then apply the construction in Fig. 33 to this minute portion.

66. Refraction and Dispersion of Light. When a ray of light, consisting of vibrations of the same wavelength (monochromatic light), passes from a rarer medium, such as air, to a denser medium, such as glass, the ray is bent toward the perpendicular to the surface separating them, as at B (Fig. 35). When the ray passes from a denser to a rarer medium, it is bent away from a similar perpendicular, as at C. This bending of the ray is called *refraction*.

If FG is perpendicular to the surface at B, then the angle FBA is called the *angle of incidence* and the angle CBG the *angle of refraction*.

Light of different wavelengths is refracted differently under the above conditions, the shorter the wavelength, the greater the refraction. Thus, since red light has a longer wavelength than yellow light, it is refracted less, and yellow light, in turn, is refracted less than blue light. If a ray of light should, therefore, be composed of light of each of these colors, the effect of passing from air to glass is illustrated in Fig. 36. This decomposition of a ray of light into its constituent colors is called *dispersion*.[1]

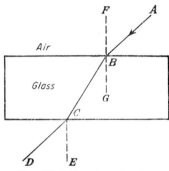

FIG. 35. Refraction of light.

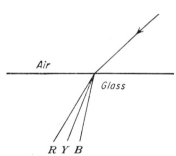

FIG. 36. Dispersion of light.

67. Path of Ray through a Prism. If a narrow beam of monochromatic light is allowed to pass through a prism of glass, the path followed is shown in Fig. 37, the amount of deviation depending on the refracting angle A of the prism, the density of the glass composing the prism, and the angle at which the beam strikes the prism face. For most purposes it is convenient to have the two angles B and C equal. In this case the beam goes through the prism parallel to the base, and the total deflection is a minimum.

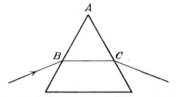

FIG. 37. Refraction of light by a prism.

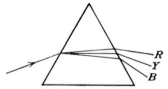

FIG. 38. Dispersion of light by a prism.

If, instead of using monochromatic light, the beam consists of light of various wavelengths, then dispersion also takes place and the beam is separated into its constituents, as shown in Fig. 38, which illustrates the effects for red, yellow, and blue light. A prism used in this way analyzes a beam of light into its constituent parts. This property of the prism is used in the spectroscope described later (Sec. 193).

[1] Note that in no case does the refracted ray cross the perpendicular.

68. The Achromatic Prism. If two prisms of the same angle and kind of glass are used, as shown in Fig. 39, their combined action is the same as if the inner surfaces were not there and we were using a plate of glass with parallel sides. The figure is drawn for a ray of monochromatic light. If the single ray is replaced by a beam of some width containing rays of various wavelengths, dispersion will come into play and the emergent beam will, in general, be a mixture except at the upper and lower borders where the light of longest and shortest wavelengths, respectively, will be found. The student will find it a good exercise to make a drawing on a sufficient scale to show this.

Fɪɢ. 39. Refraction of monochromatic light through reversed similar prisms.

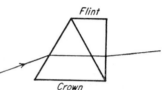

Fɪɢ. 40. The achromatic prism. Dispersion of light within the prisms not indicated.

Similar prisms made of two common kinds of glass, crown and flint, give about the same refraction for rays of light traversing them, but the flint-glass prism gives about double the dispersion of the crown-glass prism. This property of the two kinds of prisms is used if we wish to refract a beam of light without separating it into its various constituents. A crown-glass prism is combined with a flint-glass prism of about half the angle, as shown in Fig. 40. The second prism neutralizes the dispersion of the first but only half the refraction. Hence the beam of light is refracted by the combination without being dispersed. Such a compound prism is called an *achromatic prism.*

69. The Nature of White Light. If a beam of white light is analyzed by means of a prism, it is found to be made up of ether waves of all lengths from about 7800 to 3900 A. These waves of different lengths affect the eye as different colors which merge into each other in the order red, orange, yellow, green, blue, and violet as we go from the longer to the shorter waves.

By appropriate methods it has been found that white light also contains waves both longer than 7800 and shorter than 3900 A. These are called *infrared* and *ultraviolet* waves, respectively.

70. Shapes of Lenses. A lens is usually a piece of glass bounded either by two spherical surfaces or by one spherical and one plane surface. Figure 41 shows sections of the six ordinary kinds of lenses. They are called, in order, double convex, concavo-convex or meniscus, plano-convex, plano-concave, concavo-convex and double concave.

A lens is used either to converge or to diverge a beam of light. The first three are convergent and the last three divergent lenses. The convergent lenses are thicker at the center than at the edge, while the divergent lenses are thinner.

The *size* of a lens is usually designated by its diameter.

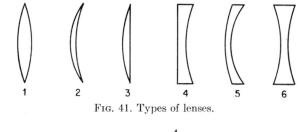

FIG. 41. Types of lenses.

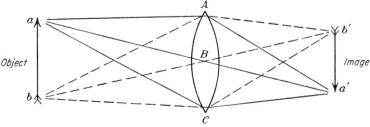

FIG. 42. Formation of an image by a convergent lens.

71. Convergent Lenses. The ordinary use of a convergent lens is to form an image of an object. A simple Kodak or camera is the best-known illustration. The use of a double-convex lens for this purpose is illustrated in Fig. 42, but the principle is the same for all convergent lenses. By means of the figure we shall trace three rays from each end of the arrow and assume that we are dealing with monochromatic light. The ray from point a which strikes the upper portion of the lens at A is bent as if the lens were a prism, and sent to a'; the ray passing through the center B is essentially undeviated; while the ray passing through C is deviated in the opposite direction from that through A so that the three unite at a'. Other rays from a which strike the lens between A and C are deviated proportionally, so that they all unite at a'.

In a similar manner the rays from b are united at b' and rays from other parts of the arrow shaft between a and b unite at corresponding points between a' and b', so that an image of the arrow is formed. This image may be seen very easily if it is allowed to fall on a piece of white paper or on a ground glass, as in the larger photographic cameras.

72. Focal Length of Convergent Lens. If a beam of light from a very distant source, such as a star, passes through a lens (the light from the source consisting of parallel rays) an image of the star is formed at a definite distance from the center of the lens. This distance is called the *focal length* of the lens and depends upon the density of the glass and the curvature of the lens surfaces. The greater the density of the glass and the greater the curvature of the surfaces, the shorter the focal length of the lens.

If it is desired to use a parallel beam of light, a point source may be placed at the focus of a lens as shown in Fig. 43. Such an arrangement is of importance in some optical instruments, such as the spectroscope.

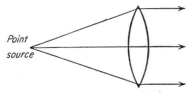

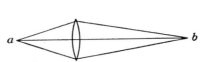

FIG. 43. Production of a parallel beam of light.

FIG. 44. Conjugate foci.

73. Conjugate Foci. In Fig. 44 let *a* represent a source of light and let *b* be the image of *a* formed by the lens. If *b* were the source, then *a* would be the image. These two points are called *conjugate foci*.

If f_1 is the distance of *a* from the center of the lens and f_2 the corresponding value for *b*, we can calculate the focal length *F* of the lens by the equation

$$\frac{1}{F} = \frac{1}{f_1} + \frac{1}{f_2}$$

If, for a certain lens, $f_1 = 10$ cm and $f_2 = 20$ cm, then

$$\frac{1}{F} = \frac{1}{10} + \frac{1}{20} = \frac{3}{20}$$

and

$$F = \frac{20}{3} = 6.67 \text{ cm}$$

74. Brightness of Image. If two lenses have the same diameters (Fig. 45), but lens *B* has twice the focal length of lens *A*, then the image of an object of appreciable angular diameter formed by *B* will have twice the length and width of the image formed of the same object by *A*.

Since we assume both lenses to have the same diameter, they will transmit equal quantities of light to the image. The image formed by lens *B* will have four times the area of the image formed by lens *A*, and hence the amount of light per unit of area in the image will only be one-fourth as much. If the lenses are to be used for photography, then lens *A* is said to be four times as fast as lens *B*.

In general it may be stated that for lenses of equal apertures the surface brightness of the image varies inversely as the square of the focal length.

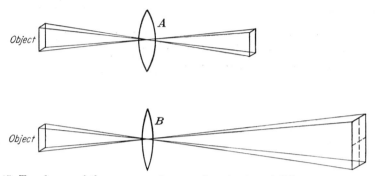

FIG. 45. Two lenses of the same aperture produce images of different surface brightness if of different focal lengths. Note that only the rays through the centers of the lenses are drawn in order not to complicate the diagram.

75. Spherical Aberration. Thus far we have considered only the general action of a convergent lens. In order to understand the telescope it is necessary to consider the matter more minutely. If rays of light from a distant point source pass through a convergent lens, it is found that the image is not formed at a point because the rays going through the lens near the edge are brought to a focus nearer the lens than those passing through near the center. This is illustrated in Fig. 46. This action of the lens is called *spherical aberration*. The thicker the lens in proportion to its diameter, the greater the spherical aberration.

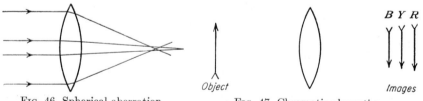

FIG. 46. Spherical aberration.   FIG. 47. Chromatic aberration.

76. Chromatic Aberration. Because of the dispersion of light by glass, a very troublesome color effect is also in evidence. The focal length of a lens for blue light is less than for yellow, and for yellow light less than for red. In consequence, if an object is sending out light of these three colors, the image formed will not be a single image but there will be blue, yellow, and red images formed at increasing distances from the lens. This effect is called *chromatic aberration*, and is illustrated in Fig. 47, the images and object alone being shown without tracing the rays.

If light of many wavelengths (white light) comes from the object, there will be an image for each wavelength—the longer the wave, the farther the image will be from the lens.

77. Divergent Lenses. A divergent lens will not form an image when acting alone. Its action for a parallel beam is illustrated in Fig. 48, and for a converging beam by Fig. 49. For the production of a con-

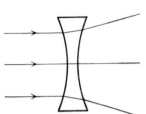
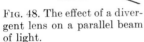

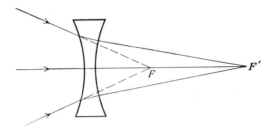

Fig. 48. The effect of a divergent lens on a parallel beam of light.

Fig. 49. The effect of a divergent lens on a converging beam of light.

vergent beam a convergent lens, in general, is necessary. The convergent beam would have come to a focus at F, but by the interposition of the divergent lens the focus is displaced to F'. This is the customary use of a divergent lens. Its application to the telescope is considered in the following section.

Divergent lenses have spherical and chromatic aberrations just like those of the convergent type.

78. The Achromatic Lens. In order to avoid the very troublesome chromatic aberration of lenses, it has been found possible to utilize the principle considered in the achromatic prism (Sec. 68). By combining a double-convex lens of crown glass with a plano-concave lens of flint glass, as shown in Fig. 50, an image is obtained which is reasonably free from color. Such a lens is called an *achromatic lens.* Lenses of this kind appear to have been made first by Chester Moor Hall of England in 1733, but they were first made for general use by the English optician Dollond, in 1758.

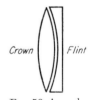

Fig. 50. An achromatic lens.

Strictly speaking, a double lens of this character will combine accurately light of only two colors or wavelengths. For some purposes it is desirable to combine three or more colors in the image. When this is the case, three or more lenses of different optical properties must be used.

In addition to eliminating the chromatic aberration by such lens combinations it is also possible to eliminate most of the spherical aberration by a proper choice of curvature of the lens surfaces. For large lenses the flint component is not plane on one side, as shown in Fig. 50, but has this side ground to a slight curve as well. Furthermore, the two convex surfaces of the crown component generally have different radii.

The direction in which light passes through an achromatic lens depends upon the maker. In some cases the crown glass is used for the front component and in other cases the flint.

EXERCISES

1. What would have to be done to lens B, Fig. 45, to produce as brilliant an image of the same object as that from lens A?

2. What would have to be done to lens A, Fig. 45, to produce as faint an image as that from lens B?

3. If the focal length of a lens is 1 m, how far from the lens will the image be formed if the object is 10 m distant? If 5 m distant? If 2 m distant? If 1 m distant?

Ans. 1.11 m; 1.25 m; 2 m; infinity.

CHAPTER 5

THE TELESCOPE

THE REFRACTING TELESCOPE

79. Invention of the Telescope. It appears uncertain who should be called the inventor of the telescope. Certain references lead some to think that the instrument was not unknown to the Greeks and Romans, but, if this was the case, it never came into general use. From the practical point of view it appears that telescopes were first made in Holland about 1608. The following year Galileo heard of the invention and constructed a number of instruments which magnified from 3 to 33 times. In 1610 he began his series of astronomical observations and discoveries and thus was the first to demonstrate the enormous value of this most important instrument to astronomy.

80. Principle of the Telescope. The principle of the telescope is exceedingly simple. All that is required is a lens (called the *object glass* or objective) to form an image of the object to be examined, a magnifier (called the *eyepiece*) to magnify the image and some device, such as a tube, to hold them the requisite distance apart.

The principle is most easily illustrated by means of a camera. If the camera is pointed at a tree, as indicated in Fig. 51, an image of the tree

Object

Image

Fig. 51. The principle of the refracting telescope.

will be formed on the ground glass at the back. For focusing purposes this image is usually examined directly by the eye, but if we magnify the image by means of a simple pocket lens, we shall have a telescope in a crude form.

The ground glass has nothing to do with the formation of the image but is a convenient device for determining the focus of the camera. If the image is examined without the ground glass, it will be found brighter than with it.

Let us now apply this principle to the telescope. Suppose the instrument is pointed at the moon (Fig. 52). An image of the moon will be formed by the objective near the eye end of the tube. This image is then

magnified by the eyepiece so that the eye will see the moon apparently much enlarged as compared with the naked-eye view.

FIG. 52. A refracting telescope.

81. The Objective. The purpose of the objective is twofold: (1) to gather as much light as possible from the object; and (2) to form an image of the object, which may then be magnified by the eyepiece. The larger the objective, the more light it can collect from the object. This is of no especial importance for a bright object like the moon, but for a faint object like a distant star it is of the utmost importance, for the image must be bright enough to affect the retina of the eye. For work on faint objects telescopes of large aperture are therefore necessary.

The diameter of the objective is used to designate the *size* of the telescope.

82. The Eyepiece. Two general types of eyepieces are in use—the positive and the negative. Each has certain advantages and certain disadvantages.

The Positive Eyepiece. This consists of two plano-convex lenses of equal focal lengths mounted in a tube which is usually of brass (Fig. 53). This type gives a very flat field of view but is not entirely achromatic. In using this eyepiece the image formed by the objective is a short distance in front of the larger lens which is called the *field lens.*

The Negative Eyepiece. This type is essentially achromatic but does not give as flat a field of view as the positive eyepiece (Fig. 53). The focal length of the field lens in the negative eyepiece is about three times that of the smaller or *eye lens.* When using this eyepiece, the image formed by the objective falls between the two lenses.

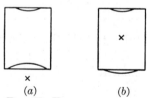

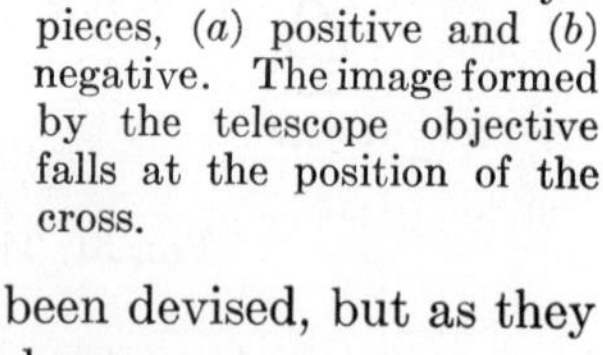

FIG. 53. Two common eyepieces, (a) positive and (b) negative. The image formed by the telescope objective falls at the position of the cross.

Other and more complicated eyepieces have been devised, but as they are more expensive, they are not in such general use.

83. Magnifying Power of a Telescope. The magnification of a telescope is defined as the number of times the diameter of an object is apparently increased when looked at through the telescope as compared with the diameter when seen with the unaided eye. Thus, suppose a planet has an apparent angular diameter of 1′ as seen by the naked eye. A magnification of 60 would make the apparent diameter 1°, or double

FIG. 54. The great refracting telescope of the Lick Observatory, Mt. Hamilton, California. Diameter of lens 91 cm (36 in.); focal length, 17.7 m (58 ft).

the apparent diameter of the moon, while a magnification of 120 would make the apparent diameter in the telescope 2°, etc.

The magnification of a telescope depends upon the relation between the focal lengths of objective and eyepiece, according to the equation

$$M = \frac{F}{f}$$

where M is the magnifying power, F the focal length of the objective, and f the focal length of the eyepiece.

The focal length of the eyepiece depends primarily upon the curvature of the lenses used and is defined as the focal length of a single lens having the same magnification. If we desire to use various magnifying powers with any objective, it is only necessary to have a set of eyepieces of different focal lengths. For small telescopes two or three eyepieces are usually sufficient, but large telescopes may require a dozen or more if the instrument is to be used effectively.

The focal length of the 41-cm (16-in.) refractor of the Goodsell Observatory is 675 cm (266 in). An eyepiece of 2.5 cm focal length will therefore provide a magnification of 270 and a 1-cm-focus eyepiece a magnification of 675.

The best magnification to use depends upon the object being studied and upon the steadiness of the atmosphere. Bright objects can be magnified more than faint ones, but the steadiness of the air plays the most important role. When the atmosphere is unsteady, the image shows tremors. Since the tremors are magnified as well as the image as a whole, it is possible to use too great a magnification and therefore actually to see less than with a lower power. Even under the best conditions it is seldom advantageous to use a power exceeding 20 to the centimeter (50 to the inch) of aperture of the objective.

84. Resolving Power. The image of a star formed by the best of objectives is never a point of light but consists of a small round disk surrounded by one or more rings of light. This form of image is due to the wave nature of light and the fact that the objective is circular. If the objective were of rectangular outline, the star would appear as a minute rectangle bounded by one or more lines.

The disk of the star image is often called the *spurious disk*. The spurious disk is brightest at the center and fades out rapidly toward the edge. The size of the disk varies inversely as the diameter of the objective. It is this fact, among others, which makes a large objective more desirable than a small one.

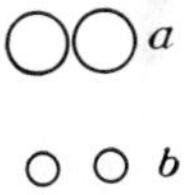

Fig. 55. Telescopic images of close stars. (*a*) The spurious disks are tangent for a telescope lens of a certain diameter. (*b*) The same stars seen with a lens twice the diameter used for *a*.

Let us suppose we observe two stars which are so close together that their spurious disks are just tangent to each other (Fig. 55*a*) as seen through a certain telescope. Then, if we observe the same stars through a telescope whose objective is twice the diameter of the first and use the same magnification, we shall see them as in Fig. 55*b*. The diameters of the disks will be only half as great compared with the distance between their centers in the larger instrument as in the smaller. Hence the larger the objective, the closer two stars may be and still be separated.

The angular distance between the centers of the spurious disks of stars which are tangent to each other as in Fig. 55a is termed the *resolving power* of the telescope.[1]

Dawes of England has given the following simple formula for resolving power in seconds of arc:

$$R'' = \frac{4.5}{\text{diameter of objective in inches}}$$

Hence a 4.5-in. objective will just separate two stars $1''$ apart, while the 40-in. Yerkes telescope will separate two stars only $0''.11$ apart.

The large telescope will not only separate close stars but will likewise show finer detail on the moon or the planets if our own atmosphere is sufficiently steady.

85. The Size of Telescopic Images. The formation of an image by a lens was considered in Sec. 71. From Fig. 42 it will be evident that angle aBb is equal to the angle $a'Bb'$, that is, the angular diameter of an object as seen from the lens is equal to the angular diameter of the image as seen from the lens.

The matter of the actual size of the image depends on where the image is formed. If the image is formed at c (Fig. 56), its size will be only half as great

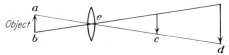

Fig. 56. The size of the image varies as the focal length of the lens. Note that only the rays through the center are drawn in order not to complicate the diagram.

as if formed at d which is twice as far from the lens. This may be stated in the form: *The linear dimensions of the image are proportional to the focal length of the lens.*

If the object in Fig. 56 represents the sun, then the angle aeb is approximately $\frac{1}{2}°$. Further, if the focal length of the lens is 100 cm, then the diameter of the image will be

$$d = \frac{1}{2} \times \frac{1}{57.3} \times 100 = \frac{100}{114.6} = 0.87 + \text{cm}$$

If two stars in the sky are $10''$ apart, then the distance between their images in the Lick refractor (focal length 1770 cm or 58 ft) will be

$$d = \frac{10 \times 1770}{206,265} = 0.086 \text{ cm} = 0.034 \text{ in.}$$

86. The Photographic Refractor. Thus far we have considered the refracting telescope as a visual instrument. The eye is most sensitive to yellow and green light, and these two colors are brought to the same focus by the lens combination. Lenses of this sort are not properly focused for the blue and violet light, which is most effective on the ordinary photographic plate, and therefore they cannot be used directly for the photography of celestial bodies.

[1] This is not an exact definition of resolving power but will serve our purpose better than one based strictly on the theory of the diffraction image.

When a refractor is to be used exclusively for photographic work, the lens is made to focus the blue and the violet light. Such a telescope is known as a *photographic refractor*. It cannot be used for visual observations and it is necessary to employ a visual telescope mounted parallel to it for guiding purposes.

Two methods have been employed to change the visual refractor into a photographic instrument. The simplest method is to use a special light filter which absorbs the blue and violet light and allows only the yellow and green to pass. Such a filter, when used with photographic plates sensitive to yellow and green light, will give excellent results except that much longer exposures must be given than if blue light were used.

Another method is to add a third lens, which can be placed in front of the visual objective and thus bring to a focus the blue and the violet light.

87. The Color Curve of a Lens. If the focal length of the convergent component of a telescope objective is measured for light of various wavelengths (colors) and these focal lengths are plotted against wavelength, then, neglecting spherical aberration, we will get a curve like that shown in Fig. 57. This is called a *color curve*. At no point is there light of more than one wavelength in focus because of the chromatic aberration of the lens.

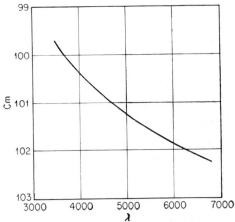

Fɪɢ. 57. The color curve of a simple converging lens. Ordinates indicate distance from lens.

The addition of the concave component of the telescope lens alters the curve as shown in Fig. 58. Curve *a* is the color curve of the 41-cm (16-in.) lens of the Goodsell Observatory. Since this is a visual objective, the shortest focal length is in the yellow-green. Curve *b* is the color curve of the 80-cm (31-in.) Potsdam photographic objective. In this case the shortest focal length is in the blue. The ordinates of the curves are measured from the point of shortest focus and away from the objective.

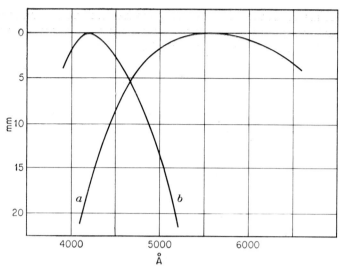

FIG. 58. The color curves of two telescope objectives: *a*, the curve of the 41-cm (16-in.) *visual* objective of the Goodsell Observatory; *b*, the curve of the 80-cm (31-in.) *photographic* objective of the Potsdam Astrophysical Observatory. The objectives are their respective focal lengths above the zero line.

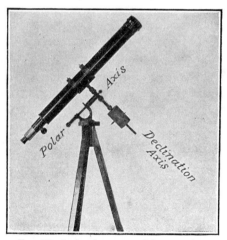

FIG. 59. A simple equatorial mounting.

88. The Telescope Mounting. Except for very small instruments, the best form of mounting is the equatorial type (Fig. 59). In this form the main axis is set parallel to the earth's axis and the other at right angles to it. These axes are called the *polar axis* and *declination axis*, respectively (see also Figs. 54, 62, 63).

When a telescope is mounted in this way, it is necessary to turn only the polar axis in order to follow an object across the sky. All larger

telescopes are equipped with a driving mechanism which turns the polar
axis at just the rate necessary to counteract the earth's rotation and thus
follow an object in the sky as long as may be desired.

THE REFLECTING TELESCOPE

89. The earliest telescopes were all refractors, but they seldom exceeded
a few inches in diameter because of the impossibility of obtaining good
optical glass in large disks and because chromatic and spherical aberrations
were so annoying in instruments of any size. Dollond's success in making
achromatic objectives eliminated the serious aberration difficulties, but
the lack of optical glass disks of any size was for many years an insurmountable barrier.

Before Dollond's time, Newton had developed the reflecting telescope,
one of these instruments being presented by him to the Royal Society
in 1671. *The statements concerning resolving power, use of eyepieces and*
magnifying power in Secs. 83 and
84 apply also to reflecting telescopes.

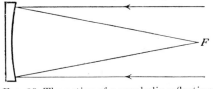

Fig. 60. The action of a parabolic reflecting
surface on a parallel beam of light.

**90. Principle of Reflecting Tele-
scope.** If a parallel beam of light
is allowed to fall on a parabolic
reflecting surface, as indicated in
Fig. 60, the rays of light are
brought to a focus at a point F.
Hence for distant objects such a reflecting surface will form an image of
the object at the focus by reflection just as a convergent lens will form an
image of an object by refraction.

The mirrors of the early reflectors were made of speculum metal (an
alloy consisting mostly of copper and tin), but the modern ones are made
of glass, the reflecting surface being coated with a thin film of silver or
aluminum. *The reflection is directly from the metallic surface, the light*
not entering the glass at all. The only purpose served by the glass is that
of a rigid form for the metallic film.

91. Types of Reflecting Telescopes. Since the image formed by the
reflector is in the axis of the mirror and on the same side as the object,
it is not in a convenient position for observation. Two methods are
in general use to obviate the difficulty. The first is to insert a small *plane*
mirror into the converging beam before it comes to a focus and reflect
the light to the side of the tube so that the image is formed near E (Fig.
61*A*). The second method is to place a convex mirror near the upper end
of the tube and reflect the beam downward through a hole in the large
mirror as shown in Fig. 61*B*. If it is not advisable to cut an opening
through the large mirror, a small plane mirror may be placed just in

front of it and the image formed at the side of the tube close to the lower end.

The first type was devised by Newton and the second by Cassegrain. The Cassegrainian form has the advantage over the Newtonian in that by using different *convex* mirrors the size of the image can be varied within wide limits. Other types have been devised but are not now in general use.

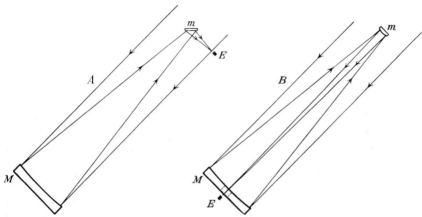

FIG. 61. Types of reflecting telescopes: (A) Newtonian; (B) Cassegrainian. Principal mirror at M, secondary mirror at m, eyepiece at E.

The introduction of a small additional mirror in the path of the incoming light reduces the light-gathering power of the instrument, but there is no way of avoiding this. Secondary mirrors are supported by thin metal strips extending inward from the main tube. These strips are the cause of the rays radiating from the images of bright stars when the reflector is used for direct photography.

Reflectors can be used as either visual or photographic instruments. When used visually, the image is viewed through an eyepiece; when used photographically, the sensitive plate is placed at the focus.

92. Relative Advantages of Refractors and Reflectors. In order to correct a telescope lens for spherical aberration it is necessary to have the focal length about 15 times the diameter of the lens (this number is called the focal ratio). The great Lick and Yerkes refractors have focal ratios of nearly 20, but some smaller instruments have been constructed in which this ratio is as low as 10. The reflector, however, may be constructed with almost any focal ratio. The large modern reflectors, such as the 254-cm (100-in.) of the Mt. Wilson Observatory, and the 183-cm (72-in.) of the Dominion Astrophysical Observatory, have ratios of about 5, and the 200-in. Hale reflector of the Palomar Observatory has a focal ratio of 3.3 (see frontispiece). Thus the refractor is from three to four times as long as a reflector of the same aperture. This is of considerable importance when considering the cost of the dome for the instrument.

The mirror has but one surface which must be brought to the proper curvature, while the lens has four. The cost is therefore much less.

FIG. 62. The great 254-cm (100-in.) reflecting telescope of the Mt. Wilson Observatory, Mt. Wilson, California. (*Mt. Wilson and Palomar Observatories.*)

A much poorer quality of glass as regards transparency can be used for the mirror than for the lens, as the light does not reach the glass of the mirror at all.

The mirror is perfectly achromatic, while no lens can be wholly so. The reflector may therefore be used for both visual and photographic observations without change.

Fig. 63. The 183-cm (72-in.) reflecting telescope of the Dominion Astrophysical Observatory, Victoria, B.C. (*Dominion Astrophysical Observatory.*)

The light-gathering power of the reflector is less than that of the refractor for apertures of 80 to 100 cm (30 to 40 in.) or less. For instruments up to this size, the loss of light due to absorption in the lens in the refractor is less than that occasioned by imperfect reflection from the metallic surface and the obstruction of light by the secondary mirror in the reflector. For larger sizes the increased absorption of the thicker lens would cause a greater loss of light in the refractor. In consequence, the reflector is more efficient than the refractor in the case of very large instruments.

A mirror must have its metallic coating renewed from time to time to keep it up to its greatest efficiency, and it is also much more sensitive to changes of temperature than a lens.

At the present time the reflector dominates the field for large instruments, but the refractor is still the favorite for apertures of 50 cm (20 in.) or less.

93. The Schmidt Camera. In 1930 Schmidt, of the Hamburg Observatory, devised a new method of overcoming the aberrations of the ordinary reflecting telescope. Instead of parabolizing the principal mirror, he used a spherical one. At the center of curvature of the mirror he placed a thin plate of glass figured in such a way that the refraction of the glass neutralized the aberration of the mirror (Fig. 64). The focal surface of

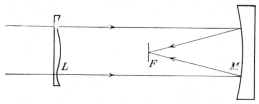

Fig. 64. A Schmidt camera: *L*, correcting lens with curves greatly exaggerated; *M*, spherical mirror; *F*, curved focal surface.

such a combination is slightly curved, but this can be allowed for by bending the photographic plate or film. The great advantage of this type of instrument lies in the fact that a large area of sky, 5° or more in diameter, can be photographed in good definition as compared with a diameter of a fraction of a degree with a paraboloidal mirror. A further advantage is that a much shorter focal ratio such as $f/2$ or even $f/1$ can be used.

Because of the large angular diameter of the field which can be photographed, the mirror must be larger than the glass correcting plate if there is to be no loss of light for the oblique rays. Figure 65 shows the Schmidt camera of the Warner and Swasey Observatory. The mirror has a diameter of 91 cm (36 in.), the correcting plate a diameter of 61 cm (24 in.), and the focal ratio is $f/3.5$.

94. The Electron Telescope. A new approach to obtain far more intense images of celestial bodies on the photographic plate has just been announced (1952) by Lallemand and Duchesne of the Paris Observatory. By means of a telescope an image of a celestial body is formed on a sensitive photoelectric film. The electrons given off by the film are focused by a combination of electric and magnetic fields on a photographic plate. The image thus recorded is fully equal to the optical

Fig. 65. The Schmidt camera of the Warner and Swasey Observatory. (*Warner and Swasey Observatory.*)

image formed by the telescope alone. The big advance, however, is that the electron image requires an exposure only about 2 per cent as long as the optical image with the same telescope. Much further work will be required to develop fully this new method, but, if the present prospects are realized, it means that photographs of faint objects, which might require an all-night exposure with a particular telescope, could be obtained in a few minutes if used in conjunction with the new apparatus. The possibilities of the new method stagger the imagination.

EXERCISES

1. What is the resolving power of an objective of 3 in. aperture?　　　*Ans.* 1″.5.

2. The great Lick refractor has an objective of 36 in. aperture.　What is its resolving power?　　　*Ans.* 0″.125.

3. The great Yerkes refractor has a focal length of 63 ft.　Calculate to the nearest hundredth inch the focal length of eyepieces required for magnifications of 250, 800, 1500.　　　*Ans.* 3.02, 0.94, 0.50 in.

4. If the moon's angular diameter is 31′, what will be the diameter of its image formed by a lens of 254 cm (100 in.) focal length?　　　*Ans.* 2.3 cm. or 0.9 in.

5. What will be the focal length of a lens which forms an image of the moon 15 cm (6 in.) in diameter if the moon's angular diameter is 31′?

　　　　　　　　　　　　　　　　　　　　　　　　Ans. 1663.5 cm or 665.4 in.

6. The 152-cm (60-in.) reflector of the Mt. Wilson Observatory has a focal ratio of $f/5$.　How large an image of Mars will be formed by this telescope when the planet is nearest the earth and has an angular diameter of 25″?　　*Ans.* 0.092 cm or 0.036 in.

7. At the eclipse of the sun on Aug. 31, 1932, the U.S. Naval Observatory used a camera lens of 65 ft focal length.　What was the size of the moon's image on the plate if the angular diameter of the moon at the time was 32′?　　　*Ans.* 7.3 in.

CHAPTER 6

THE MOON

The moon must have been one of the first of the heavenly bodies to engage the attention of primitive man. The various phases shown in the course of the month; its movement among the stars; its disappearance near the western side of the sun followed by its reappearance, a few days later, on the eastern side; the dark spots to be seen on its surface—all these gave rise to thought which resulted in various ingenious theories to account for them. Even today the moon is an object of interest, both from the popular and from the scientific point of view.

95. Distance. The moon is the nearest of the heavenly bodies. Its mean distance from the earth is 384,400 km (238,860 miles), but, on account of the eccentricity (Sec. 160) of its orbit, and the perturbations (Sec. 163) to which it is subjected, its actual distance varies from about 357,000 km (222,000 miles) to about 407,000 km (253,000 miles). The method of determining its distance has been given in Sec. 25.

96. The Moon's Orbit. The moon moves around the earth from west to east in an elliptical orbit which has an eccentricity of 0.055. The plane of the orbit is inclined to the plane of the ecliptic at an angle whose average value is 5°9'. This inclination varies about 12' either way from the mean value. The line of apsides (longest diameter extended) makes one revolution from west to east in about 9 years, while the line of nodes (the line of intersection of the plane of the moon's orbit with the plane of the ecliptic) moves from east to west and completes one revolution in about 19 years. These motions of the line of apsides and line of nodes are caused by perturbations or disturbances of the moon's motion by the sun.

The point of the moon's orbit nearest the earth is called *perigee* and the point farthest from the earth *apogee*.

97. Diameter, Mass, etc. The moon's apparent outline is circular and its angular diameter at mean distance is 31'5''. Its linear diameter is 3476 km (2160 miles). Its mass is approximately 0.0123 times that of the earth and its mean density is 3.4 times that of water. The force of gravity at its surface is one-sixth that on the earth, that is, a man who weighs 180 lb on the earth would weigh but 30 lb on the moon. If we could make a trip to the moon and live there for a time, this low value of gravity would lead to many interesting experiences.

98. The Phases of the Moon. *We see the moon because of the sunlight falling on it.* The side of the moon turned toward the sun is illuminated while the other side is in darkness. Because of the orbital motions of moon and earth the relative positions of sun, moon, and earth are constantly changing. When the moon is on the opposite side of the earth from the sun, we say it is *full*, while when it is in line with the sun it is *new*. Figure 66 illustrates these and other phases.

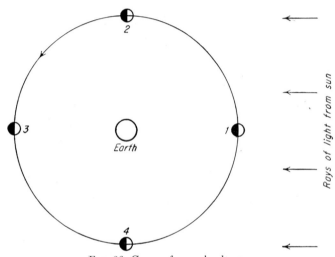

Fig. 66. Cause of moon's phases.

Since we can see only the illuminated portion of the moon which faces the earth, it is evident that, when in position 1, we cannot see the moon at all. When in position 2 we see half the surface illuminated, while between positions 1 and 2 we see the *crescent* phase. Between positions 2 and 3 we see more than half the surface illuminated. This is termed the *gibbous* phase. In position 3 the entire side turned toward the earth is illuminated and we have full moon. From position 3 to positions 4 and 1 we see the illuminated surface gradually diminish, passing through gibbous and crescent phases, until it vanishes at 1. When the moon is in positions 2 and 4, so that we see half of it, the phases are called *first* and *last quarters*, respectively.

If the plane of the moon's orbit were not inclined to the plane of the ecliptic, there would be an eclipse of the sun at each new moon and an eclipse of the moon at each full moon.

The line which separates the illuminated from the unilluminated portion is called the *terminator*. The apparent edge of the moon's disk, or the disk of any other heavenly body, is often called the *limb*.

99. The Intensity of Moonlight. At the time of full moon the light of the moon is equal to about ¼ meter-candle. Compared with sunlight it is very weak. The mean of a number of determinations yields a value of about 465,000 for the ratio of sunlight to moonlight at full moon. If the entire sky above the horizon were packed with full moons limb to limb, they would give only about one-sixth as much light as the sun.

The amount of moonlight received on the earth is not proportional to the area of moon seen illuminated as the intensity falls off rapidly either way from full so that at first or last quarters the intensity is only about one-tenth as much as at full.

100. The Sidereal Month. If observed from night to night, it will be seen that the moon moves eastward among the stars so that in time it completes a circuit of the heavens. The *sidereal month* is defined as the time it takes the moon to make one revolution about the earth with reference to the stars, that is, the time required to move around the sky from any particular star until it again reaches it. The sidereal month has a mean length of $27^d7^h43^m11^s.5$.

101. The Synodic Month. From ancient times the meaning of the word "month" has been the interval of time from new moon to new moon or from full moon to full moon. This month is called the *synodic month* and its mean length is $29^d12^h44^m2^s.8$. The diagram (Fig. 67) shows why the synodic month is longer than the sidereal month.

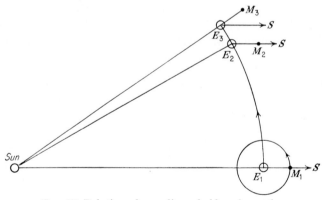

Fig. 67. Relation of synodic and sidereal months.

Let us assume that at the time of full moon the moon is in line with a star in the direction E_1M_1S. After an interval of one sidereal month the earth will be at E_2, the moon at M_2, and the line E_2M_2S will be parallel to E_1M_1S. The moon will, therefore, be in line with the same star again but, since it is not yet opposite the sun, it is not full. In order to have full moon the moon must move forward, until the line sun-earth, when continued, will strike the moon.   In the meantime the earth is also moving forward to a new position, E_3, so that the synodic month is not completed until the line $sun\text{-}E_3M_3$ is a straight line.   The additional time required for the moon to move through the angle M_3E_3S is the interval of over two days by which the length of the synodic month exceeds the sidereal.

There is a simple relationship which exists between the lengths of the sidereal and synodic months and the year.   If S_i represents the length of the sidereal month, S_y the length of the synodic month and E the length of the year, then

$$\frac{1}{S_y} = \frac{1}{S_i} - \frac{1}{E}$$

102. Earthshine on the Moon. Shortly after new moon we may see the crescent moon brightly illuminated by the sun, while the remainder of the surface is seen illuminated by a faint light.   This appearance is most marked when the crescent is narrow, and it gradually becomes less noticeable until, by the time the moon has reached first quarter, it disappears.   The faint illumination is caused by sunlight reflected to the moon from the earth and then reflected back again to the earth.   It is called *earthshine*.   Similar effects may be seen between last quarter and new moon.

103. Rotation. The moon has a slow rotation about an axis which is tipped about $6°.5$ from the perpendicular to the plane of its orbit.   A remarkable feature of this rotation is that its period is exactly equal to its sidereal period of revolution and is also in the same direction.   In consequence, the moon always turns the same face toward the earth.

The reason for this is not wholly clear, but it is probably due to tides raised in the body of the moon at a time when it may have been in a more or less plastic condition.   The friction of these tides finally produced the effect.   This explanation of the phenomenon is the best one available and appears sufficient if we grant that the moon was ever plastic.

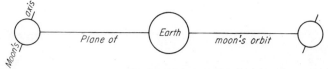

FIG. 68. Libration of moon in latitude.   Tilt of the moon's axis is considerably exaggerated.

104. Librations. Because the moon's axis[1] is not perpendicular to the plane of its orbit, we are able to see past the one pole for half of the month and past the other pole during the other half (Fig. 68).   The maximum

[1] The axis remains parallel to itself in all parts of the orbit.

amount we may see past either pole on this account is about 6°.5 of latitude on the moon. This is called the *libration in latitude*.

Another libration, known as the *libration in longitude*, is caused by the fact that, while the rate of axial rotation is constant, the velocity in the elliptical orbit is not constant. This may be understood by reference to the diagram (Fig. 69). The moon moves more rapidly in the part of its orbit ABC than in the part CDA. It therefore requires less time to move through the first 180° in the sky than through the second. Since its axial rotation, however, is at a constant rate, it will rotate less than half in the part ABC and more than half in the part CDA.

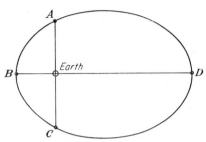

FIG. 69. Libration in longitude. The ellipticity of the orbit is greatly exaggerated.

The rotation will therefore be behind the orbital movement for part of the month and ahead in the other part. We may therefore sometimes see a little farther around the eastern side and at other times a little farther around the western side. The maximum value is nearly 8° of the moon's longitude.

A third libration of small amount has also been detected. There is some evidence that the moon is slightly elongated in the direction toward the earth. This third libration is due to a small pendulumlike oscillation of the body of the moon, and is known as the *physical libration*.

Other slight effects are due to our making observations from the earth's surface instead of from its center. The combined result of all librations is that we always have 41 per cent of the moon's surface turned toward us, a corresponding 41 per cent we never see, and of the remaining 18 per cent one-half will be turned toward us at any one time.

105. The Moon Day. The length of the day on the moon is equal to the synodic month and not the sidereal month as is sometimes stated. A consideration of the geometry of the situation in connection with Fig. 67 will make this clear.

106. Occultations. In her movement around the earth the moon necessarily passes between us and the stars. When this occurs for any particular star, it is said to be *occulted* by the moon. The occultation of a bright star, especially when it takes place at the dark limb of the moon, makes an interesting observation. The star, shining in full brightness, is suddenly blotted out. The suddenness of the occurrence is almost startling. Later the star reappears on the other side of the moon, the time between disappearance and reappearance being approximately an hour if the occultation is central.

Occultations have been used to determine the longitude of ships at sea, but this method has been superseded by more modern methods. The principal value of occultations at the present time lies in their use in determining the exact position of the moon among the stars.

Fig. 70. The moon near full. (*Lick Observatory.*)

Lists of stars to be occulted by the moon may be found in the *American Ephemeris* and in *Sky and Telescope.*

107. Telescopic Appearance. The unaided eye sees many light and dark areas on the moon. The telescope shows that, in general, the

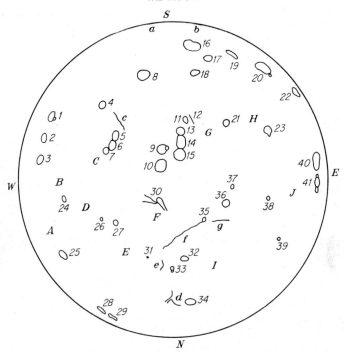

Fɪɢ. 71. Outline map of the principal features on the moon.

KEY TO MAP OF THE MOON
Seas

A. Mare Crisium
B. Mare Fecunditatis
C. Mare Nectaris
D. Mare Tranquillitatis
E. Mare Serenetatis

F. Mare Vaporum
G. Mare Nubium
H. Mare Humorum
I. Mare Imbrium
J. Oceanus Procellarum

Mountain Ranges

a. Leibnitz Mountains
b. Doerfel Mountains
c. Altai Mountains
d. Alps

e. Caucasus
f. Apennines
g. Carpathians

Craters, etc.

1. Petavius
2. Vendelinus
3. Langrenus
4. Piccolomini
5. Catharina
6. Cyrillus
7. Theophilus
8. Maurolycus
9. Albategnius
10. Hipparchus
11. Thebit
12. Straight Wall
13. Arzachel
14. Alphonsus

15. Ptolemaeus
16. Clavius
17. Longomontanus
18. Tycho
19. Schiller
20. Schickard
21. Bullialdus
22. Lagrange
23. Gassendi
24. Taurentus
25. Cleomedes
26. Jansen
27. Plinius
28. Endymion

29. De la Rue
30. Hyginus
31. Linné
32. Archimedes
33. Aristillus
34. Plato
35. Eratosthenes
36. Copernicus
37. Reinhold
38. Kepler
39. Aristarchus
40. Grimaldi
41. Hevel

Fig. 72. A great lunar plain, Mare Imbrium, and the surrounding chains of mountains. (*Mt. Wilson Observatory.*)

dark areas are comparatively smooth and the bright areas are rough. The dark areas were thought by the earliest users of the telescope to be bodies of water and were named seas. The various surface features, the seas, mountains, craters, rills, and rays, will be taken up separately.

108. The Seas. The surface of the seas is comparatively smooth and darker in color than the rest of the lunar surface. In some cases isolated mountain peaks and small craters are to be seen, but, for the most part, these areas are great plains measuring from about 250 km (155 miles) to over 800 km (500 miles) across. They are surrounded by mountains, but the extent of the larger plains is so vast that an observer standing in their center would see nothing of the mountains, as they would lie beyond his horizon (Fig. 72).

109. The Mountains. These are found either as isolated peaks or in chains. Some of the chains are named after similar formations on the earth, such as the Alps, Caucasus, and Apennines, while others are named after scientists, such as Leibnitz, Doerfel, etc.

The heights of the lunar mountains vary as do the heights of similar formations on the earth. Some peaks of the lunar Caucasus and Apennines rise to over 6000 m (19,000 ft) in elevation, while in the great Leibnitz and Doerfel ranges elevations of 8000 m (25,000 ft) and over occur.

110. Measuring the Height of Lunar Mountains. One method of determining the height of a mountain on the moon is very simple in principle. The length of the shadow cast at any time by the mountain is measured by means of a micrometer (Sec. 250). From data supplied by the *American Ephemeris* the altitude of the sun as seen from the tip of the shadow at the time can be computed and the height of the mountain determined.

In Fig. 73, let CB be the height of the mountain, AB the length of the shadow, and the angle A the altitude of the sun. The distance AB

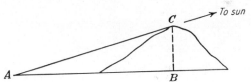

FIG. 73. Method of determining the height of a lunar mountain by means of its shadow.

will then be obtained from the micrometer measures and the angle A from the data of the *American Ephemeris*. Then by trigonometry,

$$CB = AB \tan A$$

111. The Craters. These formations bear a certain similarity to some volcanic craters on the earth, and hence the name. It must not be assumed that the name necessarily implies volcanic origin. Some observers have suggested names like *ring plains* or *ring mountains* for the larger craters.

There are many thousands of craters on the lunar surface, and these vary in size from mere pits less than ¼ km across to great ring mountains like Copernicus (Fig. 75) or ring plains like Clavius, having diameters

FIG. 74. Lunar craters.   (*Mt. Wilson Observatory.*)

of 90 and 225 km (56 and 140 miles), respectively.   In the smaller ones
we have simple depressions below the general surface, while in some of
the larger ones the surrounding rim may rise to an elevation of over
5000 m (16,000 ft) and individual peaks on the rim to even greater
elevations.   In some instances the floor of the crater is nearly at the
level of the rim, while in others it is considerably below the general level
of the region outside.

There are usually secondary craters in the floor or slopes of the main formation, while in many instances a central peak or group of peaks rises from the floor.

112. Rills. These are narrow, and usually deep, ravines or clefts which sometimes attain a length of from 300 to 500 km (200 to 300 miles). In some cases they intersect or branch and they may cross mountain and plain without a break. In other cases their course is deflected by some formation, or even interrupted, only to be resumed on the other side.

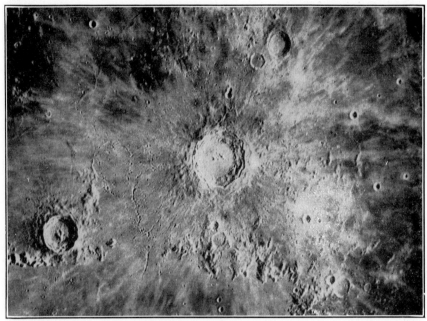

Fig. 75. Lunar craters Copernicus (center) and Eratosthenes (lower left). (*Lick Observatory.*)

Their real nature is uncertain but the idea that they were cracks which opened in the surface seems to be the simplest explanation.

113. Rays. Around many of the larger craters there is to be seen a system of white streaks, in some cases with considerable interlacing, while in others they extend almost directly away from a center, like spokes from the hub of a wheel. A good example of the first kind is found around Copernicus, while the best example of the second is found around Tycho. In the latter case some rays can be traced nearly across the entire surface of the moon (Fig. 70).

The rays seem to be entirely a surface phenomenon and cross mountain, valley, and plain without interruption. Apparently, they are white streaks on the surface itself and they are seen at their best when the sun is high for those regions on the moon.

114. Surface Materials. We do not know of what materials the surface of the moon is composed. Observations by Wilsing and Scheiner on the reflecting power of different parts in comparison with terrestrial rocks show that the dark surfaces of the lunar seas have the reflecting power of various lavas, while the bright parts of crater walls reflect as much light as volcanic ash.

The average *albedo*, or reflecting power, of the moon is low and determinations vary from 0.07 to 0.17. Russell's result is 0.073.

115. Origin of Surface Features. There are two general lines of thought in this connection. The one assumes that the craters were caused by disturbances from without and the other that they can be explained by conditions formerly obtaining within the body of the moon.

The first we shall consider may be called the meteoric theory. This assumes that in the past the moon was subjected to bombardment by great meteors, which by impact on the lunar surface melted the material and while burying themselves threw up the surrounding wall. While it is impossible to assert that the theory is wholly wrong, yet there are some grave objections to it. In the first place, it would seem that many more meteors would strike the earth because of its larger mass than would strike the moon. The striking velocity would also be higher. As a result, it would seem as if the earth should show some evidence of such a bombardment, but practically none is known. In the second place, it seems necessary to show that an adequate source of meteors was available.

All other theories start on the assumption that the moon at some time in the past was a hot molten mass. Some of these theories then merely assume that the craters are great volcanoes built up on the moon's crust. Others require the action of tides in the body of the moon pushing up molten material from the interior and then allowing any unsolidified matter to drain away through holes in the crust. Another theory assumes heated gases from the interior bursting through the crust as great bubbles, the crust bulging up and then partially collapsing, forming the rim of the crater.

It does not seem possible at the present time to decide definitely in favor of any particular theory, although it appears likely that some form of "molten moon" hypothesis is the more probable.

116. Temperature. The temperature of the lunar surface is difficult to determine. It has been shown that a considerable part of the sun's heat which falls on the moon is first absorbed and then radiated and some observers have deduced temperatures of over 100°C (212°F). This does not seem impossible, as the sun shines on a region for two full weeks without intermission. During the equally long two weeks' night, however, the temperature must fall very greatly.

From observations in 1927 Pettit and Nicholson find temperatures of

101°C (214°F) for a region with the sun in the zenith, -50°C (-58°F) for a region with the sun on the horizon and -153°C (-243°F) for the night side of the moon. According to the observers the last value is somewhat uncertain.

117. Nature of Lunar Surface. The rapid loss of heat by the lunar surface during an eclipse indicates that the high temperature under full sunlight is confined to a very thin surface layer. This layer is undoubtedly dust. The extreme temperature range during the lunar day would cause a crumbling of any rock surface exposed to it for any length of time. When such a dust layer has been formed, possibly only a few centimeters thick, it would act as a very effective insulator against transfer of heat to underlying rock. With the withdrawal of sunlight the dust layer would cool rapidly if there were no heat coming from below. Since there is no evidence of such heat we conclude that the body of the moon is cold.

118. Atmosphere. The moon possesses little or no atmosphere. The fact that there is no change in brightness between center and edge, the blackness of the shadows and the sudden disappearance of a star when occulted by the moon are evidences of an almost total absence of atmosphere. They do not prove, however, that there may not be one of great tenuity, of the order of 0.0001 of the density of the earth's atmosphere. The existence of such a thin atmosphere has not been established and it may be necessary to devise new methods of observation before this could be possible.

It has often been assumed that the moon at one time had an appreciable atmosphere and lost it because gravity at its surface was not strong enough to hold the atmospheric molecules. This assumption, however, is based on certain theories concerning the moon's origin which in themselves require proof.

The wholly wanting, or at least extremely tenuous, atmosphere precludes the existence of water in any quantity, for, if the latter existed, there would be an appreciable atmosphere of water vapor.

119. Changes on the Moon. No changes of the prominent features of the moon's surface have ever been noted. There is a certain amount of evidence that a small crater named Linné was seen a century ago as a deep crater about 10 km (6 miles) in diameter. In 1866, Schmidt of Athens reported that he could not find it and since that time it appears as a shallow bright area, about the same size as the crater formerly drawn in that region. Certain considerations, however, do not permit unqualified acceptance of a real change, although the evidence as a whole is in favor of it. A number of similar cases have since been reported.

Some years ago W. H. Pickering reported seeing periodic changes taking place within many craters, paying particular attention to Eratosthenes (Fig. 75). These consist in regular changes, occurring at each lunation, in color and outline of the different parts of the floor and inner walls of the crater. He interprets these to be in part small clouds of water vapor, deposits of frost or snow, and vegetation spreading over the surface and undergoing its life cycle within the lunar day. Observations by other observers lend support to the occurrence of these changes, but in the interpretation of the things observed there is strong disagreement at the present time.

120. Effects of the Moon on the Earth. There is a popular belief that the moon has a profound effect upon the weather; that the growth of crops depends upon the phase of the moon at the time of planting; etc. Extensive researches covering long periods have failed to find any real support for these widespread notions.

The moon, however, has one profound effect upon the earth in the formation of the tides, and in a slight degree it affects the magnetic field of the earth. The tides will be considered in Chap. 8.

EXERCISES

Assuming we might be able to live on the moon without changing the physical conditions found there:

1. Could a baseball pitcher deliver a curved ball?

2. What would be the effect of a hook or slice on the flight of a golf ball?

3. If a man could make a running high jump of 6 ft on the earth, how high could he jump on the moon?   *Ans.* About 26 ft.

4. If a man could make a running broad jump of 25 ft on the earth, how far could he jump on the moon?   *Ans.* 150 ft.

5. At a football game, would a cheer leader be of much value?

6. Could a class in astronomy be taught by the lecture method?

7. Could we see any meteors in the night sky?

CHAPTER 7

PROBLEMS IN PRACTICAL ASTRONOMY—
THE CALENDAR

There is an almost endless variety of problems in practical astronomy, but, for the purposes of this course, only a limited number require consideration. These relate to the determination of time, latitude, and longitude.

TIME

121. Sidereal Time. *Sidereal time is time measured with reference to the stars.* A good timekeeper requires a uniform rate. The best one available is the earth with its almost perfect axial rotation (see Sec. 44).

The simplest unit of time is the time required by the earth to complete one rotation with respect to the stars. This unit is called the *sidereal day.* The day begins when the vernal equinox is on the meridian. It is divided into 24 sidereal hours, the sidereal hour into 60 sidereal minutes and the sidereal minute into 60 sidereal seconds. The *sidereal time* at any instant is therefore the number of sidereal hours, minutes, and seconds which have elapsed since the last meridian passage of the vernal equinox. Another way of saying the same thing is that *the sidereal time at any instant is equivalent to the hour angle of the vernal equinox.*

The right ascensions of the stars can be measured from the vernal equinox because its position with respect to the stars is known. If a star whose right ascension is 1^h is on the meridian, we know that the vernal equinox crossed the meridian an hour ago, while if a star whose right ascension is 17^h is on the meridian then 17 sidereal hours have elapsed since sidereal noon. The sidereal time at any instant is therefore equal to the right ascension of any star on the meridian at that instant. This leads to a third way of defining sidereal time, namely, *the sidereal time is equal to the right ascension of the meridian* for the instant under consideration.

The vernal equinox, the point from which the sidereal day is measured, is moving slowly with respect to the stars (Sec. 165). The sidereal day is therefore not of the same length as if it were measured with respect to a point fixed among the stars. This difference, which amounts to approximately 0ˢ.01 per day, is the amount by which the sidereal day is shorter.

The Determination of Sidereal Time

Three instruments are ordinarily used for the determination of sidereal

time: the transit instrument or meridian circle, the chronograph, and the astronomical clock.

122. The Transit Instrument. The transit instrument is used for the determination of time by observing stars as they cross the meridian. The lens is usually from 5 to 10 cm (2 to 4 in.) in diameter. The telescope is rigidly attached to a stiff horizontal axis, which is placed in an east-west direction, so that the instrument is always pointing to the meridian as it rotates on the axis. Figure 76 shows such an instrument.

In the field of view of the eyepiece, at the focus of the objective, a series of spider threads or fine lines

FIG. 76. A simple transit instrument.

ruled on glass are placed. This is called the *reticle* (Fig. 77). The sidereal clock time when a star crosses each thread is noted and the average taken as the time when it was in the center of the field. If the instrument is in exact adjustment, this will be the clock time when the star is on the meridian. Since the right ascension of the star is known from the catalog, the difference between the observed clock time and the right ascension will be the amount by which the clock is in error. The *clock correction* is the quantity which must be *added to* the clock reading to give the correct time.

No transit instrument can be kept in exact adjustment in the meridian. Changes of temperature, etc., produce minute changes in the level and direction of the horizontal axis and in the

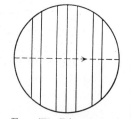

FIG. 77. Diagram of reticle of transit instrument.

direction of the line of sight with respect to the axis. The amount of these errors must be determined and allowed for in exact time determinations.

123. The Meridian Circle. This instrument (Fig. 78) is the same in principle as the transit instrument but is equipped with carefully graduated circles and various devices for refined measurements, so that in addition to observing meridian transits of stars it is also possible to

FIG. 78. The 12-cm (5-in.) meridian circle of the Goodsell Observatory, Carleton College.

determine their declinations. It is usually a larger instrument than the transit, the lens having a diameter of from 12 to 23 cm (5 to 9 in.).

124. The Chronograph. For the purpose of accurately recording the clock times as a star crosses the threads of the reticle, an instrument called a chronograph is used (Fig. 79). This consists of a cylinder about 35 cm (14 in.) long and 15 cm (6 in.) in diameter which rotates once per minute. A sheet of paper is wound around the cylinder and held by clips. In front of and parallel to the cylinder is a long screw which drives a small carriage. This carriage carries an electromagnet with a fountain pen attached to the armature of the magnet by means of a short lever. As the cylinder revolves, the pen traces a line on the paper, and, since the pen is also being moved forward slowly by the screw, the line becomes a helix.

In the circuit of the electromagnet are placed a clock and a signal key. Every even-numbered second the circuit is broken for an instant by the clock, so that the pen makes a slight jog in the line. By means of a device in the clock there is some way of indicating the end of each minute,

FIG. 79. A chronograph.

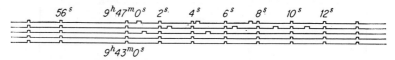

FIG. 80. A portion of a chronograph record.

either by omitting the break of the circuit at 58^s or by including one at 59^s as well. By this means definite minutes and seconds can be identified on the chronograph sheet.

Figure 80 shows a small portion of a chronograph record. In addition to the jogs caused by the clock the observer may press his signal key whenever he wishes to make a signal. This makes additional jogs on the line, whose time can then be read from the sheet by means of a suitable scale to about one one-hundredth of a second.

As the observer is watching a star cross the field of view of the transit instrument he will press the key each time the star crosses one of the spider threads of the reticle. When his observations are completed, he then reads off the clock times of the star transits across the threads.

Another type of chronograph, called the *printing chronograph*, has been developed, which prints on a strip of paper the times when the key is pressed. It is much more convenient than the type described but has not come into general use because of its much greater cost.

125. The Astronomical Clock. The astronomical clock is nothing more than a very fine clock with a seconds pendulum and a device for automatically making or breaking an electric circuit either each second or every 2 sec, usually the latter. The dial is graduated to read 24 hr instead of 12 hr, so that there is no chance of misreading the time of day.

The best clocks, however, are still subject to a change of rate with changes of temperature which affect the length of the pendulum, and by changes in barometric pressure which affect the resistance of the air to the movement of the pendulum. In order to prevent changes in the length of the pendulum with changes of temperature, the rod is made of invar, an alloy of nickel and steel whose expansion coefficient is only about one one-hundredth that of steel, and the clock is placed in a room whose temperature is kept as nearly constant as possible by means of a thermostat and some source of heat. The varying barometric pressures are also avoided by sealing the clock in an airtight case and partially exhausting the air (Fig. 81).

FIG. 81. A precision astronomical clock at the Goodsell Observatory. Note the massive concrete pier and the airtight glass case. The clock room is maintained at a uniform temperature by means of a thermostatically controlled electric heater.

A clock of this character cannot be wound by ordinary means and so an automatic electrical winding device is provided. By means of this a small weight of about 15 g ($\frac{1}{2}$ oz) is raised a short distance every 30 to 40 sec. The weight drives the clock as it falls.

No clock is perfect and none will keep absolutely correct time. The best that is hoped for is that it will gain or lose at a uniform daily rate. This amount of gain or loss is called the *daily rate* of the clock. A clock whose daily rate can be depended upon to one or two hundredths of a second is of exceptionally fine quality.

The master clock or clocks of an observatory are usually not set except when they are cleaned and oiled. This is done once in two or three years. The clock corrections are determined by the transit and chronograph and a record kept. By combining the last determined clock correction with the daily rate the correct time at any instant can be obtained.

Clocks other than the master clock are compared with the latter and may be set daily so as to show correct time. Such secondary clocks need not be of the highest quality.

There has recently been developed a new type of timekeeper, a crystal oscillator, of the sort used to control the frequency of radio broadcasting. Reports on the performance of some crystals show remarkably good time-keeping qualities, very much superior to the ordinary type of high-grade clock.

Sidereal time is not satisfactory for everyday use, for, while the vernal equinox crosses the meridian about noon on the twenty-first of March, it crosses it about 4 min earlier each day, so that by the twenty-first of September it is sidereal noon at civil midnight. This brings us to a consideration of solar time.

126. Apparent Solar Time. In general, we say that it is noon when the sun is on the meridian and that a solar day is the interval of time between two successive passages of the sun across the meridian. Time kept in this way is measured by the sun dial and is called *apparent solar time*. Since it is customary to begin the calendar day at midnight, *the apparent solar time at any instant is equal to the hour angle of the sun plus 12 hr*. This kind of time, however, is not adapted to modern conditions, for the apparent solar days vary in length as measured by an accurate clock. Thus Dec. 25 is about 50 sec longer than Sept 13 and the days in January average about 15 sec longer than the days in July.

127. The Sun's Motion in the Ecliptic. The variation in the length of apparent solar days is due to two causes: (1) The sun moves along the ecliptic and not along the celestial equator, and (2) the motion along the ecliptic is not uniform.

1. It is evident that, even if the sun moved uniformly along the ecliptic, about a degree a day, yet near the equinox a degree along the ecliptic EV would subtend a smaller angle at the celestial pole than a degree along the celestial equator QV (Fig. 82a). On the other hand, near the solstices, where the ecliptic is about 23°.5 nearer the pole than the celestial equator, a degree along the ecliptic EC subtends a greater angle at the pole than a degree along the celestial equator QB (Fig. 82b).

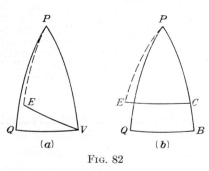

(a)   (b)

FIG. 82

Hence, in the first case the eastward component of the sun's motion would be less than in the second case and therefore the apparent solar days would be shorter near the equinoxes than near the solstices.

2. The earth moves in an ellipse and its motion, when near perihelion, is more rapid in both linear and angular velocity than when near aphelion

(see Sec. 162). As seen from the earth, the sun's motion along the ecliptic is therefore correspondingly more rapid at one time than at another. The more rapidly the sun moves eastward, the longer the interval between two successive meridian transits, and vice versa.

128. Variation in Length of Solar Day. The variation in the length of the day and the part contributed by the two causes just considered is shown very clearly in Fig. 83, which is due to S. G. Barton of the University of Pennsylvania. The effect of the eccentricity of the earth's

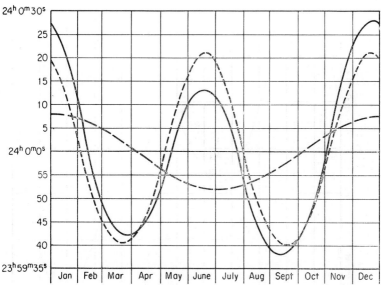

FIG. 83. Variation in length of apparent solar day. Broken line, the effect of eccentricity; dotted line, the effect of the obliquity of the ecliptic; solid line, combined effect. (*According to S. G. Barton.*)

orbit is represented by the broken curve, the effect of the angle between the planes of equator and ecliptic by the dotted curve, while the net effect is shown by the full curve.

129. Mean Solar Time. In order to have days of uniform length, a day, called the *mean solar day*, has been devised, with hours numbered from 0 to 24. It is measured by a fictitious sun, called the *mean sun*, which moves uniformly along the celestial equator. It is mean solar noon when the mean sun is on the meridian. *The mean solar time at any instant is the hour angle of the mean sun plus* 12 *hr.* This sun completes its movement around the celestial equator in the same time as the real sun does around the ecliptic, so that the mean solar day is equal in length to the average apparent solar day.

130. The Equation of Time. The difference in hour angle between the real sun and the fictitious sun is known as the *equation of time* and carries the positive sign when mean solar time is greater than apparent solar time. The variation of the equation of time in amount and sign is shown in Fig. 84.

The mean sun, being a fictitious body, cannot be observed. When high precision is not required, mean time can be obtained by observing the sun for apparent solar time and then applying the equation of time.

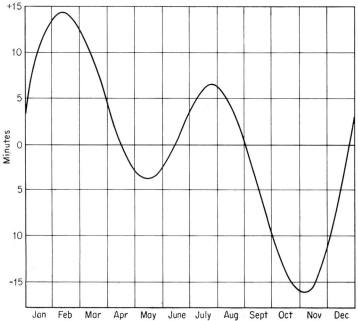

FIG. 84. Graph of the equation of time plotted as mean minus apparent time.

The sun, however, is such a large body that it cannot be observed for position with any great degree of accuracy and another method is therefore required when time of high precision is required.

131. Mean Time from Sidereal Time. The stars appear as mere points of light in the field of the transit instrument. Their meridian transits can be observed with great accuracy and sidereal time may therefore be considered as the fundamental time. Then, by means of tables and data in the *American Ephemeris* or similar publication, the sidereal time at any instant can be converted into mean time. As an example let us determine the mean time at the Goodsell Observatory for sidereal time $8^h30^m00^s$ on Jan. 5, 1953.

Sidereal time...	$8^h30^m00^s$
Longitude...	6 12 35.9 (p. 558)*
Greenwich sidereal time................................	14 42 35.9
Sidereal time Greenwich midnight........................	6 57 09.8 (p. 2)
Sidereal time interval since Greenwich midnight.............	7 45 26.1
Reduction to mean-time interval.........................	−1 16.2 (p. 576)
Greenwich mean time....................................	7 44 9.9
Longitude...	6 12 35.9
Local mean time, Goodsell Observatory...................	1 31 34.0

* The page references are to the *American Ephemeris and Nautical Almanac* for 1953.

If, instead of local mean time, the Central Standard Time (Sec. 133) had been required, then, since Central Standard Time is 6^h slower than Greenwich, the last subtraction would have been $6^h00^m00^s$ and the Central Standard Time accordingly $1^h44^m09^s.9$ on the morning of Jan. 5, 1953.

132. Civil Time and Astronomical Time. In general, it is not convenient to have the day begin at noon when the hour angle of the sun is zero, and therefore in most countries the civil day begins at midnight. *Civil time* may therefore be defined as the hour angle of the mean sun plus 12 hr.

For many centuries the astronomical day began at noon, 12 hr later than the civil day, in order to avoid changing the date during the night when observations were in progress. This advantage has not been especially great, and, by international agreement, the astronomical day was made to agree with the civil day, beginning Jan. 1, 1925.

By agreement most astronomical results involving time are now expressed in the time of the Greenwich meridian, the day beginning at midnight. This time is known by various names such as *Greenwich Civil Time, Universal Time, Weltzeit,* etc.

133. Local and Standard Time. From the definition of mean solar time it is evident that only places on the same meridian will have the same clock time, while places to the east will have later clock time and places to the west earlier clock time. The time measured by the mean sun for any particular place is called its *local mean time.*

In order to avoid having different times at practically every station, the railroads of the United States introduced what is known as *standard time.* The country was divided into four districts and the time in each district was made 1 hr earlier than that of the district to the east and 1 hr later than the district to the west (Fig. 85). These four times are known as Eastern, Central, Mountain and Pacific Standard Times and are the civil times of the 75th, 90th, 105th, and 120th meridians west of Greenwich, respectively. These meridians, in general, are located near the centers of their respective districts, although the dividing lines are not straight but are arranged so that times are not changed except at division points of the railways, or state boundaries.

Other countries have also adopted the same general plan so that now the entire civilized world is using it.

134. Zone Time. For purposes of navigation it is convenient to imagine the entire earth divided into zones 15° longitude in width. The center of each zone is 15°, 30°, etc., east and west of the Greenwich meridian. The zero zone extends from longitude 7°.5E to 7°.5W, the next zone to

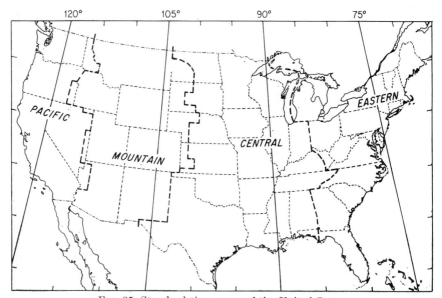

Fig. 85. Standard time zones of the United States.

westward from longitude 7°.5W to 22°.5W, etc. Each zone thus has as its central meridian one whose time differs by an integral number of hours from Greenwich Time.

The difference between Greenwich Civil Time and the standard time of each zone is known as the *zone description*. Thus the zone from longitude 37°.5E to 52°.5E, has a time 3ʰ ahead of Greenwich Time. Its zone description is accordingly −3. For the zone from 82°.5W to 97°.5W the zone description is +6.

ASTRONOMICAL LATITUDE

135. The Circumpolar Method. In Sec. 35 it was shown that the altitude of the pole is equal to the astronomical latitude of the observer. This simple relationship provides an easy method for the determination of latitude. The stars near the pole appear to describe circles around it, the polar distance of any star being the radius of its diurnal circle. In

Fig. 86 let the circle be the diurnal circle of a star near the pole and the horizontal line the horizon under the pole. By means of a suitable instrument measure the altitude of the star when at a, its greatest distance above the horizon, and again 12 sidereal hours later when at b, its least distance above the horizon. The average of these two altitudes, each corrected for refraction, will be the altitude of the center of the circle, the pole P, and this altitude is equal to the astronomical latitude of the observer.

If results of only moderate accuracy are needed, as in exploration or navigation, the observer may observe the altitude of Polaris at any time it is visible, and then, by suitable tables, obtain his latitude. With

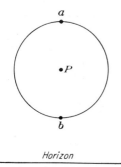

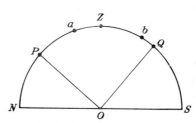

FIG. 86. The circumpolar method of determining astronomical latitude.

FIG. 87. The method of determining astronomical latitude by the meridian altitude of a star of known declination.

the time known within one minute and a good sextant or surveyor's transit it is possible to obtain the latitude correct to within 1 minute of arc.

136. The Meridian-altitude Method. Let NS (Fig. 87) represent the plane of the horizon, P the pole, OQ the plane of the celestial equator, Z the zenith of the observer at O, and a and b two stars on the meridian. From the geometry of the figure it is evident that the arc ZQ is equal to the arc PN, that is, the declination of the zenith is equal to the altitude of the pole.

Consider a star b whose declination Qb is known. By measuring its altitude above the south point S, and correcting this measured altitude for refraction, we have determined the arc Sb. After subtracting bQ, the arc QS is obtained, and by subtracting this from 90° we have ZQ, which is equal to the latitude.

If the star is at a, between zenith and pole, then the measured altitude Na, added to the declination aQ, will give the arc NPQ. Subtracting $PQ = 90°$ from NPQ will give NP, the altitude of the pole.

This method is known as the *method of meridian altitudes*.

LONGITUDE

137. Relation between Longitude and Time. Since the earth rotates uniformly at the rate of 15° per sidereal hour, it is evident that two places differing by this amount in longitude will have a difference of exactly 1 hr in their sidereal times. The same relation between angle and time holds true for all places on the earth. Hence, if we know the difference between the sidereal times of two places, we also know their difference in longitude. The problem of determining the longitude of a place therefore resolves itself into the problem of determining its sidereal time and of obtaining in some way a knowledge of the same time of some place whose longitude is known. Two methods will be considered.

138. Longitude by Transportation of Chronometers. This method consists in carrying several carefully rated chronometers, set to the time of some particular meridian. The local time will be obtained by observations of the stars. The difference between the two times willl give the difference in longitude.

More than one chronometer is used (1) in order to allow for accidents and (2) because no single chronometer can be trusted to maintain a constant rate. By averaging the time as shown by several chronometers the probability of having nearly correct time is greatly increased.

The chronometer is a portable timepiece which resembles a large watch (Fig. 88). It is built to beat half seconds. When in use on shipboard, it is swung in gimbals so that it may always remain in a horizontal position irrespective of the rolling and pitching of the vessel. In handling a chronometer it should be carefully protected against jars and sudden twists, especially in a horizontal plane, as the latter will affect the vibration of the balance wheel. A good chronometer, properly cared for, and making due allowance for daily rate, should run with an error not exceeding about 10 sec per month.

Fig. 88. A chronometer.

The weakness of this method lies in the necessity of assuming constant rates for the chronometers. It has now been superseded by the time-signal method.

139. Longitude by Time Signals. If a place whose longitude is to be determined is in telegraphic or radio communication with some other place of known longitude, signals can be sent out by the clocks of the latter, and thus its time obtained with great accuracy. The local sidereal time of the place of unknown longitude must be determined as in the preceding method.   The difference of time between the two places will correspond to the difference in longitude.

Radio time signals are now becoming so common that it seems likely that this method of determining longitude both on sea and on land will be used exclusively.

140. Longitude from Mean Time. Thus far we have stated the situation on a comparison of sidereal times, but this is not essential.   The earth also rotates uniformly with respect to the mean sun at the rate of 15° per hr of mean solar time, so that, if desired, the difference between the local mean solar times can be used instead of the difference between the sidereal times.

141. Where and When the Day Begins. Two places on opposite sides of the earth will differ by 12 hr in their time, and it is a practical question as to whether when it is one o'clock in the morning at Chicago it is one o'clock in the afternoon of the same day or of a different day in Calcutta.

By agreement the 180th meridian from Greenwich is accepted as the general line at which the day begins.   There are certain deviations from this meridian for the sake of convenience.   Some of the Aleutian Islands extend west of this meridian, and in order not to have different dates on different islands of the same group, the date line swings west of it. Similarly, it swings eastward around northeastern Siberia as well as around certain islands north and east of New Zealand.   The line as actually run is known as the *international date line*.

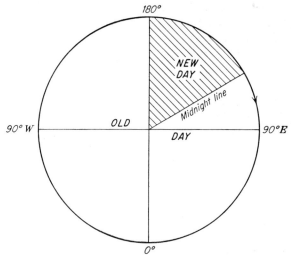

Fig. 89. Change of calendar dates over the earth.

When it is midnight at the 180th meridian, the whole earth (except for the small areas affected by the deviations of the date line from this meridian) has the same calendar day at that instant.   As the midnight line advances westward from the date line, the region between those two lines has the new calendar day (Fig. 89), while the rest of the earth still has the preceding day.   Except at this instant of midnight at the date line, the calendar days are different on the two sides of the line, the one to the west being a day later than the one to the east.   In consequence, a ship crossing the line from east to west adds a day to its reckoning, while one going in the opposite direction will go back a day.   Thus a ship going from San Francisco to the Philippines might approach the line on Tuesday.   After crossing it, the day would be called Wednesday. Another ship crossing the line at the same time but in the opposite direction would reach it on Wednesday and then call the day Tuesday after it had crossed.   For the second ship Wednesday would be repeated.

When the survivors of the Magellan expedition returned to Europe in 1522 after circumnavigating the globe, it was found that they were one day behind in their reckoning.   The ships had sailed westward in the same direction as the sun moves and in consequence the sun had risen and set once less for them than for the Europeans.   Hence the loss of a day.

NAVIGATION

The navigator requires two instruments in order to determine his position at sea: a chronometer to show Greenwich time, and a sextant to measure the altitude of the sun or a bright star.   We have already considered the chronometer in Sec. 138 and shall now study the second of the navigator's tools.

142. The Sextant. The sextant is a portable instrument for the measurement of the angular distance between two objects, such as the altitude of the sun above the horizon, etc. There are two types of sextants, the marine sextant (Fig. 90) and the bubble sextant (Fig. 92).   The marine sextant consists of a metal frame with a 60° arc of a circle of from 6 to 8 in. radius A; an index arm IM pivoted at the center of the arc; an index mirror M whose face is perpendicular to the plane of the arc and in the line of the pivot; a horizon glass H, one half of which is silvered and the other half transparent; a small telescope T; a handle B, and adjustable shade glasses to reduce the brightness of the sun.   The arc is graduated,

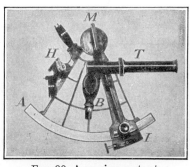

FIG. 90. A marine sextant.

half degrees being numbered from 0 to 120 for reasons given later. By means of a vernier, angles can be read to 10'' in the best instruments.

The observer holds the sextant in his right hand with the plane of the arc in the plane of the angle to be measured, moves the index arm and attached mirror with the left hand, and looks through telescope and horizon glass. The instrument is made so that, when in adjustment, and the mirrors set parallel to each other, the index arm is at zero on the arc and the observer sees two images of a distant object in coincidence in the field of view of the telescope. The one image is from the direct view through the unsilvered half of the horizon glass, and the other comes from the reflection in M and the silvered half of H. When measuring the angular distance between two objects, the one is viewed directly and M is rotated by means of the index arm until the second object is brought into the field of view by reflection from M and H.

The principle of the marine sextant is shown in Fig. 91. Suppose we wish to measure the angle between two objects whose directions from the observer are OS and OC. The mirror M is rotated until the reflected beam $SMHO$ from the one is brought into coincidence with the direct beam CO from the other. We then have to determine the relation between the angle through which M has been turned and the angle at O. Let AM and HB be perpendiculars to the planes of the mirrors. It can then be shown by elementary geometry that angle O is just twice the angle I which is the angle between the two

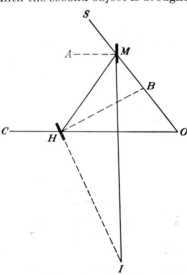

FIG. 91. The geometry of the marine sextant.

mirrors and which is measured along the arc. Since the angle O is required, the divisions on the arc are marked at double their value so that the reading gives directly the value of the angle O.

143. The Bubble Sextant. When long-distance flying became possible and the necessity of navigation for aircraft became apparent, the marine sextant alone was available. Since aircraft often must fly at high altitudes where the sea horizon is invisible because of haze or clouds some type of artificial horizon became necessary. The simplest one developed thus far utilizes a carefully mounted level, the bubble of which, when near the center of the field of view, assures that the "line of sight" is horizontal. The index glass is then rotated until the reflected image of

sun or moon is centered in the bubble.   The plane of the sextant is then
vertical and the index arm has moved along the arc to show the altitude
of the body observed (Fig. 92).

For night observations of stars the
bubble is slightly illuminated and the
star then centered in the bubble.

144. Position at Sea. Latitude and
longitude can be determined directly
from sextant observations of the altitude of a heavenly body such as the
sun, the moon, or the brighter planets
and stars, provided the observations
for altitude are made at certain times.
For latitude this means an observation
when the body is on the meridian while

FIG. 92. A bubble sextant.   (*Link Aviation Devices Co.*)

for longitude the body must be on or very near the prime vertical.   This
requirement limits the determination of position to a few minutes during
the day.   A more general method is required, particularly if the sky is
partly covered by clouds.

145. The Principle of the Sumner Method. In navigation, whether
on the sea or in the air, the earth is considered a sphere.   The error
introduced by this assumption is negligible, considering the errors that
may be involved in the relatively coarse sextant observations.

In Fig. 93 let the circle represent the earth, CS the line from the earth's
center to some celestial body such as the sun, O the position of the
observer, OS' a line from O to S, and OA a circle on the earth everywhere
equidistant from GP.   (If GP were the earth's pole, OA would be a
parallel of latitude.) GP, where the line CS intersects the earth's surface,
is the point on the earth directly under the celestial body and is often
called the *geographical point*. OH represents the plane of the observer's
horizon.   For all bodies except the moon the line OS', which is pointing
directly at S, may be considered parallel to CS.

The angle $S'OH$ is the altitude of S for the observer at O.   The same
altitude would be obtained if the observer were anywhere on the circle OA.

From the geometry of the problem it is evident that the angles $S'OH$
and OCS are complementary.   This may also be stated as follows: Angle
$S'OH$ + arc $O\,GP$ = 90°.   It is also evident that for an observer 5' of
arc nearer GP than O the altitude of S would be 5' greater than $S'OH$,
while if the observer were 10' of arc farther from GP than O, the altitude
of S would be 10' less than $S'OH$.

In Fig. 94 let A represent the point on the earth directly under one
celestial body and the arc ab part of the circle for which there is an
observed altitude of the body above A.   Similarly let A' be the point

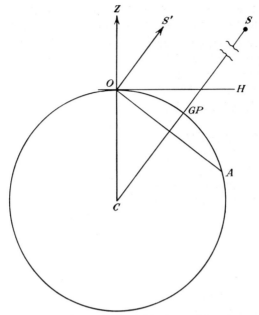

FIG. 93. A Sumner circle of celestial body at S for observer at O.

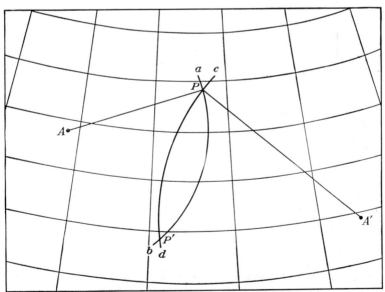

FIG. 94. Parts of two Sumner circles for two celestial bodies whose geographical points are A and A'.

under some other celestial body and cd an arc of a circle for the altitude of the second body. Since the observer must be on both arcs, he will be at either the intersection P or the intersection P'. Since the observer knows his approximate position by dead reckoning, he has no difficulty in choosing the proper intersection.

The position of the points A and A' can be obtained from tables and data in the *American Ephemeris, American Air Almanac,* or similar publications.

146. Line of Position Method. One difficulty in applying the Sumner method directly is that the arcs should be drawn on a globe. The navigator, whether on the sea or in the air, cannot carry a globe of the necessary size. The method must therefore be modified so that the navigational charts can be used.

The navigator always knows from speed and course of ship or plane his approximate position. This is called the *dead-reckoning position.* Assuming this position, by means of various tables, he can quickly compute the altitudes and azimuths of the two bodies for the time of observation.

On a chart let P, Fig. 95, be the dead-reckoning position and PA and PA' the azimuth lines to the two celestial bodies observed. Assume

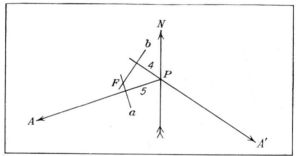

Fig. 95. Lines of position, aF and bF, whose intersection at F locates the observer.

the calculation for the dead-reckoning position gives a calculated altitude of the body in the direction PA which is 5′ less than the observed altitude. It is then evident that the observer was 5′ nearer the body than the point P. He therefore measures off 5′ along PA and draws a perpendicular to PA. This perpendicular is nothing more than a short arc of a Sumner circle and the observer is somewhere on the perpendicular. The perpendicular is called a *line of position.* Then if we assume that the calculated altitude of the body in the direction PA' is 4′ greater than the observed altitude, the observer is 4′ farther away than point P. He then measures off a distance of 4′ away from P and again draws a perpendicular. Since he was on both perpendiculars at the time of the observation, he must have been at their intersection, F. His position is thus marked on the chart.

It is obvious that observations of two bodies are necessary in order to have two intersecting lines of position. If only one body is available, only one line of position can be drawn. Even this may be worth having.

THE CALENDAR

A calendar is a method of combining days into periods of weeks, months, and years in order to serve the needs of mankind.

147. Units of Time. For different lengths of time different units are desirable. For short intervals the mean solar day is a convenient unit, but for longer intervals the synodic month and the year are not only convenient but natural. Unfortunately, these three units are not commensurable, but modern values of their lengths in terms of days make a comparison possible and not overly laborious.

The earliest calendars seem to have been predominantly lunar, and the Mohammedan calendar has remained so. Their year consists of 12 months and is reckoned as having sometimes 354 and sometimes 355 days. This kind of year does not keep step with the seasons, and gains on our year at the rate of about one year in 34.

148. Three Kinds of Year. Years are of different lengths, depending on the way in which they are reckoned. The *sidereal year* is the length of time required for the earth to make one revolution around the sun with respect to the stars. For 1950 its length is $365^d6^h9^m9^s.5$ and for the present is slowly increasing.

A second kind is the *anomalistic year*. This is defined as the time between two successive perihelion passages of the earth. It is at present $4^m43^s.6$ longer than the sidereal year on account of the slow rotation of the line of apsides of the earth's orbit toward the east. Like the sidereal year, it is also increasing in length at the present time, but at a more rapid rate.

The third kind is the *tropical year* and is the one in common use. It is defined as the interval of time between successive passages of the sun through the vernal equinox. Because of the precession of the equinoxes toward the west this year is shorter than the sidereal year. For 1950 its length is $365^d5^h48^m45^s.7$. Its value is slowly decreasing.

The tropical year is the one ordinarily used, as the seasons are thus kept in place in the calendar. If either of the other years were used, the seasons would occur earlier and earlier until spring would begin in February, then in January, etc., for the northern hemisphere.

149. The Julian Calendar. At the time of Julius Caesar there was considerable confusion in the calendar and he determined to put it in order. He summoned the astronomer Sosigenes from Alexandria and with his aid a very simple system was devised. Each ordinary year was to have 365 and each fourth year 366 days. This new calendar was introduced in 45 B.C. and the beginning of the year, which up to that time had been in March, was placed on Jan. 1.

150. The Gregorian Calendar. The Julian calendar year had been taken as exactly $365\frac{1}{4}$ days in length, about 11^m15^s too long. In the course of time the vernal equinox gradually approached the beginning of the month until toward the end of the sixteenth century it occurred on the eleventh of March instead of the twenty-first, as it did in the year A.D. 325, the year of the Council of Nicaea. To remedy this, Pope Gregory XIII issued an edict that the day following Oct. 4, 1582, should be called the fifteenth, thus bringing the vernal equinox back to Mar. 21, and that thereafter the years closing each century should not be counted as leap years unless divisible by 400. As a result of this plan 1700, 1800, and 1900 were not leap years, but 2000 will be.

The plan was adopted generally by countries predominantly Roman Catholic, but Protestant and Greek Catholic countries were slow in following. England finally adopted it in 1752, Russia in 1918, and other countries still more recently.

The length of the Gregorian calendar year is $365^d5^h49^m12^s$. This is still too long by 26^s and in the course of 3200 years the calendar will have to be corrected by one day.

151. A Modern Calendar. Various plans have been suggested to simplify the system of weeks and months. One of the simplest is the following:

Divide the year into 13 months of 4 weeks each and add 1 day, which shall belong to no month but have a special name, such as New Year's Day. On leap years add an extra day, either following New Year's Day or preferably following some month in the summer, and give it some special name. Such a plan would allow the first, eighth, fifteenth, and twenty-second days of each month to be any day decided upon, say Sunday, and a single sheet would answer for all months and years. All holidays would fall on the same day of the week in each year, and, if the ecclesiastical calendar were fixed so that Easter Sunday would fall on some particular Sunday, the entire calendar problem would be greatly simplified.

Another proposed calendar divides the year into four quarters of 91 days each, the quarter into three months of 31, 30, and 30 days, respectively. The day left over for the completion of the ordinary year is placed after Dec. 30 and the extra day for leap years follows June 30. In this plan the week days repeat every quarter.

152. The Julian Day. For some purposes the calendar involving the year, month, and day is not very convenient, particularly when long intervals of time are concerned. Calendar confusion, omitted days, and the like may cause errors. The simplest method would be to number the days consecutively. In time, large day numbers would occur, but the inconvenience would be more than counterbalanced by the increased accuracy.

In 1582, J. J. Scaliger suggested such a plan. He proposed that the beginning be made on Jan. 1, 4713 B.C., and the days numbered consecutively. His plan also involved years, but these are now seldom used. From a practical point of view, it would not have been necessary to begin so far back, as ancient dates cannot be fixed with any great degree of accuracy, but certain cycles[1] used in chronology could all be brought into step, the year 4713 B.C. being year 1 in each cycle, by the choice of this particular date. This led to its selection.

The system was adopted and is frequently used in certain classes of astronomical computations, where it has proved to be of value. The day used is called the *Julian day.*

The Julian day was made to agree with the astronomical day which began at noon, 12 hr later than the corresponding civil day. When the astronomical day was discontinued in 1925, it was also planned to change the Julian day so that it would begin at midnight. In order to avoid confusion, however, it was agreed, at the meeting of the International Astronomical Union in 1925, to continue the old plan of beginning the Julian day at noon.

January 1, 1955 was J. D. 2,435,109. From this, other Julian day numbers can be calculated.

153. Date of Easter. The dates of certain Christian festivals such as Christmas and Epiphany have gradually become fixed in the calendar, although the historical bases for these dates are uncertain. The date of Easter, however, has been set by a rule which in essence is as follows: Easter Sunday shall be the first Sunday after the first full moon on or after the vernal equinox. The application of this rule makes it possible for Easter to occur as early as Mar. 21 or as late as Apr. 26. It has been suggested that Easter be fixed as the second Sunday in April so as to avoid the present range of about five weeks, but, thus far, no widespread demand for the change has been made.

EXERCISES

1. How would Fig. 84 be changed if it showed "Std. Time — Appt. Time" for an observer in longitude 90°W? 85°W? 95°W?

2. An observer in the Northern Hemisphere measures the meridian altitude of the star Regulus as 60°46'. The declination of Regulus is +12°18'. Neglecting the correction for refraction, what is the observer's astronomical latitude?

Ans. +41°32'.

---

[1] The three cycles consist of 28, 19, and 15 years, respectively, of 365.25 days.

3. An observer in the Southern Hemisphere obtains the same value for the meridian altitude of Regulus. Neglecting refraction, what is the observer's astronomical latitude?

Ans. −16°56′.

4. If an observer found that the altitudes of the stars did not change, where would he be located?

5. The sidereal clocks at Washington and Northfield were compared by radio signals. The difference between them was 1ʰ00ᵐ24ˢ. The known corrections to the clock times were +1ᵐ17ˢ for Washington and −2ᵐ39ˢ for Northfield. If the longitude of Washington is 5ʰ08ᵐ16ˢ W, what is the longitude of Northfield?   *Ans.* 6ʰ12ᵐ36ˢ W.

6. Under what conditions might the passengers on a ship be justified in expecting two Christmas dinners?   Under what conditions might they have none?

CHAPTER 8

GRAVITATIONAL ASTRONOMY

154. Newton's Law of Gravitation. In 1687, Newton's famous "Principia" was published. In it he discussed the motions in the solar system on the basis of his law of gravitation. This law is now usually stated as follows:

Every particle of matter in the universe attracts[1] *every other particle with a force which varies directly as the product of the masses of the particles and inversely as the square of the distance between them.*

If m_1 and m_2 are the masses of two particles of matter and d the distance between their centers of mass, the force acting between the two may be expressed in the form of an equation as follows:

$$F = \frac{k \times m_1 \times m_2}{d^2}$$

where k is a constant whose value depends upon the units of force, mass, and distance used.

If the mass is expressed in grams, the distance in centimeters, and the force in dynes, the value of k becomes 667×10^{-10}. This is called the *gravitational constant* and is usually designated by G. The formula then becomes

$$F = \frac{G \times m_1 \times m_2}{d^2}$$

This means that two spheres of 1 g each whose centers are 1 cm apart attract each other with a force of G dynes.

155. The Attraction of Spheres. It is not necessary to restrict our consideration of gravitation to small particles of matter. Most of the heavenly bodies with which we have anything to do are approximately spherical, and Newton showed that a sphere whose mass is symmetrically distributed with respect to the center will act on a body outside it just

---

[1] We shall use the word "attract" as a matter of convenience without implying that gravitation is necessarily an attraction.

as if its entire mass were concentrated in a point at its center. Two spheres of masses m_1 and m_2 will, therefore, attract each other as if their

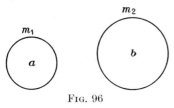

Fig. 96

masses were concentrated at the centers a and b, respectively (Fig. 96), and thus the distance betweeen them will be the distance between their centers. This holds even if the spheres are in contact.

In considering a sphere's attraction for bodies on its surface it is necessary to remember that the *distance* through which the force of gravitation acts is the radius of the sphere.

156. The Value of g. At the surface of the earth a body falling freely under the action of the earth's gravitation will fall approximately 490 cm (16 ft) the first second, three times this distance during the next second, five times this amount the third second, etc., 980 cm (32 ft) being added each second. This value of 980 cm is known as the acceleration of gravity at the earth's surface and is usually designated by g. It is not a constant quantity, but varies slightly from place to place, depending upon the elevation above sea level and the latitude. The variation depending on latitude is caused by two factors: (1) the flattening of the earth toward the poles, which allows the observer to be nearer the center of the earth the farther he is from the equator; and (2) the centrifugal effect of the earth's rotation.

157. The Universality of Gravitation. For some years before Newton's time it had been recognized that the planets moved about the sun, but no one had connected this motion with the earth's attraction for bodies at its surface. A genius like Newton was required to recognize the relationship.

While he was working on the general problem, he realized that if his formulation of the law of gravitation were true, then the earth's gravitation, which causes a free body to fall 490 cm toward the earth in 1 sec, would also be operative in compelling the moon to move around the earth, the deviation of the moon's path from a straight line in 1 sec being the amount by which it has been compelled to fall toward the earth. The proof of this follows.

Fig. 97. The earth's attraction for the moon.

In Fig. 97 let the earth be at E, the moon at M, MB the path of the moon described in 1 sec, and MA a straight line perpendicular to ME at M. The problem consists in determining AB, the amount by which the moon's motion deviates from a straight line in 1 sec. In this case the moon's orbit may be considered a circle without serious error.

The moon's orbital velocity per second is equal to $2\pi \times 384{,}000$ km divided by the number of seconds in a sidereal month. This is approximately 1.023 km per sec. The actual difference between the arc MB and the straight line MA is so small that MA can also be considered equal to 1.023 km.

In the right triangle EMA, EM is 384,000 km and MA is 1.023 km. It is therefore a simple matter to calculate the side EA. This is found to be 384,000.-0000014 km, approximately. Hence AB is equal to 0.0000014 km or 1.4 mm (0.05 in.).

The distance from earth to moon is approximately 60 radii of the earth. Hence the attraction of the earth at the moon's distance is $\frac{1}{60^2}$ that at the earth's surface. Therefore a body which falls 490 cm in 1 sec at the earth's surface would fall $\frac{1}{3600}$ of that at the distance of the moon. This is 1.4 mm, thus agreeing with the amount the moon falls toward the earth in 1 sec. This means that the earth's gravitational force is the only force required to keep the moon moving around the earth.

The extension of Newton's law to the motions of the planets was merely another step and, with the exception of Mercury (Sec. 261), it explains all these motions.

Among the stars there are certain pairs which can be observed revolving around their common center of gravity, and, within the limits of error of the observations, the same law of gravitation is operative as that which causes an apple to fall to the ground. In view of these facts we feel reasonably safe in assuming that the law of gravitation is universal.

158. The Mass of the Earth. The *mass* of a body is usually defined as the amount of matter it contains. The word "mass" must not be confused with the word "weight." The weight of a body is a measure of the gravitational effect of the earth upon the mass of the body and this varies inversely as the square of the distance of the body from the center of the earth (Sec. 155). Thus a mass of 1 kg would weigh 1 kg at the earth's surface, but, if the weighing took place at a point whose distance from the earth's center is equal to two radii of the earth, its weight would be but $\frac{1}{4}$ kg if a spring balance were used. The amount of matter in the object, however, is the same—1 kg.

One of the first attempts to determine the mass of the earth was made by the English astronomer Maskelyne, in 1774. His method was the following:

In Scotland there is a mountain Schiehallien. By observing the direction of the vertical (plumb line) on either side of the mountain (Fig. 98) it was possible to determine how much the mass of the mountain deflected the plumb line. By surveys and borings it was possible to determine the mass of the mountain. Then, knowing the distance to the center of mass of the mountain and the distance to the center of the earth, it was possible to compare the gravitative effect of the earth with that of the mountain and thus determine the mass of the earth.

The modern method of the torsion pendulum, while somewhat similar in principle, is capable of producing far more accurate results and is therefore more reliable than the mountain method. A light rod is suspended *horizontally* by means of a fine fiber, and a small ball of some heavy substance like gold or platinum is fastened to each end of the rod. If the apparatus is carefully shielded from air currents or placed in a vacuum, it will gradually come to rest in such a position that there will be no twist in the fiber. If we then rotate the rod slightly about the

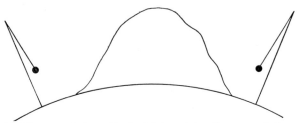

FIG. 98. The mountain method of determining the mass of the earth.

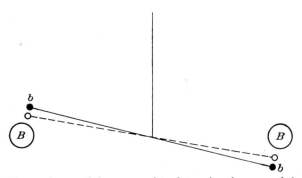

FIG. 99. The torsion pendulum as used to determine the mass of the earth.

fiber, the twist produced in the fiber will cause the rod to vibrate slowly. If we know the mass of the balls and rod, the length of the rod, and the time of vibration, we can determine the force necessary to twist the fiber through any angle. The formula

$$T = 2\pi \sqrt{\frac{k}{f}}$$

gives the time of one complete vibration in terms of the force f with which the fiber resists being twisted, and a constant k which involves the length of the rod, its mass, and the mass of the small balls. Since we can measure the quantities involved in k and can time the vibration, the formula enables us to determine f, the force required to twist the fiber through unit angle. It will be noted that this formula is very similar to that used for simple pendulums, $T = 2\pi \sqrt{l/g}$.

If the torsion pendulum is allowed to come to rest and then two large balls of lead or other heavy substance are brought into positions B, these large balls will attract the small ones and the latter will move until the twisting of the fiber prevents further movement (Fig. 99). If we then measure the angle through which the rod has turned and the distance d between the centers of the large and small balls, we have, by means of the equation given above, a direct measure of the attraction of b for B at distance d.

The attraction of the earth for the ball b is measured by its weight when corrected for the centrifugal effect of the earth's rotation at the point where the observations are made. We can then write

$$w = \frac{G \times b \times E}{R^2} \text{ or } b = \frac{w \times R^2}{G \times E}$$

where G is the gravitational constant, b the mass of the small ball, w the weight of the small ball, E the mass of the earth, and R the earth's radius.

Similarly, we can write

$$f' = \frac{G \times b \times B}{d^2} \text{ or } b = \frac{f' \times d^2}{G \times B}$$

where f' is the force between b and B at distance d.

Equating these two values of b, we obtain

$$\frac{w \times R^2}{G \times E} = \frac{f' \times d^2}{G \times B}$$

Solving this equation for E, we have

$$E = B \times \frac{w}{f'} \times \frac{R^2}{d^2}$$

which gives the mass of the earth in terms of the mass of B.

Other methods involving delicate balances or pendulums have also been devised, all yielding approximately the same values for the earth's mass.

The mass of the earth determined in some such manner comes out to be equivalent to 6×10^{21} metric tons of mass, or 6.6×10^{21} short tons.

159. Conic Sections. By analytical geometry it can be shown that if a right circular cone is cut by a plane, the intersection of the plane with the conical surface will result in three types of curves, depending upon the angle between the plane and the axis of the cone.

If the plane cuts across the entire cone (Fig. 100, a), the section is an *ellipse*, the particular shape depending upon the angle of the cone and the angle between plane and axis. If the plane is perpendicular to the axis, the intersection is a circle which may be considered as a special case of the ellipse with both axes equal (Sec. 160).

When the plane intersects the cone and is parallel to one element of the cone (*b*), the intersection is a *parabola*. It is evident that the parabola is not a closed curve.

If the plane cuts the axis of the cone at an angle which is less than the angle between the axis and the plane of the parabola (*c*), the curve is called a *hyperbola*.

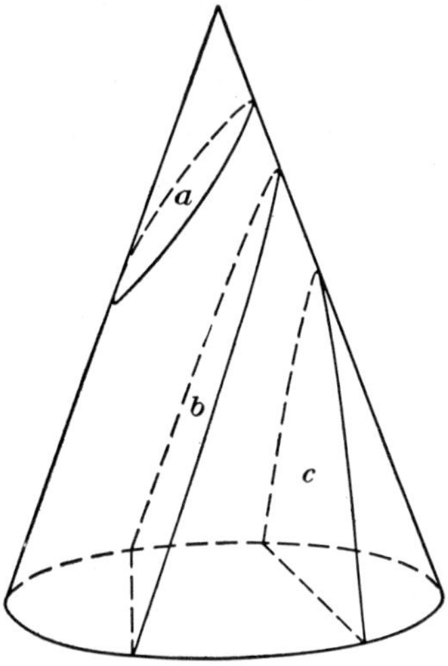

160. Properties of Conic Sections. *The Ellipse.* This curve may be defined as the locus of a point, the sum of whose distances from two given points is a con-

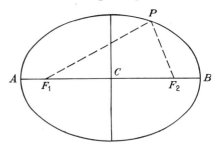

Fig. 100. Sections of a right circular cone: *a*, ellipse; *b*, parabola; *c*, hyperbola.

Fig. 101. The ellipse.

stant. If, in Fig. 101, the two points are F_1 and F_2, the length of AB the constant, and P is any point on the curve, then $PF_1 + PF_2 = AB$. The line AB is called the *major axis* of the ellipse and the points F_1 and F_2 are called the *foci*.

It is evident that if the length of the major axis AB is kept constant while the foci are moved farther apart, the resulting ellipse will be narrower than the one shown in Fig. 101, while if the foci are moved closer together, the ellipse becomes broader. If the foci are moved to the center, the ellipse becomes a circle and the major and minor axes are equal.

In order to define in a simple way the narrowness of an ellipse, the term *eccentricity* is employed. If we denote the distance from one focus to the center by c and the length of the semimajor axis by a, the eccentricity e is defined by the equation

$$e = \frac{c}{a}$$

When c is zero, e becomes zero and the curve is a circle. As c increases, e increases, the ellipse becoming narrower, and when $c = a$, the foci have moved to A and B and the ellipse becomes a straight line.

The Parabola. This curve may be defined as the locus of a point whose distance from a given point is equal to its distance from a given line. Thus, in Fig. 102, let F be the given point, CB the given line, and P any point on the curve.   Then PF, the distance to the given point, is equal to PB, the distance to the given line.

The line AK, drawn through F and perpendicular to CB, is called the *axis* of the parabola, the line CB the *directrix*, the point F the *focus*, and the point V the *vertex*.

The two sides of a parabola become more nearly parallel the farther they extend from the vertex, but they never become actually parallel.

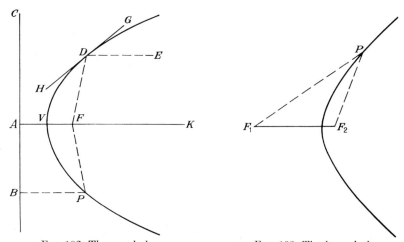

FIG. 102. The parabola.   FIG. 103. The hyperbola.

If a tangent is drawn at any point D and, from this point, DE is drawn parallel to the axis while DF is drawn to the focus, then the angles GDE and HDF are equal.   This property of the parabola is employed in the construction of the mirror of the reflecting telescope and in the manufacture of the reflectors for searchlights and the headlights of automobiles.

The Hyperbola. The property of this curve, by means of which it may be drawn, is that for any point of the curve the difference between its distances from two fixed points is a constant.   In Fig. 103 any point P is at such a distance from points F_1 and F_2 that $PF_1 - PF_2 =$ a constant.

The two sides of a hyperbola diverge more and more as the distance from F_2 increases, until, at great distances, they become practically two straight lines making a fixed angle with one another.

The points F_1 and F_2 are called the *foci* and the curve is symmetrical with respect to the line F_1F_2.

161. Gravitation and Conic Sections. It can be shown mathematically that if a body is moving about a point under the action of a force directed toward that point and varying inversely as the square of the distance from it, the path of the body must be a conic section, that is, its path will be an ellipse, parabola, or hyperbola with the point at a focus of the conic. Of the three possible paths the ellipse is the only closed one and therefore the only path in which one body may make repeated revolutions about another under the action of their mutual gravitation.

In the case of the orbits of the planets about the sun the point in the orbit nearest the sun is called *perihelion*, the point farthest removed aphelion, and the line of the major axis is often called the *line of apsides*.

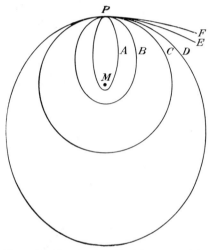

FIG. 104. Curves described by a particle *P* about a mass *M*.

The question as to which curve will be followed by any particular body depends upon the velocity of the body and its direction of motion. As a simple illustration let us assume a small particle at the point *P* (Fig. 104), projected toward the right at various velocities and then moving solely under the gravitational attraction of a mass at *M*. If the initial velocity is small, the particle will move in the narrow ellipse *A*, and the point *P* will be the aphelion point. If the initial velocity is a little greater, it will move in ellipse *B*, which has less eccentricity than *A*.

With a still greater initial velocity the orbit becomes a circle *C*. A greater velocity would compel the particle to move in the ellipse *D* with *P* as perihelion. Greater velocities still will cause the particle to move in the parabola *E* or the hyperbola *F*. Should the velocity of projection be zero, the particle would fall along a straight line toward *M*.

162. The Law of Areas. If a particle moves about a given point, the line joining the particle to the point is called the *radius vector*. *If the particle is subject to no forces except* those acting in the line of the radius vector, it can be shown that *the areas swept over by the radius vector in equal times are equal*. This holds true whatever the law according to which the total force acts,[1] provided only that it is in the line of the radius vector. Thus, in Fig. 105, let *P* be the given point and the curve be the path of a particle moving about *P* under the action of a force through *P*. Then, if the radius vector sweeps over the area *Pab* while the particle moves from *a* to

[1] It is important to realize that the *law of areas* holds not only for a force like gravitation which varies as the inverse square of the distance but also for those forces which vary in any other way as well. It holds for repulsions as well as for attractions.

b in a certain time, it will later sweep over an area Pcd which will be equal to area Pab, in an equal time interval. Since the radius vector Pa is less than the radius vector Pc, the arc ab will be greater than the arc cd. It therefore follows that the linear velocity of the particle will be greatest when at the point in its path nearest the point P.

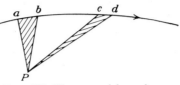

The earth's orbit about the sun is an ellipse. If the sectors Sab, Scd and Sef in Fig. 106 are equal in area, it is evident that the earth moves

Fig. 105. The general law of areas.

fastest along ab, more slowly along cd, and slowest of all along ef. Accordingly, as seen from the earth, the sun will appear to move most rapidly along the ecliptic when the earth is moving most rapidly, and vice versa. This accounts, in part, for the varying length of apparent solar days (Sec. 127).

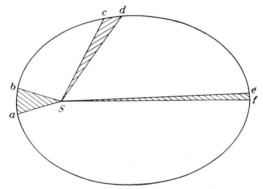

Fig. 106. The law of areas for the ellipse.

163. Perturbations. If a body such as a planet is moving about the sun, its orbit will be a smooth ellipse only in case there is no third body near them. The attraction of a third body will have an effect on both the others and these upon the third body. A simple illustration will show this.

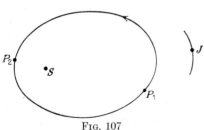

Fig. 107

In Fig. 107 let S be the sun, P_1P_2 the undisturbed orbit of an inner planet P, and J an outer planet also moving about the sun. Only a portion of the outer orbit is shown. J will attract both S and P. If P is at P_1, it will be affected more than S since it is nearer J. This difference of attraction will have the effect of pulling P forward in its orbit as well as outward toward J. If P is at P_2, then S will be attracted more than P. Hence the distance P_2S will be increased, or, so far as the effect concerns only the position of P with respect to S, we can say that near P_2 the planet P is forced away from S. It can also be shown that near P_2 there will be a force moving P ahead of its undisturbed place. Such effects of the presence of J are called *perturbations*.

The planet P will, in turn, cause perturbations of J, sometimes accelerating and sometimes retarding its motion, sometimes increasing and at other times decreasing its distance from S. These effects on J will in turn affect the motion of P.

Without considering further details, it is evident that the subject of perturbations is very complex, and it is not surprising that the problems arising when the mutual perturbations of several planets have to be taken into account are exceedingly long and difficult to solve.

164. Parabolic Velocity. There is one velocity of the motion of a body around an attracting mass which has a special interest at this time. It is the velocity required to move around the attracting mass in a parabolic

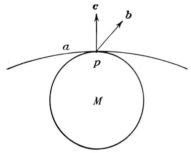

orbit. This velocity is known as the *parabolic velocity*.

In Fig. 108 let us assume that a particle is moving about M with parabolic velocity and just missing the surface of M at p. It will then leave the vicinity of M and never return. This will also apply to a particle projected from p along any other path such as b or c if the velocity of projection is equal to the parabolic velocity. Such a particle will escape from the control of M.

Fig. 108. Parabolic velocity referred to attracting mass M.

Parabolic velocity is therefore often called the *velocity of escape*. In the case of the earth the velocity of escape is 11.1 km (6.9 miles) per sec. This means that a rocket would have to attain such a velocity with respect to the earth in order to escape the earth's gravitational control and be free to wander about interplanetary space. The velocity of escape from the sun's surface would be 618 km (384 miles) per sec. For the moon it would be only 2.4 km (1.5 miles) per sec.

Another matter of interest is the fact that if a particle falls to the surface of an attracting mass from infinity, it will acquire parabolic velocity at time of impact if it starts from rest with respect to the attracting mass. The parabolic velocity can therefore also be called the *velocity from infinity*.

The velocity of such a particle, falling under the sun's gravitational force, would be 6.6 km (4.1 miles) while crossing Pluto's orbit at 40 AU and 42 km (26 miles) per sec at the earth's distance from the sun.

165. Precession of the Equinoxes. In Sec. 32 it was shown that the earth is not a sphere but a spheroid. The bulging of the earth at the equator is usually called the equatorial bulge. This bulge, with the cooperation of moon and sun, is the cause of a slow movement of the plane of the equator which is called *precession*, and, since the positions of the equinoxes are determined by the plane of the equator, their motion is called the *precession of the equinoxes*.

FIG. 109. A simple gyroscope.

Before considering the astronomical aspects of the problem it will be advisable to take up a brief study of the simple gyroscope (Fig. 109). If the wheel is rotating rapidly and the weight at the right just balances the wheel, the axis of the instrument will remain in a fixed position in space. If, however, we add an additional weight on the right, instead of the weight causing the heavier end to sink, the axis will maintain a fixed angle with respect to a horizontal plane but will slowly rotate about the vertical axis. This additional rotation involves a change in the direction of the axis of the wheel and in the plane of its rotation. This motion is called precession. The more rapidly the wheel rotates, the slower will be the precession.

The additional weight introduces a force tending to throw the wheel up, but its combination with the angular momentum of the wheel produces a motion of the axis *at right angles to the direction of the force.*

Let us now return to a consideration of the earth and its equatorial bulge. For convenience we shall consider the bulge concentrated in a ring of matter around the equator (Fig. 110), since the spherical portion does not come into play except by its attachment to the equatorial bulge.

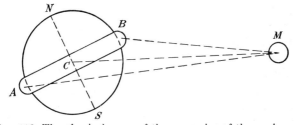

FIG. 110. The physical cause of the precession of the equinoxes.

In the figure let M be the moon, points A and B the two portions of the equatorial bulge farthest from and nearest to the moon and C the center of the earth. Since M is nearer B than A, it will exert a greater pull on the former. This will result in an effort to pull B into the line CM. If the earth were not rotating, this would be accomplished, but the great angular momentum of the rotating earth prevents B from moving toward CM, the plane of the moon's orbit, and, in combination with the additional force, the plane of the equator, while maintaining a practically constant angle with CM, gradually changes its position precisely like the plane of the gyroscope wheel.

When the moon is in the plane of the equator, as it is twice a month, this force vanishes, but the farther the moon is from the plane of the equator the greater the effect. The moon is therefore attempting to bring the plane of the earth's equator into coincidence with the plane of its orbit.

The sun, being in the plane of the ecliptic, in a similar manner attempts to bring the plane of the earth's equator into coincidence with the plane of the ecliptic. The effect of sun and moon on the rotating earth is to produce a slow change in the position of the earth's equatorial plane, although the angle between this plane and the plane of the ecliptic remains practically constant. This changes the intersections of the celestial equator with the ecliptic, that is, the equinoxes are slowly moving among the stars.

The direction of motion of the equinoxes is westward by an amount averaging 50''.2 a year. In consequence of precession, the right ascensions, declinations, and longitudes of the stars are slowly changing.

The moon's precessional effect is approximately two and one-half times that of the sun, because its proximity to the earth more than makes up for its almost insignificant mass as compared with the larger body. The planets also have a slight effect on precession, but this is practically negligible as compared with the combined effect of sun and moon.

166. Nutation. Since the precessional forces of sun and moon vanish when these bodies are in the plane of the earth's equator, it is evident that the rate of precession varies. In consequence, it is customary to break up the actual precession into two portions: a practically constant term, called the *precession constant*, amounting to 50''.2 a year, and a variable term, which is called *nutation*.

167. Motion of the Celestial Pole. The movement of the poles of the earth, described in Sec. 39, has no effect on the position of the celestial poles, for that is a shifting of the body of the earth with reference to the axis of rotation. The direction of the axis with respect to the stars is unchanged so far as this effect is concerned. The precession of the equinoxes, however, since it involves a change in the celestial equator, produces a change in the position of the celestial poles among the stars. This motion is essentially in a circle around the poles of the ecliptic, the radius of the circle being about 23°.5, the angle between the planes of the celestial equator and ecliptic. At the present rate of precession it will require about 25,800 years to complete one circuit of the celestial poles around the poles of the ecliptic.

Because of this motion of the poles various stars in turn become the pole star. About 4000 years ago the north celestial pole was less than 4° from the star α Draconis, while Polaris was then 25° from it. About 12,000 years hence the very bright star Vega will be only about 5° from the pole.

THE TIDES

168. The Tidal Forces. In Fig. 111 let A, C, and B be three points on a diameter of the earth and in line with the direction to the moon. Since A is nearer the moon than C, it is evident that the moon will attract it more strongly than C, and C more strongly than B. The effect of this attraction will be to lengthen the diameter BA if the earth is not absolutely rigid.

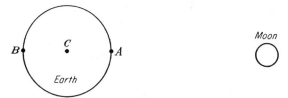

FIG. 111. The cause of the tides.

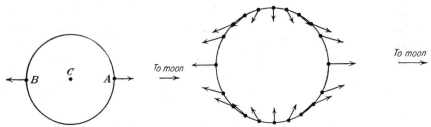

FIG. 112. The tidal forces at two ends of a diameter of the earth when referred to the center.

FIG. 113. The tidal forces around a circumference referred to the center of the earth. (*Darwin.*)

If we consider the action of the moon with reference to the center of the earth C, then both B and A are, in effect, moved away from C just as if there were two forces directed toward A and B, respectively, from C. As seen from C, therefore, we can indicate this effect by the arrows as in Fig. 112. The force at B is slightly less than that at A, since B is farther from the moon than A. When the forces with reference to C are analyzed for many points we get a result as indicated in Fig. 113.

169. Theoretical Tides. If the earth were entirely covered by the ocean, the effect of the tidal forces would be to move the waters of the ocean into two bulges, as indicated in Fig. 114, the bulge on the side toward the moon being a little greater than the one opposite. The water would be deeper near A and B and shallower around the circle CED.

If the earth rotated on an axis perpendicular to the plane of the page and in the direction of the arrow, a point, which at one time would be

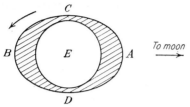

FIG. 114. Theoretical tides.

under A, would be under C, B, D, and again under A in the course of one rotation. In this time the point in question would therefore have experienced two high and two low tides. Since the moon revolves around the earth in the same direction as the earth rotates on its axis, the line joining B and A to the moon would have turned through the angle which the moon has moved. This amounts to approximately 13° a day. Hence the time when a point would be under A until it returned to the same position again would be $24^{\text{h}}51^{\text{m}}$, the additional 51 minutes being the time required for the earth to turn through the 13°.

The earth rotates on its axis once a day, while the moon revolves about the earth once in a sidereal month. It is therefore evident that unless the bulge or wave can travel westward as rapidly as the earth turns eastward, the bulge will be dragged toward the east by an amount depending upon the freedom with which the tide can move.

170. Solar Tides. The sun will cause tides precisely like the moon, except that since the tide-raising forces of the sun are less than those of the moon, the solar tides are not so high as the lunar tides, being only four-ninths of the latter.

At new moon and full moon the solar and lunar tides are superimposed, while, when the moon is at first or last quarter, the crest of the one tide is in the trough of the other. When the two tides are combined, the resulting tide is called *spring tide*, while when opposed, it is called *neap tide*.

171. The Actual Tides. The comparative shallowness of the oceans and the presence of the continents make the real tides very different from the simple theoretical situation. A tidal wave, once started, will move at a speed depending on the depth of the ocean and in a direction depending upon the direction and slope of the continental shores. The range of the tide from high to low at a port also depends upon the shape of the shore line and the shape of the bottom. The range along a comparatively straight coast is much less than at the head of a funnel-shaped bay.

RIGIDITY AND ELASTICITY OF THE EARTH

172. The Michelson-Gale Experiment In 1913, Professors Michelson and Gale of the University of Chicago carried out an experiment on the grounds of the Yerkes Observatory which gave considerable insight into the rigidity and elasticity of the earth as a whole.   Two watertight pipes, each about 500 ft long, were buried in the ground about 6 ft below the surface.   One was placed in an east-west and the other in a north-south position.   These pipes were partially filled with water, their ends closed with plate glass and devices installed which allowed the water level at the ends to be determined with great accuracy.

The theory of the experiment is as follows:

If the earth yields like a perfect fluid to the tidal forces of sun and moon, the surface of the water in the pipes will not change its apparent level. If, however, the earth has a certain amount of rigidity, the crust will not yield completely and the water in the pipes will change its level by an amount equal to the difference between the actual yielding of the earth and the amount it would yield if it were a perfect fluid.

By computation it was possible to determine the amount the earth would yield if it were a perfect fluid, while observation of the change in the water level in the pipes showed the amount the earth did not yield. The difference between these two is the amount the earth actually yielded, and this was found to be about equal to the amount a homogeneous globe of steel would yield under the tidal forces involved.   The rigidity of the earth was found to be the same in both directions.

Another result of the experiment was a determination of the rapidity with which the earth yielded to tidal stresses.   The yielding was found to be essentially as if the earth had the elasticity of steel.

A more extensive series of observations made in 1916 and 1917, with improved facilities for measuring the changes of level, confirmed the earlier work.

The results of this experiment may be summarized as follows:

The earth has both the rigidity and the elasticity of a good grade of steel.

THEORY OF RELATIVITY

173. The Einstein Theory. A book on elementary astronomy is not the proper place in which to discuss the *theory of relativity*, as it belongs properly to theoretical physics, but so much has been said about it, both in popular and in technical publications, and since the tests applied have been in the astronomical field, a very brief statement appears desirable, especially concerning that portion of the theory which applies to gravitation.

The general theory of relativity in the form presented by Einstein in 1915 sets out with the intention of molding the laws of nature into such form that they shall be invariant under any transformation of coordinates. The Newtonian law does not satisfy this criterion.   Einstein succeeded in finding a law which did satisfy it, however.   The law was very different from the Newtonian law in the *way* in which it described planetary motion.   In the Newtonian theory the thought at the back of the phenomena is one in which a mass—the planet—tends to go in a straight line with a constant velocity but is prevented from doing so and is controlled in its orbit by a force.   It is this thought, molded into quantitative form, which the Newtonian equations express.   In the general theory of relativity this thought is not dominant and the orbit becomes described in terms of a curve having certain fundamental mathematical properties. The actual orbits on the Newtonian theory and on the relativity theory are almost exactly the same.   The great difference is in the language in which the orbit is described.

The characteristics of the orbit of Mercury, and in particular its large eccentricity, are such as to make that planet specially favorable for a realization of the small departure from the Newtonian orbit predicted by the Einstein theory, a departure which is associated with the motion of the perihelion of the orbit.   The mere *existence* of a perihelion motion would not give much support to the Einstein theory as almost any departure from the Newtonian law would give such a motion.   The crucial factor in the situation is the numerical agreement of the predicted perihelion motion with that actually observed (Sec. 261).

According to the views of Einstein, his theory implies that the orbit of a light ray in passing by the sun should be the same as that which the same theory would give for the orbit of a planet which moved with the velocity of light and in this case, too, experiment confirms the theoretical prediction.   This test will be explained in Sec. 233.

To an observer who falls freely in an elevator the apparent dynamical effects of gravity are concealed.   If the observer allows a stone to leave his hand, it will stay where it is relative to him, and will not fall to the floor of the elevator.   Einstein postulates that the same acceleration which would serve to conceal the dynamical effect of gravity on the stone would also conceal whatever effect gravity might have on other phenomena such as chemical and optical phenomena.   In this way the effects of gravity are regarded as the equivalent of those obtained by adopting as our frame of reference an accelerated system of axes.   By an application of this idea Einstein was led to conclude that the effect of a strong gravitational field on the vibrations of radiating atoms would be such as to increase the wavelength of each line of the spectrum as observed by us. This test was also successfully made as will be explained in Sec. 541.

174. Einstein Theory of Mass. Another part of the Einstein theory concerns the notion of mass.   Thus far we have assumed that the mass of a body is the same under all circumstances.   The relativity theory, however, demands a variable mass, depending upon the velocity of the body.   The formula is as follows:

$$M = \frac{m}{\sqrt{1 - v^2}}$$

where M is the variable mass, m the mass of the body at rest, and v the velocity of the body in terms of the velocity of light.

For practically all bodies with which we have to deal the velocity is too small for us to detect this change of mass, but electrons emitted by radioactive substances or cathode rays in a vacuum tube have such high velocities that the question can be tested, and, within the limits of error of the observations, the results obtained satisfy the theory.

EXERCISES

1. If two homogeneous spheres of 100 g each have their centers separated 100 cm, what is the gravitational attraction between them?   *Ans.* G dynes.

2. If the earth's mass is 6×10^{27} g, the sun's mass 2×10^{33} g, and their distance apart 150,000,000 km, what is the gravitational attraction between them?

Ans. 35.6×10^{26} dynes.

3. Assuming the breaking strain of 1 cm² cross section of steel to be 5×10^9 dynes, what would be the cross section of a steel bar stretched to the breaking point which would control the earth's motion like the gravitational pull between sun and earth?

Ans. 71×10^{16} cm² or a square 8400 km on a side.

4. Assuming uniform density, show that the attraction of a sphere for a body on its surface varies as the radius of the sphere.

CHAPTER 9

THE SUN—OUR NEAREST STAR

175. Throughout the space in our vicinity are found many stars. Except on rare occasions we see them only in the night sky, because we are so near one of them that its brightness overpowers the others when our side of the earth is turned toward it. This nearest star, to which the earth is attached by the strong bonds of gravitation, is called the sun. From evidence to be presented later we shall see that the sun is a star of about average brightness, temperature, mass, density, chemical composition, etc.

The sun is in control of a planetary system. We have no evidence that any other star has a system of planets like our own, although such a situation is not improbable. While we are studying this dominant body in the solar system, we must remember that the sun is a star and try to understand the stars as a whole from a study of the only one sufficiently near to permit detailed examination.

The temperature of the earth and its general suitability as an abode for life are sustained by energy that flows from the sun. Nearly all sources of heat, light, or of other forms of energy that are of practical significance to man are derived, as we shall later see, from the sun. In turn, the sun gains its vast store of energy from atomic-energy processes going on deep in its interior.

176. Diameter. The present adopted angular diameter of the sun at mean distance is 31′59″.26. This corresponds to a diameter of 1,393,000 km (865,000 miles).

If the sun were a hollow sphere and the earth placed at its center, the moon, at its present distance from the earth, would be only a little over halfway from the center to the surface of the sphere.

The immense size of the sun as compared with the earth may more easily be realized by a comparison of their volumes. Since the volumes of spheres are proportional to the cubes of their diameters, we may write:

$$\text{Volume of sun: volume of earth: } :1,393,000^3:12,740^3$$

Solving this proportion, we find the volume of the sun is approximately 1,300,000 times the volume of the earth.

Compared with other stars, the sun is a rather ordinary body. Many stars both smaller and larger are known. Stars are known with diameters less than one one-hundredth this value. At the other extreme, Shapley has reported stars whose diameters are over a thousand times greater than the sun's, and other stars are known to exceed several hundred solar diameters in size.

177. Mass, Density, etc. Newton's law of gravitation (Sec. 154) provides us with the means to determine the sun's mass from its distance (Sec. 26) and the earth's mass (Sec. 158). By applying this law we find that the sun's mass is approximately 330,000 times the earth's mass. Since its volume is 1,300,000 times that of the earth, it follows that its mean density is one-fourth that of the earth, or about 1.4 on the water standard.

This result suggests to us a fact which more exact astrophysical analysis confirms, namely, that the sun cannot be in a solid state. Its average density is far less than that of the solid particles of the earth.

The results also allow us to determine how much greater is the force of gravity at the sun's surface than at the earth's. Using the known masses and radii of earth and sun, and applying them to Newton's law of gravitation, we find that the force of gravity at the sun's surface is nearly 28 times that at the earth's surface. A mass weighing 100 kg (220 lb) here would weigh nearly 2.8 metric tons (3 short tons) there.

As regards mass and density, the sun is also a rather ordinary star. Star densities have a wide range from about a million times that of the sun to about a millionth of the sun. Some stars thus are so dense that a piece the size of a tennis ball would weigh over 150 tons, while others are so tenuous that their average density is less than a thousandth that of air at sea level.

178. Temperature and Physical State. The surface temperature of the sun is about 6000°K.* Our theories of the sun's interior reveal that temperatures deep within the solar body probably reach up to 20,000-000°K. However, temperatures of a complex physical machine like the sun do not have a simple and unambiguous definition.

To explain what is really meant by the term "temperature" when applied to the sun goes beyond the scope of this text. It involves knowing a great deal about the laws of radiation physics as applied to heated bodies not behaving like the ideal "black-body" radiator from which we get our far simpler day-to-day

---

* The absolute temperature is usually used in the discussion of stellar temperatures. Zero degrees absolute corresponds to −273°C. To reduce absolute values to the centigrade scale subtract 273. Absolute temperature is usually indicated by K (for Kelvin).

conceptions of temperature. The temperatures given above are based on the fact that the sun's surface and interior, to a rough approximation, do behave like a black body.

The gaseous nature of the sun was foreshadowed by the sun's low average density. No body can maintain the solid or the liquid state at the high temperatures and pressures of the solar interior. The very facts, however, which complicate the radiation physics of the sun, make possible its durability and constancy, for if it were not gaseous and at such high temperatures, it could not draw upon atomic energy as its energy supply.

179. Solar Constant. Much work has been done to determine the amount of energy the sun sends to the earth. The latest results of Abbot of the Smithsonian Institution of Washington show that the amount of energy received per square centimeter of surface perpendicular to the sun's rays (after eliminating the absorption in the earth's atmosphere) is equal to 1.94 cal* per min, on the average. This quantity is known as the *solar constant.*

The solar constant is not strictly a constant quantity. It has been found to vary slightly from day to day and it may be either above or below the average value for months at a time. These variations amount to as much as 1 per cent either way from the mean.

Variations of the solar constant are probably of great significance in producing changes in weather on the earth. Many astronomers also believe that if we could detect and measure the solar ultraviolet energy that falls into the earth's upper air, but that cannot penetrate to the earth's surface because the upper air is opaque to it, we would find much larger variations than are revealed by changes in the solar constant. High-flying rockets, bearing solar telescopes and spectroscopic instruments, may soon reveal these variations and thus give us new and better methods of long-range weather prediction.

180. Amount of Energy Radiated by the Sun. If the radiation from the sun at the earth's distance amounts to 1.94 cal per cm² per min, it is evident that the total radiation must equal 1.94 times the number of square centimeters in the surface of a sphere of radius 150,000,000 km, calories per minute. This enormous amount of energy would melt a layer of ice about 11 m thick over the entire surface of the sun in 1 min. This means that each square meter of the sun's surface is radiating energy at the rate of 80,000 hp continuously.

A small part of the solar energy that reaches the surface of the earth is directly utilized by man, or is stored by natural processes that make it available for man's later uses. Thus the energy of water power used for generation of electricity and for other purposes represents simply the

* A calorie is the amount of heat required to raise the temperature of 1 g of water 1°C (from 15 to 16°C).

stored energy of sunlight. In this case the sun's energy evaporated water from low-lying oceans and seas, carried the vapor aloft against the forces of gravity, and then generated the winds and clouds that drove the water vapor against the high mountains. There it is precipitated to form the seaward-rushing streams, a tiny part of whose force runs the turbines and generators of hydroelectric plants. Similarly, the energy of burning coal and oil represents simply the growth energy of primeval forests and sea life cultured by the sunlight of ancient times and stored over geologic ages for man's use today.

181. Light of the Sun. Sunlight is merely that portion of the sun's radiant energy that falls upon the earth and that can be detected by the human eye. The sun's energy is most prolifically generated in the visible region of the electromagnetic spectrum. Part of the tiny fraction of this radiant energy that is directed toward our planet is captured at the earth's surface, where it is converted into heat, which in turn warms the abode of life. The diurnal and seasonal temperature changes of our planet result, for the most part, from the changes in the aspect of the sun relative to the earth, rather than changes in the sun's energy-production rate.

Our habits of life, even to the counting of time, are regulated by the coming and going of the sun. Starlight, by comparison, contributes negligibly to the comfort or convenience of life on earth. Moonlight, which is merely reflected sunlight, adds to the earth, even at full moon, only about a half-millionth as much visible energy as does the sun.

182. Source of Sun's Heat. The sun is not merely a hot body cooling off nor is it a body which is burning, for at the high temperature which obtains there, no chemical combinations are possible except perhaps in sunspots. If the sun's mass were composed of pure carbon and this were completely burned in oxygen, it could radiate heat at the present rate for less than 8000 years. As we shall see later, this short time interval is almost negligible in the life of the sun.

The fact that the sun is entirely gaseous and held together by the force of solar gravity suggests another possible explanation of its energy supply, the so-called "gravitational-collapse" theory. This theory seeks to explain the sun's energy as the result of a gradual decrease of its volume. By this theory the heat of the interior is provided by the collisions of the solar gas atoms as they fall ever closer into the solar nucleus from the depths of space. The source thus becomes the transformation of gravitational potential energy of the sun into kinetic energy, and thus into heat. A gaseous body so collapsing would maintain a stable temperature, as does the sun. The shortcoming of the theory is that it, too, falls short by a factor of perhaps 1000 of providing an adequate total amount of energy to explain the sun's age. Nevertheless, the gravitational collapse theory gives us our best explanation of how the sun first became hot enough to begin its atomic-energy generation, the process we now believe to be the true source of solar energy.

The atomic-energy theory, first proposed by Atkinson and Houtermans in 1929, and later developed by Bethe and others, assumes that hydrogen atoms can be transformed into helium atoms by an atomic-energy process known as a *thermonuclear reaction*. By this theory four hydrogen atoms are transmuted into one helium atom, and the process repeats on a gigantic scale every second of the sun's life. One helium atom has a mass slightly lower than the sum of the four hydrogen atoms. The difference of mass for each step like this shows up as radiant energy according to the famous Einstein equation

$$E = mc^2$$

where E equals energy; m the mass difference between the four hydrogen atoms and the one helium atom; and c the velocity of light. It was this equation which was at the foundation of the development of atomic energy for military purposes in World War II.

The enormity of the energy release in the conversion of matter to energy by this process is revealed in the fact that the conversion of 1 kg (2.2 lb) of mass into energy would produce 25,000,000,000 kwhr of energy. This is roughly equivalent to the amount of energy produced by burning three million tons of coal and is comparable to the total amount of electric power produced in the United States in a month.

Since by far the most abundant element in the sun is hydrogen, according to best present estimates, it is likely that the hydrogen stores in the sun can maintain the sun's output of energy at the present rate for at least ten billion years. The amount of helium "ash," likewise, suggests adequate fuel has been available for sustaining the sun for the approximately three billion years we believe that it has maintained its present energy output.

For the hydrogen-helium process to start, extraordinarily high temperatures and pressures, by earthly standards, are needed. Deep in the solar core, however, these temperatures exist. We estimate the central temperature to reach 20,000,000°K and the central pressures to be so great as to compress the gases there to a density 10 times that of solid steel. Gravitational collapse, as already mentioned above, probably produced the initial heat necessary for the hydrogen-helium atomic furnace to go into operation, some billions of years ago.

183. Constancy of Sun's Radiation. As stated in Sec. 179, the measurements of the solar constant indicate fluctuations from day to day and even changes in value which endure for months, but, from the evidence available, the average radiation of the sun from year to year is remarkably constant. The fruits grown today in Italy are known to be like those grown

2000 years ago. Some of the giant sequoias of California are at least 3000 years old. These trees require reasonably moderate temperatures and precipitation. We therefore conclude that, in general, there has been no marked change of climate in Southern Europe and in California for some thousands of years. Since the earth's temperature and climate are almost wholly dependent upon solar radiation, we conclude that no marked change in radiation has occurred in that interval.

Some research workers attribute the advance and recession of glaciers at intervals of hundreds of millions of years, down through the geologic ages, to minor changes of solar energy with corresponding climatic alterations. But these changes have been small percentagewise, and very small compared to the gross variations of light output that we observe in many stars.

Geological evidence carries the earth's history backward for an almost indefinite period. Fossil remains of plants and animals indicate that there has been no extraordinary change of climate affecting the entire earth for long periods of time. We are therefore justified in concluding that for possibly a billion years at least the sun has been radiating energy at about its present rate.

184. Sunspots. When Galileo first turned his newly developed telescope toward the sun in 1610, he observed on its smooth face large dark spots that he plotted on charts from day to day. These dark features are the so-called "sunspots." They generally occur in groups and change in shape and location from day to day.

A sunspot generally shows a dark center, called the umbra, usually surrounded by a less dark border, the penumbra. The penumbra exhibits pronounced structure consisting of fine filaments, when it is viewed under good conditions with a powerful instrument. The shape of a spot group often varies and even the individual spot undergoes changes, but the tendency is toward roundness.

The day-to-day motion of sunspots across the solar face reveals the rotation of the sun approximately every 27 days, as discussed in Sec. 215.

185. Size of Spots. The size of spots varies within wide limits, the smallest which can be detected being about 500 km (300 miles) in diameter, while an occasional large one approaches 100,000 km (60,000 miles).

Spots usually occur in groups (Fig. 115) and the length of the penumbra surrounding a group may be over 200,000 km (125,000 miles).

186. Development and Duration. The beginning of a sunspot is hard to determine, but usually a disturbance of some sort is noted, followed by a minute black area which enlarges rapidly to be the umbra of the fully developed spot (Fig. 116). The penumbra is not seen until the umbra is well marked.

The breaking up of a spot occurs when one or more extensions of the

penumbra shoot inward over the umbra and divide it.   If such a division
into two or more parts endures for a time, the parts move away from each
other.   The final dissolution comes when the penumbra rapidly encroaches
on and ultimately obliterates the umbra.

Sunspots appear to lie at the seat of centers of disturbance of the sun's
surface.   It is not unusual for a sunspot or a compact group of spots to

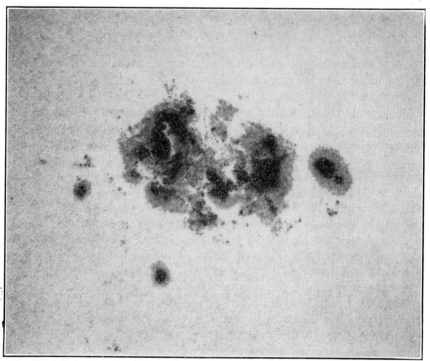

Fig. 115. Large sunspot group of May 17, 1951.   (*Mt. Wilson and Palomar Observatories.*)

rise and decline in an area that subsequently becomes the focus of an
entirely new sunspot group.   Consequently it is sometimes difficult to
decide whether a given spot is a new one or an older one, after a two-week
absence on the hidden face of the rotating sun.

The lifetimes of spots have a great range from a few hours to many
days.   Exceptional spots show lives as long as three to four months,
though in such long-extended series it is often likely that the original
spots actually died out and new spots formed in the same area.   Gnevishev
recently reported that more than half of all sunspot groups have lives
shorter than 2 days and more than 90 per cent have lifetimes shorter than
11 days.

187. Periodicity of Sunspots. About 1843, Schwabe of Dessau called attention to the periodicity of spots and showed that, on the average, the times of maximum number of spots occur about every 11 years. From the time of maximum the number gradually diminishes until, at times, weeks may pass without a spot being seen. After such a minimum the number of spots gradually increases until another maximum develops.

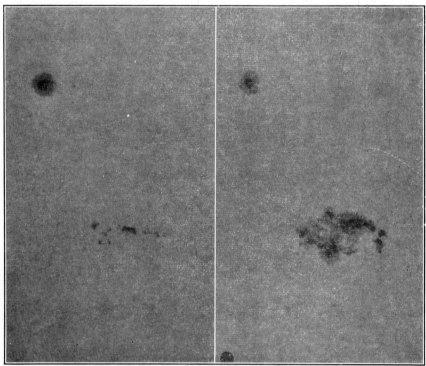

FIG. 116. Twenty-four-hour development of a sunspot, Aug. 18 and 19, 1917. (*Mt. Wilson Observatory.*)

The period and the magnitude of the fluctuation show large irregularities. Some successive maxima are separated by as few as 7 or as many as 14 years. Recent maxima have been separated by about 10 years. The rise from minimum to maximum is generally more rapid than the decline from maximum to minimum, as shown in Fig. 117.

The sunspots are not the only changeable features of the sun. Many phenomena, as we shall see, also undergo the roughly cyclical variations of the sunspots, as well as changes of shorter period. The sum of the phenomena is generally referred to as the *solar activity*. Solar-activity studies are of increasing importance because of the influences of the sun, through its variable phenomena, on such things as radio and radar reception, aurora, terrestrial magnetism, cosmic rays, and the weather.

188. Wolf's Sunspot Numbers. About 1880 Wolf of Zurich collected all available observations of spots and arranged them in accordance with the empirical formula, $N = k(10g + f)$, where N is the Wolf number, k a constant depending upon observer and instrument, g the number of spot groups, and f the total number of spots both isolated and in groups. These numbers were then plotted as shown in Fig. 117. The work has been continued by his successors, Wolfer and Brunner, who supply the results from time to time. The sunspot curve in Fig. 117 was drawn from revised values of the annual means as given by Wolfer and his successors.

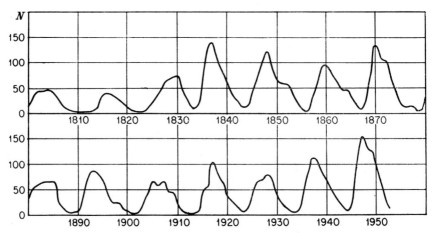

Fig. 117. Wolf relative sunspot numbers since 1800.

Wolf's sunspot numbers are only one of several measures of sunspot activity. The U.S. Naval Observatory and the Royal Observatory at Greenwich, England, for example, make regular daily measures of the total areas of sunspots. Wolf numbers have the virtue of being easily computed with no special apparatus and, therefore, of being easily measured by amateur observers. The Solar Division of the American Association of Variable Star Observers, for example, regularly publishes sunspot numbers from a great number of stations, manned by its observers, thus ensuring nearly complete day-by-day coverage of this aspect of solar activity.

189. Distribution of Sunspots. The distribution of sunspots on the solar disk is most remarkable, and thus far quite unexplained. Sunspots are seldom found beyond solar latitudes $\pm 40°$. They usually occur in about equal numbers on either side of the solar equator, when means covering several years are taken, although from 1672 to 1704 none were observed in the Northern Hemisphere. This, however, was a marked exception to the rule.

The main spot belts occur between 10° and 30° on either side of the equator. The beginning of a new spot cycle shows itself by two regions of spots at about latitude 30°N and S. The belts of disturbance gradually approach the equator and die out near latitude 10°. Spot maximum occurs when the spot regions are approximately in latitude 16°. Before the disturbances have died out entirely, new ones are beginning again at 30°. Figure 118 shows this diagrammatically. The letters in the figure will be dealt with in Sec. 192.

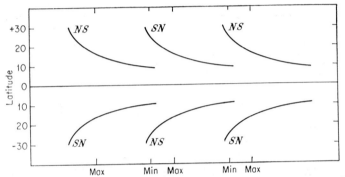

Fig. 118. The mean latitude of sunspots in successive cycles. The letters N and S show the prevailing magnetic polarity in bipolar spots.

190. Temperature in Sunspots. There is good evidence that the spot umbra is considerably cooler than adjacent bright portions of the sun. The lower temperature is largely responsible for the relative darkness of the umbra. Nicholson and Richardson of the Mt. Wilson Observatory find temperatures as low as 3800°C in large spots.

As in the case with the surface and interior of the sun (Sec. 178) ambiguities of the definition of temperatures arise for sunspot temperatures. Thus temperatures determined in different ways do not always agree in value. On the whole, however, sunspot temperatures are generally about 1500 to 2000° cooler than the surrounding solar surface. Even though a sunspot looks dark by comparison with the surrounding solar face, it is intrinsically very bright.

191. The Nature of Sunspots. The nature of sunspots has been the subject of much speculation ever since their discovery. Sir William Herschel thought they might be openings in a bright outer shell of the sun through which we could look and see a dark interior. Others held them to be openings in the photosphere caused by an explosive uprush of gases from the interior. Another theory, due to Faye, was that they are analogous to the cyclonic whirls in our atmosphere. As we shall see, this part of

Faye's theory is borne out by modern investigation, although other details of it, which need not concern us, are not corroborated.

Even though the sunspots have been known for over 300 years, many of their principal characteristics still defy explanation. The darkness, and therefore the lower temperature, is usually explained as the refrigerating effect of the sudden expansion of uprushing solar gases as they flow from deeper within the sun. This theory gains confirmation from the fact that we have clear observations showing that the gases are seen flowing away from the spot, a phenomenon known as the Evershed effect.

A principal observed feature of sunspots is their intense magnetism. The sunspot spectrum is strongly affected by the powerful magnetism in the spots, as shown by Hale. Yet the sunspot magnetism is quite unexplained.

Sunspots, when observed in a spectroheliograph tuned to take a picture showing the distribution of hydrogen gas (Sec. 205), are surrounded by whirls or vortices, as shown in Fig. 119. The whirl structure near the spot somewhat resembles the appearance of the spot penumbra seen in an ordinary telescope, but still quite unexplained. It is evident that a sunspot is a complicated phenomenon.

The long-period regularities in sunspot behavior are probably symptomatic of causes lying deep below the solar surface, and probably connected with the strange fact that the sun's equator completes a full rotation faster than the higher latitudes. But nothing definite is known concerning the cause of spots or of their magnetism, nor why they vary in number, nor why spot zones appear in middle latitudes and gradually approach the equator, as shown in Fig. 118. In spite of the gradual evolution of new and promising sunspot theories, such as those of Alfvén and Walen, these problems as well as others are still unsolved.

192. The Law of Sunspot Polarity. According to their magnetic properties, spots may be classified as unipolar, bipolar, and complex. *Unipolar* groups are either single spots or groups of spots exhibiting the same magnetic polarity, like one end of a bar magnet. *Bipolar* groups, in their simplest form, are composed of two spots quite close together and showing opposite magnetic polarity. *Complex groups* are those in which the polarities are irregularly distributed.

Bipolar groups are most common, 61 per cent of all groups classified at the Mt. Wilson Observatory since 1908 being of this character. In general, the line joining the two spots is approximately parallel to the solar equator. On account of the sun's rotation, one spot leads the other as they pass across the disk of the sun. The first is called the *preceding* and the other the *following* spot.

In 1925, Hale and Nicholson announced the following important discovery:

"The sunspots of a new 11.5-year cycle, which appear in high latitudes after a minimum of solar activity, are of opposite magnetic polarity in the northern and southern hemispheres. As the cycle progresses the mean latitude of the spots in each hemisphere steadily decreases, but their polarity remains unchanged. The

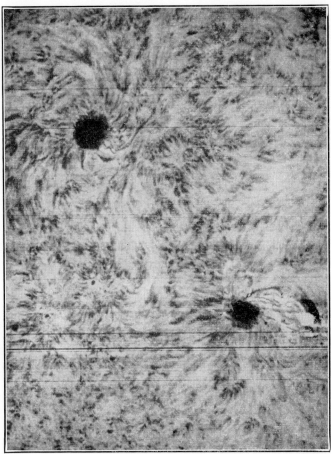

FIG. 119. Vortex motion in sunspots. Note that whirls in opposite direction are indicated for the two spots. (*Mt. Wilson Observatory.*)

high-latitude spots of the next 11.5-year cycle, which begin to develop more than a year before the last low-latitude spots of the preceding cycle have ceased to appear, are of opposite magnetic polarity."

This law of reversal of polarity in successive cycles was found to hold in all but 41 cases out of a total of 1735 bipolar groups. It is therefore evident that the full spot period, at least that referring to magnetic polarity, is 23 years and not 11.5 years as it is for spot frequency. Turner of Oxford has also shown that there is a difference between successive

FIG. 120. The great tower telescope of the Mt. Wilson Observatory especially designed for solar investigation. Total height 52 m (170 ft). (*Mt. Wilson and Palomar Observatories.*)

periods of spot frequency which points to the double period as well.   We may therefore ultimately find that the true spot period, as to both magnetic polarity and frequency, has a mean duration of 23 years.

The law of spot polarity is indicated in Fig. 118.   The pairs of letters, N and S, refer to the two spots of a bipolar group, the letter at the right indicating the preceding spot of the pair.   North-seeking poles are indicated by N and south-seeking poles by S.

THE SPECTROSCOPE

For a better understanding of the nature of the sun it is necessary to consider a new instrument, the spectroscope, which in the modern observatory is second only to the telescope in importance as an astronomical instrument of research.   It has unlocked many doors which appeared forever closed to the astronomer of 100 years ago, and many results have been achieved of which he had not even dreamed.

193. Principle of the Spectroscope. The instrument, in simplest form, consists of three parts: the collimator, the prism, and the view telescope (Fig. 121).

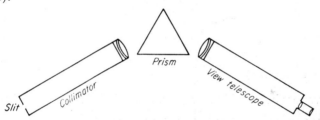

Fig. 121. The spectroscope.

The Collimator. A narrow slit with movable slit jaws is placed at the focus of an achromatic lens.   Light entering the slit and passing through the lens is therefore sent into the prism as a parallel beam.

The Prism. The purpose of the prism is to analyze the light coming from the collimator so that the light of the various wavelengths is separated. If greater dispersion is desired, more than one prism may be used.   For very high dispersion a diffraction grating is used in place of a train of prisms.   For the theory of the grating the student is referred to any standard text on physics.

The View Telescope. The lens of the telescope brings the dispersed beam of light to a focus, where it is examined through the eyepiece.   This dispersed beam as seen in the telescope is called a *spectrum.*[1]

---

[1] If the spectrum is to be photographed instead of being observed visually, the eyepiece is removed and a photographic plate placed at the focus of the telescope lens. This converts the view telescope into a camera and the entire instrument is then called a *spectrograph*.

If the slit is illuminated by monochromatic light, there appears in the eyepiece a line of light of the same color as passed through the slit. *This line is an image of the slit.*[1]

In practical use spectroscopes and their photographic counterparts, called spectrographs, take many forms and sizes. At one end of the scale we find very small, high-speed reflection spectrographs for obtaining spectra from extremely faint objects like distant nebulae or the night airglow.[2] At the other end of the scale are the powerful high-dispersion diffraction-grating spectrographs used for studying the fine structural detail of the spectrum of full sunlight. There are many degrees and forms of intermediate-sized spectrographs and spectroscopes used in nearly every branch of astronomy.

194. Bright-line Spectra. If light from a fluorescent lamp or from a hydrogen, helium, or neon tube is examined by means of the spectroscope, the spectrum is found to consist of a series of bright lines. Luminous

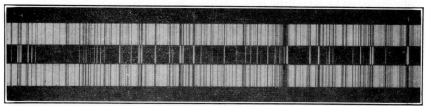

Fig. 122. Portion of solar spectrum (top and bottom); spectrum of iron vapor (middle). (*Mt. Wilson Observatory.*)

metallic vapors behave likewise (Fig. 122, middle). No two chemical elements have the same series of lines and no two lines in the spectra of any two elements have exactly the same wavelength. This principle, the first law of spectroscopy, may be stated as follows:

1. *The luminous gas or vapor of a chemical element, when under low pressure, gives a spectrum of bright lines and each element exhibits its own characteristic lines.*

Low pressure is specified, since only at low pressures are the atoms of a gas sufficiently far apart to allow each one to act more or less independently.

195. Continuous Spectra. In Sec. 69 it was stated that white light consisted of waves of all lengths from red to violet. Examination of white light with a spectroscope will therefore show a continuous band of color, running without interruption through red, orange, yellow, green, blue, and violet. Such a spectrum is called a *continuous spectrum.* Since

---

[1] It is very important that the student realize this point and it is desirable to perform experiments to demonstrate it by using small apertures of various shapes in place of the ordinary slit.

[2] The "airglow" is the permanent aurora found at all locations and on all nights. Its study forms an important new field of astronomy.

white light can be obtained from an incandescent solid or liquid, or from a
luminous gas under high pressure, the second law of spectroscopy is as
follows:

2. *An incandescent solid or liquid, or a luminous gas under high pressure,
produces a continuous spectrum.*

We would also expect such a result, for when atoms are closely packed,
there must be great interference with the freedom of motion of the electrons, so that jumps of all sorts might be expected and thus light of all
wavelengths emitted.

196. Absorption Spectra. If light from a source giving a continuous
spectrum is allowed to pass through a cooler gas at low pressure, the cooler
gas will absorb some of the energy from the continuous radiation.   The
absorption, however, is not general but is primarily of those light waves
having the frequency which the atoms of the cooler gas have when they
act as radiators of energy themselves.   Under these conditions there will
be gaps in the continuous spectrum, the gaps falling at precisely those
places where we would find bright lines if the cooler gas were giving a
spectrum of bright lines.   Such a spectrum with gaps or dark lines is
called an *absorption* spectrum (Fig. 122, top and bottom).   The third law
of spectroscopy is as follows:

3. *If light from a source of continuous radiation passes through a cooler
gas under low pressure, it loses energy of precisely those wavelengths which
the gas itself would emit if radiating alone.*

These three laws are often called *Kirchhoff's laws* because they were
first stated, in approximately their present form,
by the German physicist Kirchhoff (1858).

197. The Comparison Spectrum. In order to
determine whether a certain element is present in
a heavenly body, a simple device is used.   In
front of the slit of the spectroscope two small
total-reflection prisms are placed so that light from
a known source may be sent into the spectroscope
as at *a* and *c* (Fig. 123), while the light from the
heavenly body is sent through the slit at *b*, or vice
versa.   If some of the lines in the spectrum of the
heavenly body agree in position with lines from
the known source, we have the proof that the
known substance is to be found in the heavenly
body (see Fig. 122, which compares the spectrum

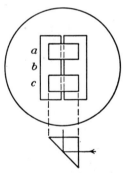

Fig. 123. Prisms for
comparison spectrum in
front of slit of spectro-
graph.

of the sun with that of iron).   The spectrum of the known substance is
called a *comparison spectrum*.

198. Doppler's Principle. A passenger on a train passing a crossing bell
may note a drop in the pitch of the sound from the bell—the greater the

speed of the train, the greater the change in pitch. This phenomenon may be explained by a diagram (Fig. 124).

The pitch of the bell is determined by the number of sound waves reaching the observer per second. If the observer is stationary at a, as many sound waves will strike his ear as the bell emits per second, say 400. If the observer moves toward the bell a distance ab in 1 sec, then not only will all the waves passing a strike his ear, but also eight more, the waves a-b. The pitch of the bell will therefore be higher than if the observer had remained at rest.

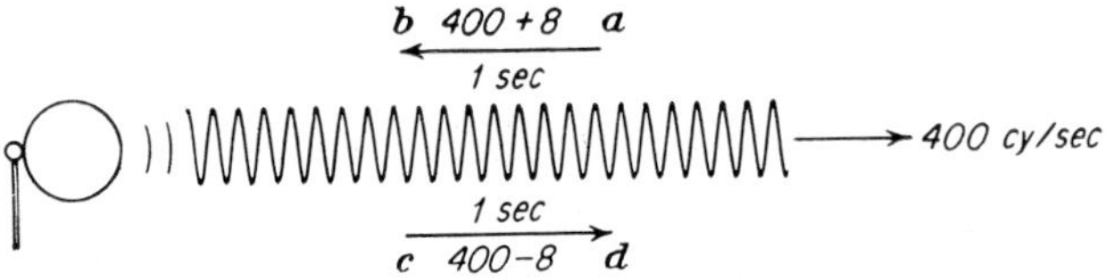

FIG. 124. The Doppler principle.

Again, suppose the observer at rest at c. He will hear the sound of the same pitch as when at rest at a, for the same number of sound waves will reach his ear at the one place as at the other. Let him now move from c to d in 1 sec. It is evident that the eight waves c-d, which would have passed him had he remained at c, have not yet done so. Eight fewer waves have reached him, and the pitch of the bell will be lower.

Summarizing this in a different way, we may say that when an observer approaches a source of sound, the observed wavelength of the sound (as indicated by the pitch) is decreased, while when he recedes from the source, the observed wavelength is increased.

It is evident that the amount of the change in observed wavelength depends upon the velocity of the observer and is proportional to his velocity. This can be expressed in the form of a proportion as follows:

$$\frac{v}{V} = \frac{\Delta \lambda}{\lambda}$$

where v is the velocity of the observer, V the velocity of sound, $\Delta \lambda$ the change in wavelength, and λ the wavelength for an observer at rest. Solving the equation for v, we have

$$v = \frac{V \times \Delta \lambda}{\lambda}$$

a formula which will allow us to determine the velocity of the observer if we know the velocity of sound, the change in wavelength, and the wavelength of the sound for the observer at rest.

The above formula is not exact, but will answer, within the limits of accuracy of observation, so long as v is small as compared with V. If both source of sound and observer are in motion, then v is the relative velocity of the two.

As early as 1845 Buys-Ballot made some experiments in Holland, using locomotives to carry sounding bodies, and found good agreement between theory and experiment.

This principle of change of wavelength with velocity is known as *Doppler's principle*.

199. Doppler's Principle Applied to Light. The same considerations which have been applied to sound can be applied to light. If the distance between a source of light and an observer is decreasing, the wavelengths of the lines of its spectrum will be decreased, while if the distance between source and observer is increasing, the wavelengths of the lines in its spectrum will be increased. We may state this as follows:

If the distance between an observer and a source of light is increasing, the lines in the spectrum of the source are displaced toward the red; while if the distance is decreasing, the lines of the spectrum are displaced toward the violet, the displacement being proportional to the velocity.

Examples illustrating this principle will be found in Secs. 346, 434, and 435.

200. Elements in the Sun. A long and careful study has been made of the elements in the sun which betray their presence by dark lines in the solar spectrum.

The method is that of comparing the position of the dark lines with a bright-line spectrum of the various elements as obtained in the laboratory. Iron is responsible for nearly 3300 lines in the spectrum of the sun (Fig. 122), titanium nearly 1100, calcium about 127, sodium 22, etc.

Sixty-seven elements have thus far been identified by Mt. Wilson observers as certainly existing in the sun, and there are a few others whose existence is probable,[1] out of a total of about 100 elements known in the laboratory. In general, the elements of low atomic weight are represented by more lines in the solar spectrum than those of high atomic weight, but there are exceptions to this rule.

The absence of an element in the spectrum of the sun is not a proof of its absence in that body. The conditions under which an element will exhibit spectral lines differ among the elements, and it may be, therefore, that the missing elements are present, but the conditions in the reversing layer (Sec. 203) are not right for them to show absorption lines.

The abundances of the different elements of the sun can also be determined roughly from spectroscopic analysis, though the problem is far more difficult than simple atomic identification. Russell has pioneered in ascertaining abundances from spectroscopic data.

[1] See list of elements in the Appendix.

In addition, the relative brightnesses of different lines of the spectrum corresponding to different physical states of the atom yield knowledge of solar temperatures. Thus, spectrum analysis can tell us about temperatures both in the umbrae of sunspots and in the sun's atmosphere.

Spectroscopic analysis of sunspots frequently reveals spectrum lines that gather together in closely clustered groups known as "bands." Laboratory studies have shown that such bands arise from molecules rather than from simple atoms. From analyses of these sorts we have found the spectra of simple chemical compounds like titanium oxide and hydrides of magnesium and calcium in sunspots.

Magnetic fields reveal themselves to the spectroscope by widening and splitting some lines of the spectrum. Spectroscopic analysis, therefore, gives us the magnetic strength of nearly all sunspots that are observed and has also shown that many stars have powerful general magnetism. Magnetic studies of the sun, as a whole, have revealed conflicting results. At some times, at least, the sun's general magnetism, if present, is very weak.

In 1940 Minnaert, Houtgast, and Mulders prepared a monumental spectroscopic atlas giving all lines of the sun's spectrum on a very accurate graphical scale. In 1950 the McMath-Hulbert Observatory compiled and published a similarly magnificent work covering the infrared spectrum far beyond the range of the human eye, but a region of equal astrophysical importance. Tens of thousands of spectrum lines appear in these catalogs.

201. The Photosphere. The apparent surface of the sun is called the *photosphere*. It was formerly believed that this surface was formed by a layer of clouds composed of small liquefied particles of the less easily volatilized elements composing the sun. This view can no longer be held, for at the high temperature known to exist at the photosphere all known elements would be in the gaseous state. Since the internal temperature is very much higher than that at the surface, it is necessary to assume that the sun is wholly gaseous, the density increasing with the depth below the outer boundary.

For the sun a remarkable physical process discovered by Wildt renders the solar photosphere astonishingly opaque in spite of the tenuity of its gases. This process, known as the *continuous opacity of the negative hydrogen ion*, explains why light reaching the eye usually comes from within a few hundred kilometers of the surface of the photosphere. It also explains why the sun, in spite of being gaseous throughout, has a perfectly sharp edge, even when viewed in a powerful telescope. We shall not explain the negative-hydrogen-ion theory but refer the reader to modern astrophysical texts for the explanation.

At the earth's distance from the sun the depth of the layer of gas involved in the transition between essentially transparent and essentially opaque gases is hardly of appreciable thickness.   This apparent luminous surface is called the *photosphere*.

202. Appearance of Photosphere. The photosphere is not a surface of uniform brightness but has a mottled appearance (Figs. 115 and 116) to which the older observers gave the name of "rice-grain structure."   The "grains" are from 300 to 800 km in diameter, about the smallest area that can be distinguished easily on the solar surface.   The probable explanation of the mottled appearance is that there are ascending and descending currents of gases at the photospheric level, the ascending ones bringing up hotter material from lower levels and the descending ones carrying down cooler, and therefore darker, matter.   Individual grains last only a few minutes and then fade away, to be replaced by new ones.

Occasional sunspots will also be seen.   These look like black areas in the photosphere.   Around the spots bright areas, called *faculae*, make their appearance, but they usually can be seen only near the limb of the sun.

The general brightness of the photosphere is greatest at the center of the sun's disk and decreases rapidly near the edge.   This is especially well seen on photographs (Fig. 125).   It is easily explained as an absorption effect, since the light from the limb must take a much longer path through the sun's atmosphere[1] than that coming from the center of the disk.

The faculae apparently lie a bit higher than the photosphere, and thus suffer less absorption than the photosphere as they near the edge of the sun.   This is why they show up bright around the sunspots at the edge of the sun, but not near the center.

203. Formation of Absorption Lines. The photosphere of the sun is a region of extreme interest.   The pressure, even at the bottom of the photosphere, is only about one-tenth of the atmospheric pressure at sea-level. It is in this region that the absorption lines of the spectrum of the solar surface are produced.   Some years ago astronomers held a rather simple theory of the formation of these spectrum lines in a "reversing layer" of cooler gas lying above the continuously emitting photosphere.   By this theory, the cooler gas absorbed from the continuous spectrum the same radiations it would emit when excited in the laboratory, thus producing the dark-line or Fraunhofer spectrum of the sun.

We now know that our simple theory of the reversing layer is inadequate.   The true situation is far more complicated.   In our present theories the absorption lines are produced in the photosphere itself. When we look in just the wavelength corresponding to an absorption line, we are seeing to a smaller depth of the photosphere where the temperature is lower and the brightness less.

[1] The term "atmosphere" as applied to the sun means that portion lying above the level of the photosphere.

In spite of the complexity of the situation modern astrophysics gives us a reasonably satisfactory mathematical theory for the formation of the absorption lines of the sun's spectrum. It describes their width, blackness, and relative intensities in terms of the temperatures, pressures, and other physical properties of the gaseous atoms of the photosphere. To

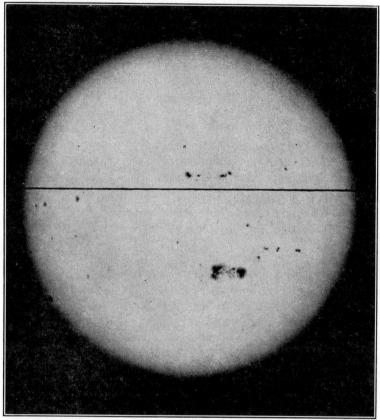

Fig. 125. Direct photograph of the sun showing sunspots, faculae, and absorption effect near edge. (*Goodsell Observatory.*)

explain the present state of our knowledge of the formation of these lines is, however, beyond the scope of this text.

Lying directly below the photosphere is a transition zone where the physical composition of the gas changes drastically. The region is below the sun's visible surface, but astrophysicists have been forced to invent it to explain the flow of energy from the sun's interior to the photosphere, where the energy is radiated from the sun principally as light. The hypothetical region, perhaps 500 km in depth, is known as the *convective layer* and must be in turbulent motion. We believe that in this region are formed the minute streams of gas that exhibit themselves as the grains mentioned in the preceding section. When the streams of gas impinge upon the photosphere, they cause local hot spots which in turn look like grains. The grains thus are the visible evidence for the existence of the convective zone, which otherwise is purely hypothetical.

204. The Chromosphere. Just above the visible solar surface, the photosphere, lies another important region known as the *chromosphere*. It is almost perfectly transparent. The solar continuum and the Fraunhofer lines pass through it virtually unaltered. The layer is normally virtually undetectable in spectroscopic observation of the sun. At total eclipse, however, the chromosphere shows as a spectacular color band that led the English astronomer Lockyer to name it "chromosphere." For a mere second or two the light of the chromosphere flashes into brilliant visibility, giving us the famous "flash spectrum" so intensively studied by means of the spectrograph over the past three-fourths of a century. Here

K H $H\delta$ $H\gamma$ $H\beta$

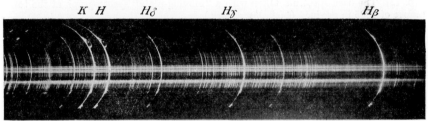

Fig. 126. The flash spectrum at the total eclipse of Aug. 31, 1932. The scale of the spectrum is approximately the same as that of Fig. 127. (*Lick Observatory.*)

we have a "luminous gas under low pressure" emitting a spectrum consisting of bright lines.

Owing to the small depth of the layer and the distance of the sun, it is not necessary to use a collimator on the spectrograph used to photograph the "flash." The narrow arc at the limb of the sun left uncovered by the moon is obviously curved. In consequence, the lines, instead of being straight, are curved and the length of the crescent is an indication of the height to which the element rises in the solar atmosphere. Figure 126 is a reproduction of the flash spectrum obtained by Menzel and Chappell, of the Lick Observatory, at the eclipse of 1932.

Most of the lines of the chromospheric flash spectrum have their origin in a layer of gas within 2000 km (1200 miles) of the photosphere, but some of the lines, notably some belonging to hydrogen and calcium, have sources extending to 12,000 and 14,000 km, respectively, above the photosphere.

Campbell of the Lick Observatory devised a special type of spectrograph for use in eclipse work which is known as the *moving-plate spectrograph*. By means of it the changes in the character of the spectrum lines can be followed. Figure 127 is a reproduction of a portion of a spectrogram taken with this instrument. The lower portion shows the lines as absorption lines which gradually changed to bright lines above as the moon eclipsed the sun. The length of the bright lines is determined by the height of the emitting gases in the solar atmosphere.

At the Mt. Wilson Observatory it has been possible to photograph the lines of the flash spectrum without eclipse by using a large solar image of 46-cm (18-in.) diameter, but a very steady and large image is required. This method, however, does not give the elevations of the gases in the solar atmosphere.

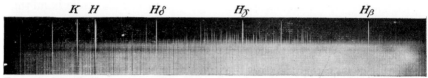

Fig. 127. The flash spectrum taken with a "moving-plate" spectrograph at the total eclipse of 1905 in Spain. (*Lick Observatory*.)

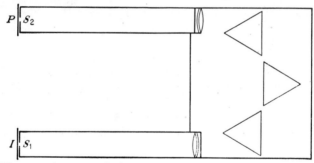

Fig. 128. Diagram of a spectroheliograph. The solar image formed by a telescope is at I; S_1 is the first slit and S_2 is the second slit which allows the light of a selected spectrum line to fall on the photographic plate at P.

The spectrum of the chromosphere may be observed at any time with appropriate apparatus and ordinarily consists of bright lines of calcium, helium, and hydrogen. When there is a disturbance of the solar surface at the point of investigation, however, gases from lower levels are brought up and hundreds of bright lines become visible.

205. The Spectroheliograph. This instrument consists of a spectrograph so mounted that it can be moved with respect to the image of the sun and the photographic plate (Fig. 128). By means of a second slit, placed immediately in front of the plate, the light coming from only a single line of the spectrum is allowed to reach the sensitive film. At any instant, therefore, the impression obtained gives the relative intensities of the light in this line as distributed across the sun. By the motion of the instrument across the image of the sun, and also by moving it at the same rate with respect to the plate, a complete photograph of the sun is obtained, showing the distribution across the sun of the element whose line has been used.   Photographs thus obtained are called *spectroheliograms*.

The spectroheliograph was developed independently by Hale in this country and Deslandres in France about 1892.   It is used especially for the study of the distribution of calcium and hydrogen in the sun's atmosphere and the photography of prominences.   Lines of other elements than calcium and hydrogen can be used, but since other elements have less prominent lines in the solar spectrum, the spectroheliograms are not so easily obtained.

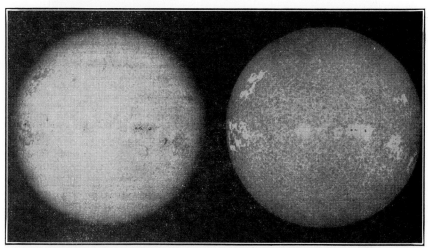

Fig. 129. Spectroheliograms of the sun showing the distribution of hydrogen (left) and calcium (right) in the solar atmosphere.   (*Mt. Wilson Observatory.*)

Recently a new instrument to accomplish monochromatic photography of the sun was developed independently by Lyot of France and Öhman of Sweden.   This device is a color filter that transmits a very narrow band of wavelengths.   It utilizes birefringent crystals and polarizers and is generally termed a *birefringent filter*.   Its advantage over the spectroheliograph is its smallness, its luminous efficiency, and the fact that it has no moving parts.   Its principal disadvantage, at this stage of development, is the fact that it is not easy to change the wavelength for which it is tuned or the width of the spectrum band transmitted.

Another recent development of significance in solar research was the application of motion-picture techniques to the study of the sunspots, prominences, and other features on the sun.   The first application of motion-picture techniques was made by McMath of the McMath-Hulbert Observatory.   Many observatories have now adopted these methods of observation and analysis for solar phenomena.

206. Prominences. From time to time there may be observed above the level of the chromosphere immense clouds of luminous gases, which are called prominences. These vary in height from those which can just be detected to some which rise over 800,000 km (500,000 miles) above the solar surface. Elevations above 150,000 km are rare.

The spectrum of prominences is essentially the same as that of the chromospheric flash observed at eclipse, though differences exist not only

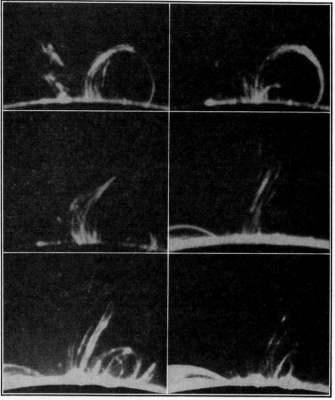

Fig. 130. Hydrogen spectroheliograms showing loop-type prominences. (*McMath-Hulbert Observatory, University of Michigan.*)

between different prominences but probably also between prominences and the chromosphere in the relative brightness of different lines. The differences give the astrophysicist clues to temperature- and electron-density variations in these solar phenomena.

Prominences tend to fall into two principal classes, early recognized by Secchi and others. One class includes the *active-region prominences* that cluster about sunspot groups. These are characterized by rapid vertical motions, sharply knotted character, and by loops and short streamers, as shown in Fig. 130. Motions of several hundred kilometers per second are not unusual in such prominences and are characterized by a predominance of downflow to the solar surface, punctuated by occasional intensely violent ejections known as *surges*. When viewed on the face of the sun with a spectroheliograph, these surges and downflowing knots frequently show as dark absorption features, with their principal absorption displaced from the normal wavelength by the large effects of its motion, according to the Doppler principle. Figure 133 shows such a dark feature, while Fig. 130 exhibits the appearance of a similar object at the edge of the sun.

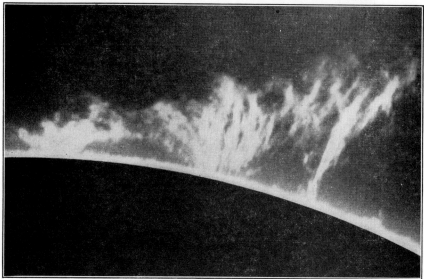

FIG. 131. Quiescent prominence 128,000 km (80,000 miles) high. (*Mt. Wilson and Palomar Observatories.*)

The other principal type of prominence is a "quiescent" prominence. It usually makes a brilliant feature at the solar limb (Fig. 131). These quiescents, in sharp contrast to the active-region prominences form preferentially in regions free of marked solar activity. Occasionally a quiescent prominence undergoes a sudden transformation and erupts from the sun as a giant expanding arch (Fig. 132) moving with great speed.

Seen on the disk of the sun with the aid of a spectroheliograph or birefringent filter, quiescent prominences frequently reveal themselves as long streaklike markings known as "dark filaments" (Fig. 133).

Prominences of one sort or another can be seen at all times. In regions where no more spectacular features can be found, the upper fringe of the chromosphere appears to break up into multitudes of minute spikelike prominences known as *spicules*. The spicules are generally visible near the solar poles.

207. Solar Flares. One particular form of prominence of spectacular behavior is the so-called solar "flare" or "chromospheric eruption" (Fig.

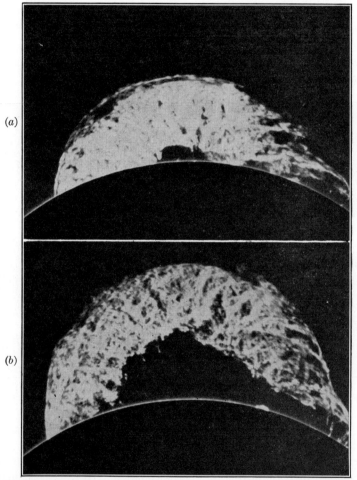

(a)

(b)

FIG. 132. Large eruptive prominence, June 4, 1946. Time between *a* and *b* 33 min. Height of prominence in *b* over 320,000 km (200,000 miles). (*High Altitude Observatory, Climax, Colo.*)

134). This prominence, an active-region type of extreme sort, has an explosive rise of brightness, often in a few seconds. It accompanies pronounced radio-reception effects and other effects, as we shall show in Sec. 213. So marked are the phenomena of flares that some astronomers class them as a different form of activity from prominences.

208. Plages. Hale's early study of the solar surface with the spectro-heliograph showed many great clouds of luminous calcium vapor in the solar atmosphere. He called these *flocculi*. Modern usage tends toward elimination of this term which Hale assigned to a relatively wide range of phenomena. The term "plage" describes the luminous calcium and hydrogen clouds formerly termed "bright flocculi." The plages are closely related to the continuous-spectrum faculae which generally appear

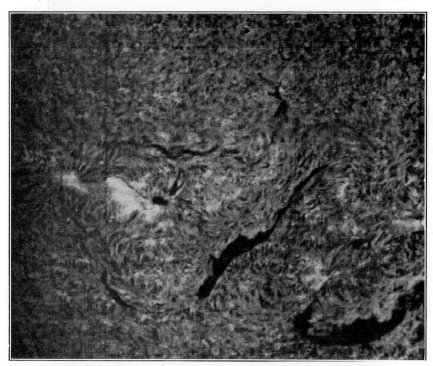

Fig. 133. Quiescent prominences projected against sun as dark filaments.

in the same regions. Plages, however, unlike faculae, appear over the entire solar disk.

209. The Corona. At the time of a total eclipse of the sun, there appears around the sun an exquisitely beautiful halo of pearly white light which is called the *corona*. Near the edge of the sun the corona is quite bright, but the brightness falls off rapidly with increasing distance. Thus far it has been impossible to see the corona as a whole except during a total solar eclipse.

The shape of the corona varies a great deal, but, in general, at spot minimum there are long equatorial streamers and short polar rays, while at spot maximum the polar rays are longer and the equatorial ones shorter.

so that the extension from the sun is approximately uniform in all directions.   At spot maximum the corona extends about one solar diameter or
less from the sun's edge, but at spot minimum equatorial streamers may
extend outward several diameters (Figs. 135 and 136).   At the eclipse
of 1878 two streamers were traced outward a distance of 10 diameters, or

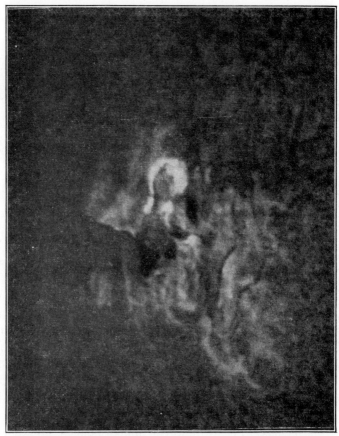

Fig. 134. A bright solar flare, May 19, 1951.   (*High Altitude Observatory, Climax,
Colo.*)

about 15,000,000 km (9,000,000 miles).   So far as the author can find,
this is the maximum length of coronal streamers on record.   According to
Mitchell, the maximum and minimum types of corona precede spot maximum and minimum by a year or two.

Unlike the prominences, the corona exhibits relatively gentle motions.
It apparently rotates as a whole with the sun, as shown by the artificial
eclipse studies by Lyot with the coronagraph described in Sec. 210.
Measures of the motions of fainter streamers of the corona at eclipse sug-

gest motions of the order of some tens of kilometers per second, but these must be regarded as still inconclusively established.

210. The Coronagraph. In 1930 the French astronomer Lyot developed a new type of solar telescope known as the coronagraph. The development ranks with the spectroheliograph in astronomical importance. With it Lyot was first able to establish the day-to-day changes of the coronal spectrum and continuous emission, and to discover new lines of the coronal spectrum.

Fɪɢ. 135. The solar corona of Jan. 25, 1944. Typical corona of sunspot minimum. (*Expedition of Tacubaya and Tonantzintla Observatories to Peru.*)

Coronagraphs have now been established in Switzerland, the United States of America (Fig. 137), Germany, Sweden, and Russia, and are planned for other places. The coronagraph has also aided greatly in studies of solar prominences.

211. Coronal Spectrum. The spectrum of the corona appears to be composite. The dark lines of the solar spectrum are found, but the continuous background is brighter. This is interpreted to mean that there are particles reflecting the ordinary solar spectrum and that, in addition, either there are some particles hot enough to give a continuous spectrum which is superposed on the absorption spectrum, or else the continuous spectrum is due to scattering of ordinary sunlight by high-speed particles which would obliterate the absorption lines.

In addition to this, there are a number of bright lines, especially one in the green at λ 5303, which at times are very prominent. It has recently been shown by Edlèn that these lines are probably due to highly ionized atoms of calcium, iron, and nickel. The very high ionizations suggest extremely high temperatures in regions subject to large deviations from the black-body laws of temperature equilibrium.

Fig. 136. The solar corona near sunspot maximum. (*Photographed by the Swarthmore College Eclipse Expedition to Sumatra, Jan. 14, 1926.*)

212. Nature of the Corona. We now believe the corona to consist of three principal parts as follows:

1. The emission-line corona, discussed in Sec. 209.

2. The "electron corona" comprising high-speed electrons moving so fast that their Doppler effect "smears" out the Fraunhofer lines giving the scattered light[1] the appearance of continuous light. The coronal streamers arise from this component, and its light is polarized.

3. The Fraunhofer corona, consisting of light diffracted and scattered into a halo by particles of dust and meteoric material between the sun and

[1] The light is scattered by the process known as *Thomson scattering*, which the reader can investigate in advanced physics texts.

the earth, was proposed independently in 1948 by van de Hulst and Allen. Particles all the way to earth contribute to this element of the corona, which is actually not truly a solar feature at all. Near the sun these particles are evaporated and do not contribute to the halo.

We know that the density of the corona, even close to the sun, is exceedingly low. The great comets of 1843 and 1882 almost grazed the sun's

Fig. 137. The Lyot-type coronagraph of the High Altitude Observatory at Climax, Colo.

surface and at the time were moving with a velocity of about 500 km (300 miles) per sec. Both comets went through at least 1,000,000 km of the corona at this great velocity without suffering the slightest appreciable retardation.

The total brightness of the corona is small. Observations by Stebbins and Kunz at the eclipses of 1918 and 1925 by means of the photoelectric cell, and by Pettit and Nicholson at the eclipse of 1925 by means of the thermocouple, agree in making the total light of the corona almost exactly one-half that of the full moon. Stetson's observations at the eclipse of 1926 in Sumatra give a value 70 per cent that of the full moon.

213. Solar Activity and Related Phenomena. The sunspot curve given in Fig. 117 shows the variation of one form of solar activity. The corona, prominences, faculae, plages, and other features of the visible surface of the sun all appear to vary in related fashion. Some phenomena, like solar flares, are rare except during sunspot maxima, while others, like the corona, are always present but vary in form and spectral character in unison with sunspot changes.

The relationship of the different aspects of solar activity to terrestrial phenomena like weather, radio reception, etc., is a field of astrophysics of ever-increasing practical importance.

Large solar flares, for example, are always accompanied by severe long-distance radio communications blackouts, instantaneously affecting most of the sunlit hemisphere of the earth. The effects, astronomers believe, are the result of ultraviolet light or X rays falling on the earth's upper atmosphere and changing the character of the layers of the radio-reflecting ionosphere upon which long-distance radio messages depend.

Magnetic storms and *aurorae*, on the other hand, appear to be produced by a slower-moving stream of ejected solar particles, presumably largely hydrogen ions and electrons, a part of which find their way to earth and spiral into the earth's atmosphere, being deflected poleward by the earth's magnetism. When they collide with upper-air atoms, they excite them to produce the well-known *northern lights*.

Effects of solar activity have also been reliably established for certain types of cosmic-ray changes, for the rate of growth of trees in some areas, for weather influences, and for a small number of other phenomena. Moreover, the sun has been found to emit radio waves of very short wavelength that can interfere with man-made radar and other electrical services, under some conditions.

In addition to these, many other variable phenomena, ranging from the flight of insects to the price of wheat, have been thought to show a periodicity which is analogous to the sunspot curve. How much reliance should be placed in these ideas it is difficult to say, but for the present it seems best not to consider them too seriously.

214. Sun's Rotation. The sun rotates on an axis from west to east, just like the earth. The plane of the sun's equator makes an angle of $7°11'$ with the plane of the ecliptic. The earth is at the intersection of the two planes about June 6 and Dec. 8. The north pole of the sun is turned toward the earth $7°$ about Sept. 8 and the south pole similarly about Mar. 7.

There are several ways of determining the sun's period of rotation, but we shall consider only two, the spot method and the application of Doppler's principle.

215. Rotation by Spot Method. Sunspots are seen to move across the sun's disk (Fig. 138), disappear from view at the western edge, and, if of sufficient duration, reappear later at the opposite edge and again cross the disk.   Observations of this character show that the average time between two successive transits across the sun's central meridian is about 26.8 days.   This period is called the sun's *synodic rotation period.*

The synodic period is not the actual rotation period, for the earth has moved ahead nearly 30° in its orbit in the interval, so that the apparent central meridian is not the same.   After allowing for the effect of the earth's motion, the sun's period of rotation, called its *sidereal period*, is found to be approximately 25 days.

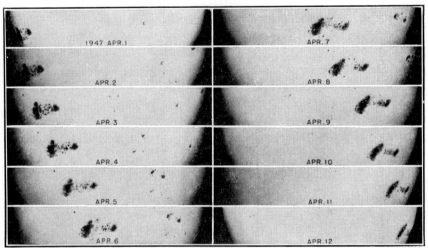

Fig. 138. Sections of photographs of sun showing its rotation as indicated by the motion of sunspots across the solar disk.   (*Mt. Wilson and Palomar Observatories.*)

216. Rotation by Doppler's Principle. An interesting application in solar research of Doppler's principle is to be found in the spectroscopic study of the sun's rotation.   At several observatories series of spectrograms have been taken giving light first from the east edge of the sun and then from the west.   The spectrum lines arising from the different elements of the sun are all shifted toward the blue end of the spectrum for the east edge and to the red for the west, showing that the east edge approaches us and the west edge recedes from us.   The amount of shift is very slight, corresponding to a velocity of rotation at the equator of about 2 km per sec.   Figure 139 illustrates the effect.

217. Law of Solar Rotation. Observations of sunspots have shown the remarkable fact that the rotation period depends upon the solar latitude of the spots used.   Many series of observations have been made to study this phenomenon, but we shall give only the values obtained by E. W. and

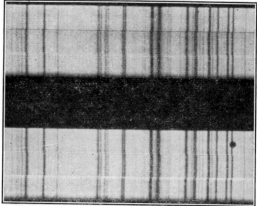

Fig. 139. Solar rotation as shown by Doppler effect. (*Royal Observatory, Arcetri, Italy.*)

A. S. D. Maunder from the Greenwich photographic observations of 1879 to 1901. These results, depending on 1871 spot groups which lasted 6 days or more, may be summarized as shown in Table II.

TABLE II

Spot latitude, degrees	Period, days	Spot latitude, degrees	Period, days
0	24.6	20	25.2
5	24.7	25	25.6
10	24.8	30	25.8
15	25.0	35	26.6

Few spots are found beyond 40° latitude, either north or south, so that the spot method is not available for higher latitudes. To study rotation there Doppler's principle must be called upon. One series of observations of this character, made by Plaskett and De Lury, gave the following results:

TABLE III

Latitude, degrees	Period, days	Latitude, degrees	Period, days
0	25.3	35	28.0
5	25.4	40	28.7
10	25.6	50	30.4
15	25.8	60	32.2
20	26.2	70	33.8
25	26.7	80	35.0
30	27.3	90	35.4

The two methods agree moderately well in results. Each shows the shortest period at and near the equator, the period increasing with the latitude. No satisfactory reason has been found to explain this peculiar law of solar rotation. There is some evidence also that there is a variation in the period, depending upon the level in the solar atmosphere of the element whose lines are used, in the sense that the higher the level the more rapid the rotation.

EXERCISES

1. If the smallest sunspot readily seen is 500 km in diameter, what is its angular diameter? *Ans.* 0''.69.

2. How long would it take to travel around the sun on a great circle at the average speed of 500 km per hr? *Ans.* 1 year.

3. The leading spot of the large spot group in Fig. 138 moved 133° in solar longitude from Apr. 1 to 11. (*a*) What is the synodic period of the sun's rotation? (*b*) Assuming that the earth revolved around the sun through an angle of 10° in that time, what is the sidereal period of the sun's rotation? *Ans.* (*a*) 27.1 days; (*b*) 25.2 days.

4. In 1912, Schlesinger at the Allegheny Observatory determined by means of the spectrograph that the sun's equatorial velocity was 2.0 km per sec. What was the sun's sidereal rotation period? *Ans.* 25.3 days.

CHAPTER 10

ECLIPSES

ECLIPSES OF THE MOON

218. Cause of the Lunar Eclipse. An eclipse of the moon occurs when the moon passes into the earth's shadow. In Fig. 140 let the plane of the page represent the plane of the ecliptic, S the sun, E the earth, M the moon, and the dotted line HJ a portion of the moon's orbit around the earth.

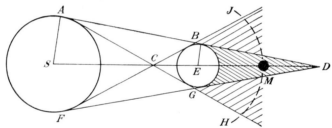

FIG. 140. Eclipse of the moon.

From the figure it is clear that within the region BDG we have a cone-shaped space which is occupied by the earth's shadow and from which the sunlight is excluded. In the region around the cone like JBD the sunlight is only partially excluded. The shadow cone is called the *umbra* and the surrounding region, JBD, the *penumbra*. The boundary between umbra and penumbra is not sharp because the earth's atmosphere forms no definite shadow (Fig. 11).

219. Length and Diameter of the Earth's Shadow. The mean length of the earth's shadow cone is approximately 1,379,000 km (857,000 miles), a value easily calculated by the use of the similar right triangles ASD and BED. The diameter of the shadow at the moon's mean distance is about 9200 km (5700 miles). The length of the shadow varies slightly, owing to the earth's varying distance from the sun. The diameter at the moon will vary for the same reason as well as because of the moon's varying distance from the earth. Both variations are small and can be disregarded in an elementary discussion.

220. Lunar Eclipse Limits. If the moon's orbit lay in the plane of the ecliptic there would be an eclipse at every full moon, but, since this is not the case, eclipses occur only under certain conditions.   In Fig. 141 let NC represent the plane of the ecliptic, NB the plane of the moon's orbit, N the node[1] of the moon's orbit, M the moon, and E the cross section of the earth's shadow at the moon's distance.   From the figure it is evident that

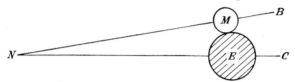

Fig. 141. Lunar eclipse limits. E is the earth's shadow and M the moon.

if full moon and shadow were farther from the node than indicated, there would be no eclipse; if nearer, an eclipse would be certain.   Hence the shadow must be near a node at the time of full moon in order that an eclipse may occur.   This distance from the node is called the *lunar eclipse limit*.   This limit is not constant, owing to the slight variation in the inclination of the moon's orbit and to the varying diameter of the shadow at the moon's distance.   Hence it is customary to give maximum and minimum values such that if the shadow's distance from the node exceeds the maximum, no eclipse is possible; while if less than the minimum, an eclipse is certain.   These maximum and minimum values are $12°.2$ and $9°.5$, respectively,[2] as seen from the earth.

221. Duration of Lunar Eclipse. If the eclipse occurs when the shadow and the full moon are quite near one of the nodes of the moon's orbit, the moon will pass entirely into the shadow.   This is known as a *total eclipse*.   If the entire body of the moon does not pass into the shadow, a *partial eclipse* occurs.

In Fig. 142 the numbers 1, 2, 3, and 4 represent four positions of the moon with respect to the shadow. Position 1 is called *first contact*, position 2 *second contact*, etc.

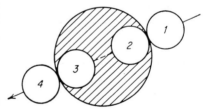

Fig. 142. Contacts of moon with earth's shadow in the case of maximum duration of totality.

In the figure it is assumed that the moon's center passes through the axis of the shadow.   The student should draw a similar figure and study the circumstances of the eclipse when the moon's path does not cut the axis.

[1] The intersection of the moon's orbit with the plane of the ecliptic is called the *node*.

[2] As usually defined, the lunar eclipse limits are the distances of the sun from the node opposite N.   The values are the same since the two nodes are precisely opposite and the sun is always just 180° from E.

When the moon passes through the center of the shadow, the time from first to fourth contact is about 4 hr; from second to third contact about 2 hr.   If the eclipse is not central, the duration will be less and less until a small partial eclipse may be only of a moment's duration.

222. Phenomena of a Lunar Eclipse. For some time, possibly half an hour, before the moon reaches the shadow, the eastern side of the moon may be seen to darken gradually.   When it reaches the shadow, the darkening is very marked, looking almost black by contrast.   The edge of the shadow appears sharp to the unaided eye, but even in a field glass the sharpness disappears.   If the eclipse is total, the surface of the moon appears of a dull-orange hue, the intensity varying considerably from one eclipse to another.   This is caused by the refraction of the sun's rays into the shadow by the earth's atmosphere.   The rays most strongly refracted have passed through a large mass of air, and accordingly have lost their blue light.   If that portion of the lower atmosphere through which the sun's rays might pass is filled with clouds, very little light may be refracted into the shadow.   This occurred at the total eclipse of Oct. 4, 1884, when the moon's disk was invisible to the naked eye.

223. Visibility of Lunar Eclipses. From Fig. 140 it is clear that an eclipse of the moon is visible over an entire hemisphere of the earth.   The various phases of the eclipse will also occur at the same instant and be visible wherever the moon is above the horizon.   If the eclipse is of long duration, it will be visible over considerably more than a hemisphere because of the rotation of the earth.

ECLIPSES OF THE SUN

224. Cause of the Solar Eclipse. An eclipse of the sun occurs when, at new moon, the moon passes so near the line between earth and sun as to cut off some or all of the sun's light.   In Fig. 143 let S represent the sun,

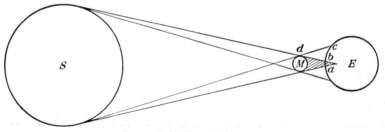

FIG. 143. Eclipse of the sun.

M the moon, and E the earth.   The moon's shadow is cone-shaped, with the base of the cone at the moon.   If the shadow cone touches the earth, an observer within the cone will find all the sunlight cut off, as at ab.   An observer in the region *bc* will see only part of the sun's disk hidden by the moon. The first observer will see a *total* eclipse, while the second will see a *partial* one. The shadow cone itself is called the *umbra*, while the portion surrounding it, as *cbd*, is called the *penumbra*.

225. Length and Diameter of Moon's Shadow. The length of the moon's shadow varies from about 367,000 to 380,000 km (228,000 to 236,000 miles). Since its distance from the earth varies from 357,000 to 407,000 km, it is clear that sometimes the tip of the shadow may not reach the earth at all. If this is the case, an observer within the prolongation

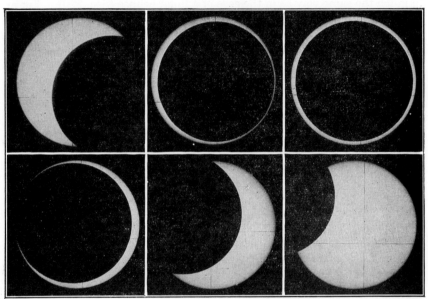

Fig. 144. Annular eclipse of the sun. (*Photographed by Mexican National Observatory, Tacubaya, D.F., in Chihuahua, Mexico, Apr. 7, 1940.*)

of the cone of the shadow will see a narrow ring of sunlight around the body of the moon. Such an eclipse is an *annular eclipse* (Fig. 144).

The maximum cross section of the moon's shadow at the earth is 269 km (167 miles), but since the earth's surface is seldom perpendicular to the axis of the shadow cone, the outline of the shadow on the earth will, in general, be an ellipse of greater dimensions than the cross section.

226. Angular Diameters of Sun and Moon. Because of the elliptical character of the orbits of earth and moon the angular diameters of sun and moon vary as seen from the earth.

The sun's angular diameter ranges from 31′31″ to 32′36″, while that of the moon ranges from 29′27″ to 33′30″. In order that an eclipse of the sun be total, the angular diameter of the moon must be at least equal to that of the sun. The more the moon's apparent diameter exceeds that of the sun, the longer will be the time of totality. The maximum length of totality requires, among other things, the maximum diameter of the moon to occur at the time of new moon and when the sun has the minimum angular diameter.

227. Solar Eclipse Limits. Because of the inclination of the moon's orbit to the plane of the ecliptic the sun is not obscured at the time of every new moon. Only when sun and moon are near one of the nodes of the moon's orbit is an eclipse possible. Hence the distance of the sun from the moon's node at the time of new moon is the determining factor in much the same way as in the case of a lunar eclipse (Sec. 220). For an eclipse of the sun to be certain, the sun must be within 15°.2 of the node at the time of new moon, while if more than 18°.5 from the node, an eclipse is impossible. For the eclipse to be central, either total or annular, the corresponding limits are 9°.9 and 11°.8, respectively.

228. Velocity of Moon's Shadow. The velocity of the tip of the moon's shadow with respect to the earth's center is, of course, essentially equal to the moon's velocity in her orbit, 3370 km (2100 miles) per hr. The velocity with respect to the earth's surface, however, depends upon the region touched by the shadow, since the moon's motion and the earth's rotation are both eastward. At the poles of the earth the rotation effect is negligible, hence the shadow passes at the rate of 3370 km per hr. At the equator, however, the earth's eastward rotation is about 1675 km (1040 miles) per hour, so that the shadow moves at the rate of 1695 km (3370 minus 1675) per hr for an observer located there. At latitudes 30° and 60° the velocity of the shadow will be 1930 and 2575 km (1200 and 1600 miles) per hr,[1] respectively.

229. Duration of Total Eclipse. If we know the velocity of the shadow and its width for any particular point on the earth, it is a simple matter to find the duration of the eclipse for that point. Under the most favorable conditions possible the duration of a total eclipse is about 7.5 min. Such conditions, however, do not occur more than once in some thousands of years. The average duration is about 3 min. If the tip of the shadow cone just grazes the earth, the duration will be only an instant at the point of contact.

230. Visibility of Total Eclipses. At any particular instant a total eclipse is visible only to those within the small area of the earth's surface on which the shadow falls. The oval outline of the shadow is carried across the surface of the earth with the velocity given in Sec. 228. The narrow strip of the surface along which the shadow passes is called the *path* of the eclipse, or the *shadow path*. The width of the path averages

[1] These velocities for regions at some distance from the poles hold only when the sun is on the meridian at the time of the eclipse. If the eclipse occurs near sunrise or sunset, the velocity with respect to the earth's surface will be considerably higher.

about 160 km (100 miles) in the temperate and torrid zones, although, under favorable circumstances, greater widths are possible.

The eclipse may be observed as total only by those within the narrow shadow path. For this reason a total eclipse of the sun is a very rare phenomenon at any particular place on the earth. Young estimated that

FIG. 145. Total solar eclipse of June 30, 1954, as seen at Minneapolis, Minn. (*Minneapolis Star.*)

at any one station a total eclipse will be visible once in 360 years, in the long run.

Outside the shadow path and within the limits of the penumbra the eclipse will be seen as partial.

231. Phenomena of Total Solar Eclipse. About 1 hr before the total phase the moon may be seen gradually encroaching on the disk of the sun. About 15 min before totality the light wanes perceptibly and the landscape takes on peculiar color tones not usually seen. Animals show signs of uneasiness. The portion of the sun remaining visible is a narrow crescent (Fig. 145), and crescent-shaped images may be seen on the ground where the sunlight filters through the foliage of trees or other small apertures. During the last 2 or 3 min before the sun disappears, peculiar wavelike shadows, called *shadow bands*, may usually be seen moving over the ground. These also appear after totality.[1]

A few seconds before totality the brighter parts of the corona become visible and an observer who has a clear horizon toward the west may note the approach of the shadow.

FIG. 146. Eclipse station near Khartoum, Anglo-Egyptian Sudan, for total eclipse of Feb. 25, 1952. (*Official U.S. Navy photograph.*)

At the beginning of totality the corona appears in all its beauty (Fig. 147). At the same time solar prominences may be seen projecting outward beyond the edge of the moon and some of the planets and brighter stars appear. The darkness is usually very marked, but a large watch face can be read with comparative ease. A fall of several degrees in the air temperature is also common.

At the end of totality the sudden return of the sunlight brings a feeling of relief, the corona and prominences fade away, the shadow bands again become visible for a minute or two, and, finally, about an hour after totality, the moon passes off the sun's disk.

232. Eclipse Problems. There are various problems which can be attacked only at the time of a total eclipse. Some of these are the corona, the flash spectrum for determining the heights at which the various elements give their characteristic lines, the search for small planets inside the orbit of Mercury, the exact path of totality for checking the position of the moon, and the deviation of a ray of light passing close to the sun (Sec. 233).

[1] Shadow bands have occasionally been seen during totality.

It has been estimated that if an observer were to observe all total eclipses which occur in reasonably accessible regions of the earth in half a century, and taking into consideration the possibility of cloudy weather, he would probably have less than a total of 1 hr in which to carry on observations during totality. Considering the limited time during which total eclipses have been observed with modern equipment, it is evident

FIG. 147. The corona at total solar eclipse of Feb. 25, 1952. (*Taken by Hagen and Hawkins, Naval Research Laboratory, Joint NRL-HAO eclipse expedition near Khartoum.*)

that every reasonable opportunity must be used to study the eclipsed sun if progress is to be made in solving eclipse problems.

233. The Einstein Eclipse Problem. Einstein had predicted, on the basis of his theory of gravitation, that a beam of light just grazing the edge of the sun would be deflected through an angle of 1".74, the path of the beam becoming concave toward the sun, and that the deflection would vary inversely as the distance of the beam from the sun's center. The only way to test the prediction consists in photographing the stars which can be seen in the immediate neighborhood of the sun during a total eclipse and comparing these photographs with similar ones taken of the same star field when the sun is not there. The deflection, if found, would be of such a nature that the stars would be farther from the center on the eclipse plates than on the others.

The first test of the prediction was made at the eclipse of 1919 by two English expeditions under Eddington and Crommelin in Africa and South America, respectively. After rejecting poor plates the others yielded values of 1″.61 and 1″.98 for the two sets of plates when the measures were reduced to the edge of the sun.

The next test was made by parties from the Lick Observatory and from Canada at the eclipse of Sept. 21, 1922, in Australia. The results of the Canadian party, from quite limited material, gave a value of 1″.78 (mean of three solutions), and the Lick party, from much more extensive material, obtained 1″.75—values very close to the predicted amount. At the eclipse of May 20, 1947, Van Biesbroeck obtained a value of 2″.01 and at the eclipse of Feb. 25, 1952, a value of 1″.70.

234. The Shadow Bands. These wavering shadows, which are usually but not always seen immediately before and just after totality, within the eclipse path, were also observed outside the path at the eclipse of Jan. 24, 1925. From all the observations available it appears that these shadows are produced in our own atmosphere, but the exact conditions necessary to produce them are not wholly clear, since they have not been seen at every eclipse.

235. Number of Eclipses. Since eclipses of sun and moon are possible only when the sun is near one of the nodes of the moon's orbit, eclipses, in general, will occur at intervals of about six months. Since the lunar eclipse limits are smaller than the solar, it is possible that no eclipses of the moon will occur in any calendar year. Two solar eclipses must occur under these conditions, however. In this century there are 14 years when only two solar and no lunar eclipses take place. Under the most favorable circumstances there may be as many as seven eclipses, two of the moon and five of the sun or three of the moon and four of the sun, in any one year. During the remainder of the twentieth century the first combination will not recur, but the second will occur in 1982.

From A.D. 1901 to 2000 there will be a total of 375 eclipses, according to Oppolzer's "Canon der Finsternisse," 228 of the sun and 147 of the moon, an average of nearly four per year.

236. The Saros. Because of the revolution of the moon's nodes westward at the rate of 19°.5 annually, the sun meets the same node in 346.62 days. This interval is called the *eclipse year*. The relation between this and certain values is as follows:

Days

242 returns of moon to a particular node	6585.36
19 returns of sun to the same node	6585.78
223 synodic months	6585.32

In the interval of 6585 and a fraction days we therefore expect sun and moon to return to approximately the same positions with respect to one of the nodes of the moon's orbit. In consequence, if an eclipse has occurred at any time, we may expect a similar eclipse to occur again at the end of this interval. If we note a series of eclipses in the interval, we may expect an analogous series in the following interval.

This recurrence of eclipses was known to the ancients and the time interval of 223 synodic months or 18 years 10 or 11 days (depending on how many leap years occur) was called the *saros*.

The return of the same eclipse will not be for the same region on the earth, owing to the ⅓ day over the 6585 days. The earth will have turned about 120° in this time, so that the eclipse will take place about 120° of longitude farther west than before. The total eclipse of the sun of Sept. 10, 1923, was the return of a similar eclipse of Aug. 30, 1905. The latter was well located for observation in Spain and its repetition in California one saros later.

A lunar eclipse repeats itself 48 or 49 times before the small deviations from exact commensurability eliminate it entirely. Such a series lasts about 865 years. A solar eclipse also has from 68 to 75 returns, the series lasting about 1260 years, according to Young.

The total number of eclipses in one saros is about 70, of which number 41 are usually solar and 29 lunar. Of the solar eclipses, 14 are partial, 17 annular, and 10 total.

EXERCISES

1. Would it be possible for the plane of the moon's orbit to have an inclination to the plane of the ecliptic which would make eclipses of the moon impossible?

2. If the plane of the moon's orbit made an angle of 1° with the plane of the ecliptic, how often would we have an eclipse of the moon? An eclipse of the sun?

3. If the moon's diameter were reduced 10 per cent, would it be possible to have a total eclipse of the sun?

CHAPTER 11

THE PLANETARY SYSTEM

The solar system consists of the sun, planets, and satellites, asteroids, comets, and such meteor swarms as are moving under the gravitation of the sun. This system forms a unit, which, *so far as we know*, is unique in the universe.

237. The Planets—Definition and Names. The term *planet* is usually applied only to any one of the nine larger bodies which, like the earth, move about the sun.   Their names, in order of distance from the sun, are Mercury, Venus, Earth, Mars, Jupiter, Saturn, Uranus, Neptune, and Pluto.

According to size, the planets fall into two groups, the first four usually being termed the *terrestrial planets*, because they are not very different from the earth in size, and the next four the *major planets*, because, as a group, they are very much larger than the first four.   Pluto, for the present, is in a class by itself.

There are, in addition to the nine known planets, many small bodies called *minor planets* or *asteroids*, which are also moving about the sun. About three thousand of these, having diameters of 800 km (500 miles) or less, have been discovered in the last 150 years.   In many ways they resemble the large planets, but as a group they show a marked difference.

In our study of the planets we shall find many things to consider, such as their apparent and real motions in the sky, their distances from the sun, the eccentricities of their orbits and the inclinations of the orbit planes to the plane of the ecliptic, their periods of revolution about the sun, their diameters, masses, densities, rotation periods, physical conditions, satellite systems, etc.

The terms *rotation* and *revolution* are ordinarily used as synonyms, but in astronomy it is agreed to use rotation only when it refers to the turning of a body about an axis through its center of mass, while revolution is applied to the motion of one body about another.   Thus, the earth *rotates* on its axis in a sidereal day, but it *revolves* around the sun in a sidereal year.

If viewed from the direction of the north pole of the ecliptic, the planets and asteroids revolve about the sun in a counterclockwise direction. This kind of motion is called *direct* motion. Motion in the opposite direction is called *retrograde* motion. As seen from the earth, direct motion is from west to east and retrograde motion is from east to west. Similarly the motion of a satellite around its primary is said to be direct or retrograde, that is, whether it moves counterclockwise or clockwise as seen from a point north of the plane of the ecliptic.

238. Inner and Outer Planets. There is a second way of grouping the planets—those whose orbits lie inside and those whose orbits lie outside the earth's orbit. Mercury and Venus belong to the first group, and Mars, Jupiter, Saturn, Uranus, Neptune, and Pluto to the second. All asteroid orbits known, with three exceptions, lie outside the orbit of the earth. Planets and asteroids move about the sun in the same direction, from west to east, and at velocities which decrease with increasing distance from the sun.

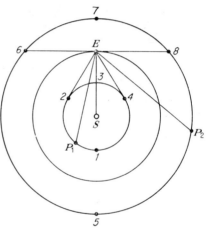

FIG. 148. Elongations of inner and outer planets.

239. Positions Relative to Earth and Sun. The *elongation* of a planet is the angle at the earth between the lines drawn to planet and sun.

In Fig. 148 let the inner circle represent the orbit of an inner planet, the second circle the earth's orbit, and the outer circle the orbit of an outer planet, S the sun, and E the earth. The elongation of an inner planet at P_1 would then be the angle P_1ES and the elongation of an outer planet at P_2 would be P_2ES.

If the earth is at E when an inner planet is at 1, the elongation is zero and the planet is said to be in *superior conjunction*. When the inner planet is at 3, the elongation again is zero and the planet is at *inferior conjunction*. When the planet is at 2 or 4, the elongation is at maximum value and is called *greatest elongation*.[1] The elongations are either *east* or *west*, depending on the direction of the planet from the sun.

The outer planet is in *conjunction* at 5 (elongation zero), in *opposition* when at 7 (elongation 180°), and in *quadrature* at 6 or 8 (elongation 90°).

240. Apparent Motions of the Planets among the Stars. In Fig. 149 let the outer circle represent the earth's orbit and the inner circle the orbit of an inner planet. If the planet is at inferior conjunction, it will be at

[1] The lines $E2$ and $E4$ are tangents to the orbit of the inner planet.

P_1 when the earth is at E_1. Later the planet reaches greatest western elongation at P_2 when the earth is at E_2, and, when the earth is at E_3, the

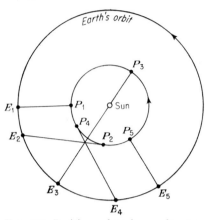

planet will be at superior conjunction at P_3. Still later will come eastern elongation with planet and earth at P_4 and E_4, respectively. Finally, inferior conjunction occurs with the two bodies at P_5 and E_5. This series of positions will appear from the earth as a slow vibration of the planet, first to one side and then to the other of the sun. The motion of the planet, when combined with the sun's motion eastward among the stars, gives a comparatively complicated movement of the planet among the stars.

FIG. 149. Positions of an inner planet as seen from the earth.

For the outer planets a different series of positions will be found. Beginning at conjunction E_1P_1 (Fig. 150), the planet will appear to move gradually eastward and at E_2P_2 quadrature will occur. After quadrature

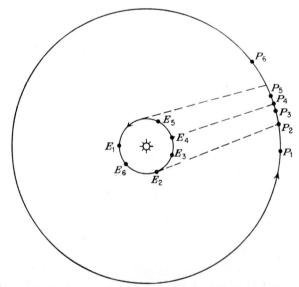

FIG. 150. Positions of an outer planet as seen from the earth.

the planet will continue to move eastward until it reaches P_3, a short time before opposition. From this time onward, past opposition E_4P_4, and until position E_5P_5 the *EP* line will swing westward, owing to the earth's greater orbital velocity. After positions 5 the planet's apparent motion will again be eastward until and after conjunction E_6P_6.

241. The Astronomical Unit. The mile is too small a unit for measuring planetary distances. In consequence a much larger unit, the mean distance from earth to sun, is now in general use and is called the *astronomical unit* (abbreviated AU). Its length is 149,670,000 km (93,000,000 miles) according to the best determination, but this is still uncertain by possibly 10,000 km. This unit will be used in stating distances in the solar system.

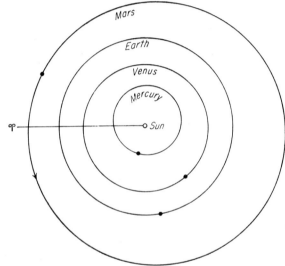

FIG. 151. Orbits of the four planets nearest the sun. Perihelion points marked by dots.

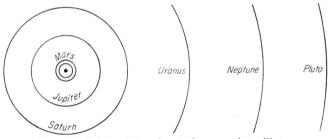

FIG. 152. Orbits of the planets from earth to Pluto.

242. Planetary Distances. The mean distances of the planets from the sun vary from 0.387 for Mercury to 39.5 for Pluto. Figure 151 shows the relative dimensions of the orbits of the four planets nearest the sun and Fig. 152 similarly the orbits from the earth outward.

The orbits of the asteroids, in general, lie between those of Jupiter and Mars.

243. The Bode-Titius Law. In 1772, Bode brought to the general attention of the astronomical world a series of numbers which had been discovered by Titius six years earlier. This series is usually called *Bode's law*, and may be stated as follows:

If we write a series of 4's and to the second 4 add 3, to the next 6, to the next 12, etc., we obtain a series of numbers which represent approximately the relative distances of the planets from the sun.

4	4	4	4	4	4	4	4	4
	3	6	12	24	48	96	192	384
4	7	10	16	28	52	100	196	388

Table IV gives these numbers divided by 10 and the actual mean distances for comparison.

TABLE IV

Planet	Bode's law	Actual distance
Mercury	0.4	0.4
Venus	0.7	0.7
Earth	1.0	1.000
Mars	1.6	1.5
Asteroids	2.8	1.1–5.8
Jupiter	5.2	5.2
Saturn	10.0	9.5
Uranus	19.6	19.2
Neptune	38.8	30.1
Pluto	77.2	39.5

There is no physical reason known underlying Bode's law and it seems likely that it is merely a chance arrangement of numbers which breaks down completely for Neptune and Pluto.

244. The Orbits. The orbits of the planets are all ellipses with moderate eccentricities varying from 0.007 for Venus to 0.25 for Pluto.

The orbits also lie nearly in the same plane. Using the plane of the earth's orbit as the reference plane, the orbit of Pluto makes the greatest angle and this amounts to only 17°09'.

In comparison with the orbits of the planets the asteroid orbits have both greater eccentricities and inclinations. Thus, as an extreme case, the orbit of the asteroid Hidalgo (944) has an eccentricity of 0.653 and an inclination to the plane of the ecliptic of 43°.

245. Period. A planet has two periods of revolution, a sidereal period and a synodic period. The *sidereal period* is the time required by the planet to complete one revolution about the sun with reference to the stars. The *synodic period* is the time required from any elongation to the same elongation next following, such as from superior conjunction to superior conjunction for an inner planet or from opposition to opposition for an outer one.

The relation between the two periods may be expressed by the equation

$$\frac{1}{S_i} = \frac{1}{E} \pm \frac{1}{S_y}$$

where S_i represents the sidereal period, S_y the synodic period, and E the earth's period. The upper sign is used for inner planets and the lower for outer planets.

246. Kepler's Laws. Tycho Brahe, the last great astronomer before the invention of the telescope, had accumulated a great mass of observations of planetary positions. His assistant, Kepler, spent many years in a careful study of these observations and during this period announced the discovery of three laws of planetary motion now known as *Kepler's laws.* These are as follows:

1. *The orbit of every planet is an ellipse with the sun at one focus.*
2. *The radius vector of a planet sweeps over equal areas in equal times.*
3. *The cubes of the mean distances of the planets from the sun are proportional to the squares of their sidereal periods.*

1. From the historical standpoint the first law is the most important. From the earliest times until Kepler it had been assumed that the orbits of the planets had to be of a circular character because the circle was the only perfect curve and therefore the only one in which heavenly bodies could possibly move. Ptolemy, one of the great astronomers of antiquity, had assumed that all the heavenly bodies revolved about the earth as a center and had built up an elaborate system of circles (sec. 247) to explain the motion of the planets. His system held sway until Copernicus, in 1543, published his great work "De Revolutionibus Orbium Caelestium," in which he showed that the sun was the center of the planetary system and that the apparent rotation of the heavens could be explained on the assumption that the earth rotated on its axis. Copernicus, however, still held to circular planetary orbits, although he found it necessary, like others before him, to put the sun out of center and it remained for Kepler to discover the real shape.

2. We have already considered this under the *law of areas* (Sec. 162).

3. As an illustration of the third law, let us compare the earth and Neptune and determine the period of the latter. The law may be applied as follows:

$$\frac{(\text{Earth's distance})^3}{(\text{Neptune's distance})^3} = \frac{(\text{Earth's period})^2}{(\text{Neptune's period})^2}.$$

This may be simplified by using periods in years and distances in astronomical units. The proportion may then be written

$$\frac{1^3}{30^3} = \frac{1^2}{x^2}$$

Hence $x^2 = 30^3$ years $= 27,000$ years, whence $x = 164.2$. The actual value is 164.8 years, which value would be more nearly obtained if, instead of using the approximation of 30 for Neptune's distance, we had used 30.07. The law as stated, however, does not hold absolutely except for a system where all of the planets are of negligible mass.

247. The Ptolemaic System. The ancients assumed the earth to be the center of the visible universe and that it was fixed in space. They explained the apparent diurnal rotation of the celestial sphere as a real rotation. Since moon, sun, and planets moved with respect to the celestial sphere, they required special treatment. The plan developed by Claudius Ptolemy of Alexandria and described in his Almagest (about 138 A.D.) has been called the *Ptolemaic system* and was generally accepted for nearly 1500 years.

In this system the distances from the earth assigned to the seven known moving bodies were in the order Moon, Mercury, Venus, Sun, Mars, Jupiter, and Saturn. Each of these had a circular orbit centered at the earth and known as its *deferent*. Moon and Sun moved around their respective deferents without further complications, but the planets showed not only direct but also retrograde motions. Each of the planets was accordingly provided with a separate circle, called its *epicycle*. The real planet moved around its epicycle and the center of the epicycle moved around the planet's deferent (Fig. 153).

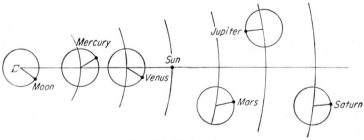

Fig. 153. The Ptolemaic system.

The period of revolution in its epicycle was what we now call the synodic period, while the revolution of the center of the epicycle along the deferent occurred in the sidereal period. The combination of these motions supplied the necessary "theory" to explain the motions of the planets.

In later times, as knowledge of planetary motions became more exact, it was found necessary to place the earth out of the center of the deferents and to add some additional epicycles so that the system became exceedingly cumbersome. It should be recognized, however, that this system, however erroneus, could be used to predict the positions of the planets with the accuracy required at the time.

248. Elements of an Orbit. In the consideration of an orbit there are six constants which are termed the *elements* of the orbit. These define the shape and the size of the orbit, its inclination to the plane of the ecliptic, the direction of the intersection of the orbit plane with the plane of the ecliptic, the direction of the perihelion point from the sun, and the position of the planet in the orbit at a definite time. By means of these elements the position of the planet can be calculated for any time, past or future, if the elements are accurate and as long as they are not changed by perturbations. Figure 154 illustrates the geometrical relations.

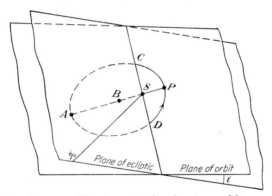

FIG. 154. The elements of a planetary orbit.

In the figure the plane of the orbit makes an angle with the plane of the ecliptic, the intersection of the two planes being along the line CD, which is called the *line of nodes*. The point D is called the *ascending node* and the point C the *descending node*,[1] since the planet when passing D goes to the northern side of the ecliptic and when passing C to the southern side. Since the sun S is in the plane of the planet's orbit as well as in the plane of the ecliptic, it will be on the line of nodes. The line AP represents the major axis of the orbit and the line $S\Upsilon$ the direction of the vernal equinox from the sun. B is the midpoint of the major axis.

The *eccentricity* of the orbit e is the ratio of BS to BP and defines the shape.

The length of the *semimajor axis BP* determines the size of the orbit and is usually denoted by a. It is also known as the *mean distance* of a planet from the sun.

[1] The ascending node is indicated by the symbol ☊ and the descending node by ☋.

The angle between the planes of the orbit and ecliptic is called the *inclination i*.

The angle ΥSD is called the *longitude of the ascending node* and is denoted by Ω. There is no ambiguity between this use of the symbol and its other use as stated above.

The angle DSP, denoted by ω, gives the direction of the perihelion point P from the line SD. These five geometrical relationships fix the size, shape, and position of the orbit in space.

The sixth element, the *epoch*, is designated by E and gives the time when the planet is in a given position in its orbit. Frequently E is the time when the planet was at perihelion.

As matters of interest there may be added to the tabulation of the six necessary elements such others as the sidereal period and the distance of the perihelion point from the sun, but these are not essential since they can be computed from the six elements.

249. Orbit Computation. The *determination* of the orbit of a planet or comet consists in the computation of the elements of its orbit. Such a computation is based on at least three observations of the right ascension and declination of the body as seen from the earth, on the fact that the orbit lies in a plane which passes through the sun, on the law of areas, and on certain other quantities which are known or can be determined. The relations of these various factors are such that, in general, the elements of the orbit can be computed from them.

In the case of a newly discovered comet or asteroid it is of the greatest importance to obtain the three observations of position in order that a preliminary orbit may be calculated so that if bad weather prevents further observations for a time, the object will not be lost. Except in very rare cases, it is necessary to have the three observations made at least a day apart in order to allow for changes in direction which are sufficient to permit a satisfactory calculation of the elements.

The observations are obtained either by measuring the positions of the new body on photographs with reference to stars on the same photographic plate or by measuring the positions in the sky by means of a micrometer (Sec. 250) attached to the eye end of a telescope.

After receiving the three observations a good computer is usually able to calculate a preliminary set of elements in from 6 to 8 hours by the use of logarithms. The recently developed electronic computers have reduced the time to minutes.

250. The Micrometer. The micrometer is a device used in connection with a meridian circle or equatorially mounted telescope to measure the angular distance between two objects in the field of view of the eyepiece. Several kinds of micrometers have been devised, but the only one now in general use is known as the filar (or thread) micrometer (Fig. 155).

In its simplest form it consists of two parallel spider threads, one fixed and the other movable. The motion of the latter is controlled by a finely made screw with a graduated head and a device for counting the number of revolutions of the screw. By suitable methods the exact

FIG. 155. A filar micrometer.

angular distance which the movable thread traverses with one turn of the screw[1] can be determined. This may be of almost any value from 10″ upward. Besides the motion of one thread with respect to the other, both may be rotated about the line of sight of the telescope so that they may be set at any angle with respect to a north-and-south line in the sky.

If it is desired to measure the distance between a comet and a *star whose position is known*, the threads are first rotated until they are either exactly north and south or east and west. A reading of the graduated head of the screw is taken when both threads[2] are in coincidence. The star is then placed on the fixed thread and the movable thread set on the comet (Fig. 156). By again reading the screw-head the number of revolutions and a fraction of the screw through which the thread was moved is obtained. When this is multiplied by the angular value of one revolution, the angular distance between star and comet in a north-south or east-west direction is obtained.

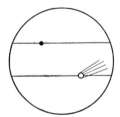

FIG. 156. The use of the filar micrometer.

The final step in this type of micrometer work consists in applying the

---

[1] This is called *the value of one revolution of the screw.*
[2] The threads of a micrometer are often called *wires.*

measured distances to the known position of the comparison star and thus obtaining the right ascension and declination of the comet.

The filar micrometer is usually limited to measuring small distances, as both objects should be in the field of view at the same time.

251. Distance of a Planet in Terms of Earth's Distance. If it is possible to make a series of observations of a planet at intervals of its sidereal period, it is possible to determine its distance from the sun in terms of the earth's distance.

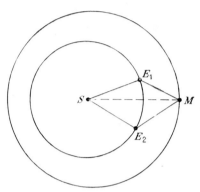

If we wish to determine the distance of Mars in this manner, we observe its elongation from the sun SE_1M (Fig. 157) by means of a meridian circle when Mars is at M and the earth at E_1. At the end of 687 days Mars will again be at M, but the earth will be at E_2. The elongation SE_2M is again measured. In the quadrilateral SE_1ME_2 we have measured the angles at E_1 and E_2, the angle E_1SE_2 will be the angle the earth passes over in 43 days (730 − 687) and SE_1, SE_2 are radii of the earth's orbit. We can therefore solve the quadrilateral and determine SM in terms of SE_1. By similar observations of Mars at various points in its orbit its mean distance from the sun in terms of the earth's mean distance can be obtained.

Fig. 157. Method of determining a planet's distance from the sun in terms of the earth's distance from the sun.

The same method can be applied to any other planet.

252. Mass of a Planet. One of the important quantities of any astronomical body is its mass. Upon its mass will depend its gravitative effect on other bodies such as a planet or satellite. If a planet has a satellite whose period and distance are known with reference to the planet, we can determine the planet's mass in terms of the mass of the sun by the equation

$$\frac{m}{M} = \frac{a^3}{t^2} \times \frac{T^2}{A^3}$$

where m is the planet's mass, a the satellite's mean distance from the planet, t the satellite's mean period, M the mass of the sun, T the earth's period, and A the earth's mean distance from the sun.

Let us apply this formula to determine the earth's mass in terms of that of the sun:

$$\frac{m}{M} = \frac{240,000^3}{27.3^2} \times \frac{365.2^2}{93,000,000^3}$$

On carrying out the calculation we find the value of m/M is equal approximately to 1/325,000 in fair agreement with the value given in Sec. 177.

253. The Zodiac. A narrow belt of the sky about 16° wide, extending along the ecliptic and bisected by it, is called the *zodiac*. Within this belt all planets known to the ancients as well as sun and moon are found.

The zodiac seems to have had an important place in the astronomy of all ancient civilizations. It was usually divided into 12 parts or constellations. These constellations, being of unequal extent, made unequal divisions, but this was changed by Hipparchus, the greatest of ancient astronomers of whom we have any record. In the second century B.C. he divided the zodiac into 12 sections of 30° each. These sections were called signs, corresponding to the constellations falling within their limits. The signs are still in use, although they have shifted from their constellations, owing to the precession of the equinoxes.

EXERCISES

1. Construct a figure similar to Fig. 157 for an inner planet and show how its distance from the sun in terms of the earth's distance may be determined.

2. Determine the sidereal period of Pluto by Kepler's third law if the mean distance is 39.5 AU.   *Ans.* 248.2 years.

3. If the earth's orbital motion were stopped, how long would it take the earth to fall to the sun?   *Ans.* 64.6 days.

NOTE: Assume the path to the sun to be one-half of an extremely narrow ellipse with the sun at perihelion and the earth's present orbit at aphelion. Then apply Kepler's third law.

4. If the moon were moved to half its present mean distance from the earth, what would be the length of the sidereal month?   *Ans.* 9.65 days.

5. What would be the sidereal period of a satellite of the earth whose mean distance was 6400 km (4000 miles)?   *Ans.* 1.4 hr.

6. If the earth kept the same mass but had its radius reduced to one-half its present value, how would the weights of bodies at its surface be changed?

7. If the earth's diameter were doubled without changing its mass, how would the weights of bodies at its surface be changed?

8. Assume that a mass M is moving along the straight line AB with uniform velocity past a point P (this means that the force between M and P is zero). Show that the law of areas is maintained between M and P (Fig. 158).

9. If a comet moves around the sun in an ellipse of eccentricity 0.5, show that its orbital velocity at perihelion is three times as great as at aphelion.

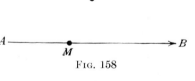

Fig. 158

10. If the perihelion velocity of a body is four times that at aphelion, what is the eccentricity of the orbit? If ten times as great?   *Ans.* 0.6; 0.81.

11. If the moon's orbit were in the plane of the earth's equator, would the precession of the equinoxes cease? Why?

12. What would be the approximate value of the precession constant under the conditions in Exercise 11?   *Ans.* About 14″ a year.

CHAPTER 12

THE TERRESTRIAL PLANETS AND THE ASTEROIDS

MERCURY

254. Elongation, Orbit, Period. Mercury is the innermost of the planets. It is never seen very far from the sun, its greatest elongation being about 28°.

The planet's mean distance from the sun is 0.387 AU. Its orbit has both the greatest eccentricity, 0.206, and the greatest inclination to the plane of the ecliptic, 7°0′, of any of the planets except Pluto.

The *sidereal period* is very nearly 88 days and the *synodic period* 116 days.

255. Dimensions, Mass, etc. The diameter of Mercury is 4847 km (3012 miles). This makes it the smallest of the planets with the possible exception of Pluto. Its volume is about one-eighteenth that of the earth.

The mass of Mercury is not easily determined, but a value of one-eighteenth that of the earth is probable. The density is therefore approximately that of the earth. The surface gravity[1] is about one-third that at the earth's surface.

256. Albedo. The reflecting power of the planet is low, approximately 93 per cent of the sunlight falling on it being absorbed and only 7 per cent reflected. This reflecting power is called the *albedo*.[2]

The stellar magnitude (Sec. 399) varies from −1.9 downward.

257. Telescopic Appearance. Mercury is difficult to observe, as it is so near the sun. When the sun is below the horizon, the altitude of the planet is very small, even at greatest elongation, and the unsteadiness of the air at low altitudes makes observation unsatisfactory. If observed during the daytime, the air is less steady than at night; the strong sunlight is also a drawback.

---

[1] The value of gravity at the planetary surfaces will be given in terms of that at the earth's surface throughout the book.

[2] The albedos of the planets and moon used in this book are those given by Russell in his two papers in the *Astrophysical Journal*, vol. 43.

A few observers claim to have seen various markings on the planet's surface, but there is no satisfactory agreement as to the markings. Under ordinary conditions little or nothing can be seen.

Mercury shows phases like the moon. Figure 159 illustrates these phases and the relative apparent diameters as the planet revolves about the sun.

The planet has no known satellite.

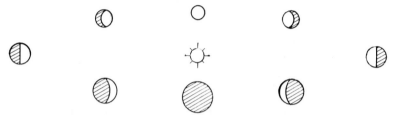

Fig. 159. Phases of Mercury.

258. Rotation. The rotation period of the planet has not yet been determined with certainty. Some observers have thought they had evidence of a period of approximately 24 hours but there are good reasons for questioning this value. Schiaparelli reported many observations in which there was only a minute shift of markings on consecutive days and therefore inferred that the planet always kept the same face toward the sun. Antoniadi's observations in recent years appear to confirm this. We may therefore tentatively assume a rotation period of 88 days.

259. Atmosphere and Physical Conditions. The low albedo of Mercury indicates a very limited atmosphere and suggests that we probably see the actual surface of the planet. Spectrographic tests by Adams and Dunham failed to show any atmospheric absorption bands and particularly none of oxygen or water vapor. When the planet is nearly in line with the sun, it is not surrounded by a ring of light as in the case of Venus. All this indicates little or no atmosphere around Mercury.

Antoniadi reports that at times certain faint markings he has seen on the planet's surface disappear under a dull veil and then reappear again. He attributes this phenomenon to possible dust clouds in a thin atmosphere. Dollfus also finds some indication of a tenuous atmosphere of the order of 0.003 of the earth's by testing the light from Mercury for polarization. The light from the cusps shows greater polarization than the light from other parts of the disk. This effect would be expected if there is a thin atmosphere.

Because of its nearness to the sun the planet receives approximately seven times as much heat and light per unit of area as the earth. If the sky is cloudless, this great amount of energy would heat the surface exposed to it to a high temperature. Radiometric measures made at both the Mt. Wilson and Lowell Observatories agree in finding the temperature of the subsolar point (the point where the sun is in the zenith) to be somewhat above 300°C (572°F) at the planet's mean distance from the sun. This is approximately the melting point of lead, 327°C.

Attempts to measure the radiation from the dark side of the planet have not been successful except to show that the temperature is low, but no figures can be given.

260. Transits. Occasionally the planet passes directly between earth and sun so that it can be seen projected against the disk of the sun (Fig.

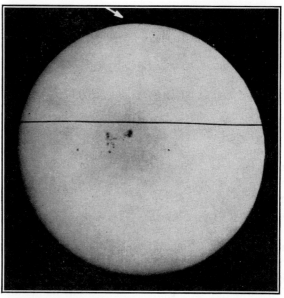

Fig. 160. Transit of Mercury. The planet is the small black spot near the top as indicated by the arrow. (*Yerkes Observatory.*)

160). Such a phenomenon is called a *transit* across the sun. The last transit occurred on Nov. 14, 1953, and the next three will occur in May, 1957, November, 1960, and May, 1970.

During a transit the planet appears as a small black disk, about 12″ in diameter. This is much too small to be seen with the unaided eye. The transits are of no particular astronomical importance; nevertheless they are interesting phenomena to observe.

261. Motion of Perihelion. A comparison of the positions of the perihelion point shows that this point is slowly moving eastward at the rate of 574″ per century. After allowing for the perturbations of the orbit by all the known planets, there remains about 43″ of this motion (according to Clemence) which could not be accounted for. The presence of unknown masses in the form of small planets or dispersed meteoric matter within the orbit of Mercury might account for this, but their presence in sufficient quantity has not been proved.

The Einstein theory of relativity achieved its first success by accounting for practically the entire amount. According to this theory, Newton's law of gravitation is not absolutely exact and requires a small correction. As a result of this, the line of apsides of a planet should move forward in the same direction as the planet moves by a certain fraction of a revolution, $3v^2/c^2$, during each revolution (in this formula v represents the orbital velocity of the planet and c the velocity of light).

Calculation by De Sitter gives 43″ per century as the amount of rotation of the line of apsides of Mercury's orbit in satisfactory agreement with the 43″ required.

INTRAMERCURIAL PLANETS

262. The question of possible planets within the orbit of Mercury has often been raised. In a number of cases observers have reported seeing such bodies, but, from the evidence now available, they seem to have been mistaken.

During total eclipses of the sun many efforts have been made within the last half century to photograph possible intramercurial planets but none has been found. If any exist, they must be very small, certainly less than 40 miles in diameter.

VENUS

263. Orbit, Period, etc. Venus is the second planet in order from the sun. Its mean distance is 0.723. The orbit has an eccentricity of 0.007 and is inclined 3°24′ to the plane of the ecliptic.

The *sidereal period* is nearly 225 days and the *synodic period* 584 days. Its greatest elongation from the sun is about 46°.

264. Dimensions, Mass, etc. The diameter of Venus is 12,205 km (7584 miles), a value almost equal to that of the earth.

The mass of Venus, like that of Mercury, is somewhat uncertain, but it is about 0.82 that of the earth. Its mean density is therefore about 5.2. The surface gravity is about five-sixths of the earth's.

265. Brightness, Albedo. Venus is the brightest of the planets. It attains its greatest brilliance, stellar magnitude −4.4 (Sec. 399), about five weeks after greatest eastern elongation and an equal time before greatest western elongation. It is so bright that it may be seen by the unaided eye in full daylight for many weeks near greatest elongation if the sky background is blue. When it is above the horizon at night, it will cause shadows.

The planet's great brightness is due in part to proximity to sun and earth and in part to its high albedo, 0.59. A good white paper reflects only about 10 per cent more light than Venus.

266. Telescopic Appearance. Venus shows phases like Mercury, but the apparent change in size is much greater, for at inferior conjunction the apparent diameter may be a little over 1', while at superior conjunction it is only about 11'' since at superior conjunction it is nearly six times as far from the earth as at inferior conjunction (Fig. 161).

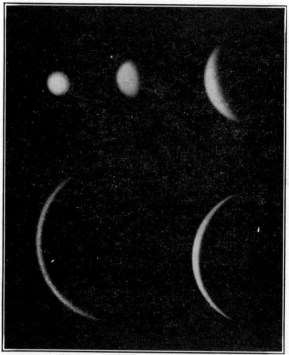

FIG. 161. Phases of Venus showing the great range in apparent diameter as the planet passes from superior to inferior conjunction. (*Lowell Observatory.*)

The usual telescopic appearance is that of a very bright white surface with occasional dimly seen shadings. Some observers have reported spots of various kinds and others somewhat more definite markings. Such appearances, however, are usually evanescent and make it appear probable that the actual surface of the planet is not seen.

During 1927, F. E. Ross photographed Venus in light of different colors at the Mt. Wilson Observatory. No detail of any consequence was shown except in the ultraviolet photographs. Figure 162, reproduced by Ellerman from the original negatives, shows the character of the detail in some of these.   In all probability only the upper levels of the atmosphere of Venus are responsible for these changes in appearance.

267. Atmosphere. The evidence in favor of at least a moderate atmosphere seems quite conclusive.   At the times of inferior conjunction and transits a fine thread of light completely encircling the disk of the planet has often been seen.   This can be explained either on the assumption that the light of the sun is sufficiently refracted by a fairly dense atmosphere to be bent around the edge of the planet's disk or that it is a twilight effect in an atmosphere of moderate density.

The extreme brightness of the disk and the lack of permanent markings afford strong evidence in favor of the view that the atmosphere of Venus is heavily cloud-laden.   St. John and Nicholson of the Mt. Wilson

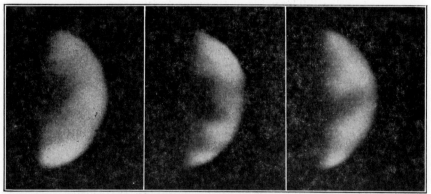

Fig. 162. Ultraviolet photographs of Venus on June 6, 24, and 26, 1927.   (*Mt. Wilson Observatory.*)

Observatory have failed to obtain spectrographic evidence of water vapor, but clouds of dust would produce essentially the same effects as clouds of water droplets.   Such a possible dust cloud 700 miles long was seen by E. C. Slipher 30' from the point of the sunlit crescent several years ago. The cloud was of a reddish color.

Menzel and Whipple have recently suggested (1954) that it is possible, under certain conditions, that the clouds of Venus may be composed of water vapor.   One of these conditions is a surface covered with water. Further study will be necessary before this suggestion can be properly evaluated.

Investigation of the composition of the planet's atmosphere by means of the spectrograph shows neither water vapor nor oxygen in detectable amounts.   In 1932, Adams and Dunham found heavy absorption lines of carbon dioxide and later Adel, by more detailed analysis, found evidence of at least an amount of carbon dioxide equal to a thickness of 400 m at atmospheric pressure. Kuiper's more recent work raises this to about 1000 m. This is several hundred times the amount in the earth's atmosphere.

268. Physical Conditions. Venus receives from the sun twice as much heat and light per unit of area as the earth, but we do not know how much of this penetrates the atmosphere and cloud envelope and actually reaches the surface of the planet. Measures of the temperature of Venus by Pettit and Nicholson at crescent phase give the low value of −20°C (−4°F) for the illuminated part of the planet and about the same value for the unilluminated part. This value of the temperature is undoubtedly that of the atmosphere at the top of the cloud envelope. Measures by Coblentz and Lampland give temperatures near 0°C.

The problem of the possible temperature at the surface of the planet is not easy to solve. The value of the solar constant at Venus' distance is known, but how much of this energy is reflected, how much absorbed, depends on various assumptions it is necessary to make in the course of the calculation. The amount finally available depends upon these assumptions. Adel believes the surface temperature to be at least above 50°C (120°F) while Wildt holds it to be above 100°C. Such temperatures at the bottom of a moderately dense atmosphere combined with planetary rotation might easily produce violent winds. If little or no water is present, the surface would be desert. High winds over a desert area would easily explain dust clouds in the atmosphere of Venus. The theory is attractive because of its simplicity but the most that can be said for it is that it is worth investigating.

269. Rotation. Some observers, by watching the elusive spots and shadings through the telescope, obtained a rotation value of about 24 hr; others insisted that Venus presents the same face to the sun continuously and therefore has a rotation period of 225 days.

Spectrographic attempts have failed to show a measurable rotation. If one as short as six days existed, it would have yielded to this method of attack.

The radiometric measures which show nearly the same temperatures for bright and dark parts of the planet seem to demand at least a slow rotation. If the rotation period coincided with the period of revolution about the sun, then the illuminated side would be intensely hot and the dark side extremely cold, possibly so cold as to condense any gaseous constituents of the atmosphere. This would, in time, lock up the atmosphere on the dark side. Since this has not occurred, and since the dark side gives off some heat, the only possible way in which these facts can be brought into agreement is by assuming a rotation period which is longer than six days and considerably shorter than 225 days. The location of the hypothetical rotation axis is of course unknown.

270. Transits. Transits of Venus across the solar disk are rare.   The last two occurred on Dec. 9, 1874, and Dec. 6, 1882, and the next two will occur on June 8, 2004, and June 6, 2012.   These transits have been used to determine the distance from earth to sun, but the results have not been satisfactory and better methods have been developed.

271. Satellites. Venus has no known satellites.   If any exist, they must be very small.   Several astronomers of the seventeenth and eighteenth centuries thought they saw a fairly large satellite, but the fact that it has not been seen in the last 150 years seems conclusive proof that they must have been mistaken.

MARS

272. Distance, Orbit, Period. Mars is the outer one of the group of terrestrial planets.   Its mean distance from the sun is 1.52 AU.

The orbit has an eccentricity of 0.093, so that its distance from the sun varies 21×10^6 km (13×10^6 miles) each way from the mean.   The orbit is inclined 1°51′ to the plane of the ecliptic.

The *sidereal period* is nearly 687 days and the *synodic period* nearly 780 days.

273. Dimensions, Mass, etc. The mean diameter of Mars is 6792 km (4220 miles), and there is a slight flattening at the poles.   The volume is a little more than 0.151 and the surface about 0.28 that of the earth.

The mass is equal to 0.108 that of the earth, and the mean density is 4.0.   The surface gravity is equal to 0.38, that is, an object weighing 100 lb at the surface of the earth would weigh 38 lb at the surface of Mars.

274. Albedo, etc. The mean albedo of the planet is about 0.15, but the determinations by various observers are not in the best agreement.

When Mars is very near the earth, as it was on Aug. 22, 1924, its stellar magnitude is −2.7, thus making its apparent brightness greater than that of any other planet except Venus.   This exceptionally high value was possible because Mars was near perihelion while the earth was near aphelion.   Its apparent diameter was 25″.1.   The stellar magnitude near conjunction may be fainter than +2.0 and the apparent diameter only 3″.8.

275. Rotation, etc. The rotation of the planet is easily seen when observed for an hour or more and the period is readily determined because of a number of well-marked surface features which have been under observation for centuries.   By using old drawings, made by Huyghens about 300 years ago, in connection with modern observations the rotation period has been determined with great accuracy.   It is found to be $24^h37^m22^s.7$.

The rotation axis is not perpendicular to the plane of the orbit, but is inclined about 24° to this perpendicular.   In consequence, we can sometimes see about 24° beyond the pole which is turned toward us. The southern pole is the one thus situated when Mars is nearest the earth. As a result, the southern hemisphere is more easily studied than the northern.

276. Atmosphere. The atmosphere around Mars appears to be comparatively thin. Clouds are seen at rare intervals, but there is no certain way of telling whether they are of water vapor or dust. In 1908, V. M. Slipher found spectroscopic evidence of very small amounts of water vapor and oxygen. More recently Adams and Dunham, with much more powerful instrumental equipment, found no evidence of either. They report that if the oxygen content of the Martian atmosphere had been as much as one part in a thousand of that over equal areas on the earth's surface, their spectrograms would almost certainly have shown it. The area investigated by them was near the equator. The region best suited for the investigation of the water-vapor problem lies in the polar areas but Mars was unfavorably situated for this purpose.

In 1947 Kuiper detected some carbon dioxide in Mars' atmosphere amounting to possibly twice that in our own.

277. The Polar Caps. The most conspicuous features on the surface of Mars are white areas around the poles. These vary in size with the seasons. During spring and summer in the northern hemisphere the north-polar cap shrinks rapidly, while the south-polar cap increases in size. When it is summer in the southern hemisphere, the reverse process may be observed. The polar cap of the southern hemisphere has been studied in greater detail because it is turned toward us when the planet is nearest the earth.

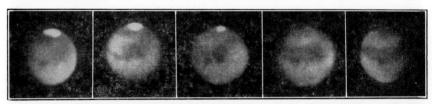

Fig. 163. South polar cap of Mars on Martian dates corresponding to May 11, May 29, June 23, July 31, and Aug. 20 for the earth's Northern Hemisphere. (*Lowell Observatory.*)

Kuiper has found that infrared reflection spectra of the polar caps are similar to those obtained in the laboratory from frost or snow. Accordingly there must be some water in the Martian atmosphere, even though no water-vapor absorption bands can be detected in the ordinary spectrum. The caps therefore correspond to the snow fields of the earth which form in higher latitudes during the winter of the corresponding hemisphere and shrink toward the poles during the spring and summer.

Figure 163 shows a series of photographs of the south-polar cap of Mars taken by E. C. Slipher at the Lowell Observatory. They show clearly the shrinking of the cap with the advance of the warm season. The dates given are the Martian seasonal dates which correspond to like dates for the earth's Northern Hemisphere. It can also be noted that the markings in the tropics are darker in the later photographs.

278. Surface Temperature. Until very recently we have had no knowledge of the surface temperatures of Mars. Various calculations had been made based on a variety of assumptions and the results varied as widely as the assumptions.

During the oppositions of 1922, 1924, and 1926 Coblentz and Lampland at the Lowell Observatory investigated the problem by means of specially devised thermocouples used in connection with the large reflector of that observatory. Their results for 1926, for late summer for the southern hemisphere of Mars, gave values for the actual surface temperatures as follows: south-polar region 0 to $+20°C$; south temperate zone 20 to 30°C; center of disk 30 to 40°C; north temperate zone 15 to 25°C; north-polar region -15 to $-30°C$; sunrise region $-10°C$; sunset region 20°C. When a region was cloudy the temperatures at the cloud layer were from 15 to 30°C lower. Observations at the Mt. Wilson Observatory by Pettit and Nicholson in general support these values.

279. Surface Colors. Aside from the polar caps the surface of Mars has two predominant colors, orange and bluish green. Formerly, it was supposed that the orange regions were land and the bluish-green areas water, but modern observations have shown that there is much detail to be observed in the latter and that no large bodies of water exist. Some observers hold that the bluish-green areas are regions supporting some vegetation and the orange regions deserts. This does not seem improbable.

Kuiper's spectrographic observations show that the spectra of the blue-green areas agree with those of our lichens and not with the spectra of seed-bearing plants or ferns. It might therefore be assumed that a low form of vegetable life is responsible for the blue-green areas on Mars. The orange regions are almost certainly deserts.

McLaughlin has recently (1954) made a most interesting suggestion concerning the nature of the blue-green regions. He holds that owing to the relative smoothness of Mars' surface a well-defined system of planetary winds has been developed—particularly the trade winds. These distribute dust along their path. He also assumes that the blue-green color is not due to vegetation but to weathered rock which may be a greenish tone under the atmospheric conditions prevailing on Mars. This hypothesis is contrary to Kuiper's spectrographic data, but Pickering's observations of shifting canals support it.

280. The Canals. In 1877, Schiaparelli announced that he had observed many fine lines over the orange-colored surface of Mars, and in 1881 he

further announced that in many cases these lines first appeared single
and later double.   He applied to them the Italian name "canali," which
means channels and which has been translated canals.   Since that time
many observers have seen these markings, those at the Lowell Observatory at Flagstaff, Ariz., paying especial attention to them and construct-
ing charts of the planet showing many hundreds.   Some of the more conspicuous ones have also been photographed at Flagstaff.

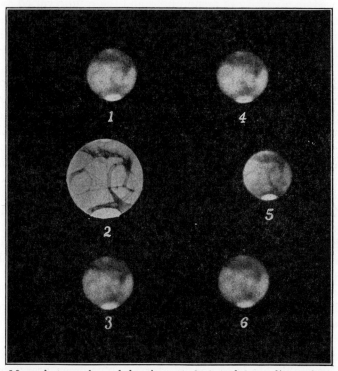

Fig. 164. Mars photographs and drawing.   1, 3, 4, and 6 are direct photographs of
Mars on Feb. 11, 1916; 2 is an independent drawing of the planet on Feb. 10, 1916;
5 is a photograph of the drawing placed at a distance and photographed with the same
telescope used for 1, 3, 4, and 6.   (*Lowell Observatory.*)

The success with which it has been possible to photograph the canals
and other features may be judged in part by Fig. 164.   Numbers 1, 3, 4,
and 6 are direct photographs of the planet, while 2 is a drawing and 5 is a
photograph of the drawing on the same scale as the photographs.   The
photographs and drawing were made by E. C. Slipher of the Lowell
Observatory.

Many observers of Mars deny the existence of this network of fine
straight lines, claiming that the markings are not only much broader
individually but that there are considerable variations in width and

direction. At the present time the majority of astronomers seem to favor the latter view.

An explanation of this marked difference of opinion may be as follows: There are on the surface of Mars many details which cannot be seen individually but which the eye unconsciously integrates into lines and spots. If this is the case, we would expect small telescopes to bring out the fine network while large telescopes, having a greater resolving power, would be able to bring out more detail and thus destroy the appearance of the network. Figure 165 is a reproduction of drawings by Hamilton and Trumpler showing the same regions on Mars. Hamilton used a 28-cm (11-in.) and Trumpler a 91-cm (36-in.) telescope.

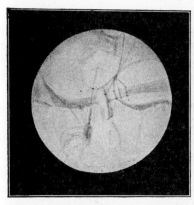 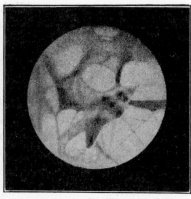

(a)   (b)

FIG. 165. Drawings of Mars, showing the same surface features as seen by different observers: (a) drawn by Hamilton at Mandeville, Jamaica, Sept. 8, 1924, using a 28-cm (11-in.) refractor; (b) drawn by Trumpler at the Lick Observatory, Sept. 11, 1924, using a 91-cm (36-in.) refractor. (*Popular Astronomy, March,* 1926.)

281. Life on Mars. In the popular mind this question usually means, "Is Mars inhabited by intelligent beings?" For us, however, it is necessary to distinguish carefully, first, between vegetable and animal life, and, second, between low forms of animal life and highly intelligent beings.

There seems to be little question about the existence of some sort of vegetation on Mars. Change in the color of the dark regions with change in season appears well established, and Kuiper's spectrographic observations indicate that this vegetation resembles terrestrial lichens.

If plant life exists, it does not seem impossible that at least low forms of animal life also may be there, but no observations have been brought forward to establish this.

The question of intelligent life on Mars hinges almost exclusively on the interpretation of the canals. The argument is as follows: Nowhere in nature do we find long straight lines. Our experience on the earth is that

only man produces projects, such as canals or railways, which follow
essentially straight lines for long distances.   The network of fine straight
lines therefore clearly implies an artificial and not a natural system of
markings.   Hence there are intelligent beings on our neighboring planet
who are responsible for these markings.   Water seems scarce on Mars,
so these intelligent beings constructed a great system of water courses
leading from the warmer equatorial regions toward the poles in order to
carry the water from the melting polar caps to regions where crops may
be grown.   The markings seen and called canals are not the artificial
water courses themselves but the irrigated regions of growing crops along
their sides.

It will be seen that the argument depends essentially on the straightness
of the canals.   Some of the world's keenest observers, however, using the
most powerful telescopes fail to see this network of fine straight markings,
although they see a great amount of what we may term "natural detail."
Accordingly, the argument for the existence of intelligent Martians
capable of carrying out great engineering works is seen to rest on very
insecure foundations.

W. H. Pickering has made many observations which indicate a shifting
of the positions of many of the canals and thinks that at least some are
strips of vegetation which shift in position with changes in the precipitation as the prevailing winds may affect the latter.

282. The Satellites of Mars. Mars has two satellites which were discovered by Hall at Washington in 1877.   The outer one was named
Deimos and the inner one Phobos.   They are very faint and so small they
show no measurable diameters.   Deimos is the fainter of the two.
Assuming both have the albedo of Mars, various observers have estimated
their diameters by their brightness, but there is marked disagreement
among them.   Deimos is probably about 8 km (5 miles) and Phobos
about 15 km (10 miles) in diameter.

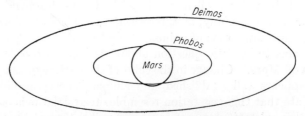

Fig. 166. The orbits of the satellites of Mars.

The orbits of both satellites are practically circular, the smaller with a
radius of 9300 km (5800 miles) and the larger with a radius of 23,500 km
(14,600 miles).   Both orbits lie very nearly in the plane of the planet's
equator.   Their periods of revolution are 7^{h}39^m and 30^{h}18^m, respectively.

Phobos is the only satellite known which goes around its primary in a period shorter than the rotation period of the latter. Because of the rapid revolution it rises in the west and sets in the east, while Deimos rises and sets in the usual way, although it requires about 132 hr between successive risings or settings.

For considerable periods near the times of the equinoxes on Mars the two satellites will transit the disk of the sun at each new moon and both will be eclipsed at full moon.

THE ASTEROIDS

283. Early Discoveries. The possibility of the existence of a planet between Mars and Jupiter had been recognized as early as the time of Kepler in the seventeenth century. When Bode's law was announced over a century later, the possibility became a probability and led to an organization in Germany for the purpose of looking for the unknown planet. Apparently, however, no great efforts were expended on the search and the actual discovery of the first asteroid fell to Piazzi in Palermo, Sicily.

While observing a certain region of the sky on the night of Jan. 1, 1801, he came across a telescopic star which had moved appreciably by the following night. He followed it with care for 6 weeks and was then forced by illness to abandon the work.

News of the discovery reached Germany in March, but the planet, to which Piazzi had given the name Ceres, was then too near the sun to be observed, and it was necessary to wait until fall before the search could be continued. The question at that time, however, was where to look for it. During the summer the mathematician Gauss attacked the problem and devised his famous method of determining orbits. Applying the method to Piazzi's observations, he predicted where the planet might be found and Ceres was rediscovered at the end of the year.

A few months later Olbers discovered a second asteroid which he named Pallas; Harding discovered Juno in 1804 and Olbers found a fourth, Vesta, in 1807. For nearly 40 years these four were the only ones known and it was not until 1845 that Hencke, an amateur astronomer, found the fifth. Since 1847 no year has passed without new discoveries and about 1600 have been assigned definite numbers. Besides these, probably an equal number have been discovered, but so few observations obtained that satisfactory orbits could not be computed.

284. Probable Number. The question of the total number of asteroids has occasionally been raised. There is no good basis upon which to theorize. Various assumptions have to be made and various numbers have been obtained, depending on the assumptions. Baade has recently made such an estimate which is as reliable as can be expected.   He concludes that there are between 30,000 and 40,000 asteroids brighter than the nineteenth magnitude (Sec. 399), which is about the limiting brightness for a large reflecting telescope with moderate exposure.

285. Methods of Search. For many years the search was carried on visually by making charts of the faint stars near the ecliptic and then comparing these with the sky.   If a starlike object was found which was not on the chart, it was carefully observed, and, if found to be in motion, sufficient observations were obtained so that an orbit could be computed.

Fig. 167. Trail of asteroid Egeria.   (*Yerkes Observatory.*)

The modern method, inaugurated by Wolf of Heidelberg, consists in photographing regions near the ecliptic with special cameras of large aperture and field.   The camera is mounted so that it is moved by clockwork to follow the stars across the sky.   When exposures of some duration are made, the stars will give round images, but if an asteroid is in the field, its motion will produce a short line or trail (Fig. 167) which betrays its presence.

286. Designation. The asteroids were originally named, but when their number mounted into the hundreds, it became difficult to find suitable names.   Later each asteroid on discovery was given a provisional designation, such as 1920HZ, which shows the year of discovery and the order. The next one in the same year would be 1920JA, the next 1920JB, etc., the letter I being omitted.   When sufficient observations have been obtained to compute an accurate orbit, the asteroid is given a special number enclosed in parentheses if it proves to be a new one. Thus 1920HZ became (944). About 1600 have been assigned permanent numbers.

Beginning with Jan. 1, 1925, a new method of designation has come into use. The letters of the alphabet are divided according to the months, allotting two letters to each month but omitting I and Z. Following these letters, the letters are used a second time from A to Y if necessary (excepting I) as follows:

The first asteroid of the year, if discovered in the first 15 days of January, 1925, is designated 1925AA, the second 1925AB, etc. Those discovered from the sixteenth of January onward would be 1925BA, BB, etc. Similarly the February asteroids would be 1925CA, CB, etc., and 1925DA, DB, etc. For 1926 the letters would be used again as in the preceding year, the only change made being in the number of the year.

The discoverer is still at liberty to assign a name but frequently the right is not used.

287. Diameter, Shape. Most of the asteroids have diameters less than 100 km, but a few are large enough to be measured. Thus Barnard found values of 768, 489, 385, and 193 km (477, 304, 239, and 120 miles) for Ceres, Pallas, Vesta, and Juno, respectively, by using powers of 1000 to 1700 with the Lick 36-in. and Yerkes 40-in. refractors. Most of them, however, are too small to show a measurable disk and some are without doubt less than 10 km in diameter. Thus, judging from its brightness, Albert (719) probably has a diameter of not over 4 or 5 km, and some, discovered by large instruments, can hardly be over 1 km in diameter.

The larger asteroids are presumably spherical in shape but there is no reason for assuming this for the smaller ones. In the case of Eros (Sec. 294) there is some evidence of a marked departure from sphericity.

288. Orbits. Most of the asteroids have mean distances from the sun between 2.0 and 3.5 AU, but the range is from 1.07 for Icarus to 5.8 for (944). The shortest perihelion distance is 0.23 for Icarus, while the greatest aphelion distance is 9.6 for (944). The present-known asteroid belt therefore extends from well within the orbit of Mercury to the orbit of Saturn. Exceptional cases may still be discovered which will increase the width of this belt.

The eccentricities vary from 0.00 to 0.887, but most of the values are below 0.30.

The inclinations to the plane of the ecliptic vary from 0° to 43°, but most of them are less than 16°.

The period of the average asteroid is about 4.5 years, but Icarus revolves about the sun in 1.1 years, while (944) requires 14 years.

289. Eros (433). This asteroid was discovered photographically by Witt of Berlin in 1898. The computation of its orbit showed it to be an exceptional one. Its mean distance from the sun is 1.46 and its eccentricity of 0.22 brings it at times very close (about 22,000,000 km) to the earth. In 1900 it came within about 47,000,000 km and the favorable opportunity was utilized to organize an international campaign for the determination of the distance between earth and sun, with the result that we knew this value more exactly than ever before (see Sec. 26). In 1931 it came much nearer than in 1900, and many observatories joined in securing observations for an even more exact value of the astronomical unit. Final results of this work became available about 10 years later. The value of the solar parallax, 8".80, which had been used for many years, was reduced to 8".79.

290. Apollo (1932HA). This asteroid was discovered by Reinmuth at Heidelberg in April, 1932. It proved to be moving rapidly westward which made it remarkable and its discovery was announced by cablegram. It was followed by a number of observers until May 15 after which it moved into the day sky. At its closest approach it was only 3,000,000 km (2,000,000 miles) from the earth. When the orbit was computed it was found that at perihelion Apollo penetrates several million kilometers within the orbit of Venus and may, at a favorable opposition, pass even closer to the earth than it did when discovered.

It so happened that Apollo was observed such a short time and its position with respect to earth and sun was so unfavorable that it proved impossible to calculate accurate orbit elements, the period being the one of greatest uncertainty. Every effort was made to find it after it passed the sun but without success. It must therefore be listed among the lost asteroids. Should it be recovered accidentally some time in the future, the error in the present assumed length of its period can be determined and thereafter it should be possible to keep track of it. It may then be used instead of Eros for determining the value of the astronomical unit as it approaches the earth much nearer than Eros.

Since the discovery of Apollo three other asteroids, Adonis, Hermes, and Icarus have been found whose orbits also pass inside the orbit of Venus. The first two have been lost because observations extending over a sufficient length of time to permit the computation of accurate orbital elements could not be made.

291. Icarus. In 1949 Baade discovered another short-period asteroid, which, fortunately, has been observed at more than one return to the sun and is therefore not "lost." Its mean distance from the sun is 1.066, but the eccentricity of its orbit is so great (0.789) that at perihelion it comes within 34,000,000 km (21,000,000 miles) of the sun, while at aphelion it reaches a distance of 285,000,000 km (177,000,000 miles). Its period is only 1.1 years. In this time it completes a trip from well inside the orbit of Mercury to a point nearly 65,000,000 km (40,000,000 miles) beyond the orbit of Mars and return.

292. The Trojan Group. Thirteen members of this group are known at present. All have mean distances from the sun differing but little from that of Jupiter. It has been shown that if three bodies, essentially at equal distances, move about their common center of gravity in a plane, they will maintain their relative distances at the vertices of an equilateral triangle. These 13 asteroids, each in connection with Jupiter and the sun, very nearly fulfill these conditions. Two additional members were suspected in 1949, but they were lost before enough observations could be made to obtain satisfactory orbits.

293. Perturbations by Jupiter and Saturn. All the asteroids are influenced to a marked degree by Jupiter and perturbations by this planet cause great changes in the orbits. Saturn also has some influence, but much less than Jupiter. On this account an asteroid orbit, however carefully determined, will not suffice to predict its future position for any length of time without the calculation of the perturbations by Jupiter and Saturn. This is a rather long and tedious process. Watson, one of the chief American discoverers of asteroids in the last century, realized that the 22 bodies discovered by him might be lost[1] on account of the changes in the orbits and at his death left a sum of money to the National Academy of Sciences, Washington, D.C., in order to have tables of the perturbations calculated so that it would be a simple matter to determine and apply the corrections to the ever-changing orbits. This work was put into the hands of Leuschner of the University of California and is now completed.

294. Variation in Brightness. All of the asteroids vary in apparent brightness, depending on their distance from sun and earth, but in a number of cases they also undergo other variations in brightness which seem to indicate possible rotation effects by presenting light and dark sides alternately toward the earth. It is possible, too, that some of the smaller asteroids are not even approximately spherical but more or less angular. If this is the case we would expect variations in brightness depending upon whether a more or less flat side or an angle is turned toward the earth.

One of the best known cases of variability is that of Eros. The period is approximately 5.3 hr. Since the range of variation was from practically 0 to 1.5 magnitudes (Sec. 399), it seemed evident that Eros might be of irregular shape and have a rotation about an axis. The amount of the variation would then depend on the direction of the rotation axis with respect to the observer.

In February, 1931, when Eros was very near the earth, van den Bos and Finsen of the Union Observatory at Johannesburg saw the image of the asteroid distinctly notched, somewhat like a figure 8, and could see the notched image rotate in a period of 5^h17^m, the period of variation. The length of the image was about $0''.18$.

---

[1] In fact, one of the 22, Aethra (132), was lost within a few weeks after discovery in 1873 and not recovered until found by chance in 1922.

This is the first case in which the surmised irregularity of figure of a variable asteriod has been detected.

Kuiper and others reported recently (1953) on a study of the light variations of 10 asteroids made at the McDonald Observatory. Analysis of the light curves support the idea that these asteriods are rotating masses of irregular shape.

295. The Masses. We have little knowledge of the masses of the individual asteroids, but it is probable that the combined mass of all those known barely exceeds 0.001 that of the earth.

296. Origin. When the first asteroids were discovered, Olbers suggested that they might be the fragments of a disrupted planet. This idea is now generally given up. It appears more probable that they are the material from which a planet might have been formed had not the presence of Jupiter prevented it by the disturbances induced in the motions of the small masses concerned. The meaning of this statement will be clearer when the theories of the origin of the solar system are considered in Chap. 22.

EXERCISES

1. If an intramercurial planet had a period of 19 days, what would be its mean distance from the sun?				*Ans.* 0.139 AU.

2. Look for Venus in the daytime. Use the *American Ephemeris* to determine its position relative to the sun.

3. Assuming that the rotation period of Mars given in Sec. 275 depends on the early drawing of Huyghens dated Nov. 28, 1659, and one made at the Lowell Observatory on Aug. 22, 1924, what change would be made if it should be discovered that Huyghens had made an error of one day in his date?				*Ans.* About $0^s.9$.

4. At what distance from the surface of Mars would a satellite revolve about Mars in the same time as the planet rotates on its axis? *Ans.* 17,000 km or 10,600 miles.

5. If an asteroid had a diameter of 8 miles and a mean density equal to that of the earth, what would be its surface gravity as compared with the earth's?
						Ans. 0.001.

6. If a high jumper is off the earth about 1 sec during his jump, how long would he be off the ground of the asteroid in Exercise 5?				*Ans.* 1000 sec.

7. If the jumper of Exercise 6 raises the center of gravity of his body about 4 ft when making his jump on the earth, how high would he go on the asteroid?
						Ans. About 4000 ft.

CHAPTER 13

THE MAJOR PLANETS

JUPITER

297. Distance, Orbit, etc. Jupiter is one of the brightest of the planets. Its mean distance from the sun is 5.20 AU (778 $\times$ 10^6 km or 484 $\times$ 10^6 miles). The orbit has an eccentricity of 0.048, which allows a variation of over 37 $\times$ 10^6 km (23 $\times$ 10^6 miles) each way from the mean distance. The orbit is inclined 1°18′ to the plane of the ecliptic and the plane of the equator is inclined only 3° to the orbital plane.

The *sidereal period* is 11.86 years and the *synodic period* 399 days.

298. Dimensions, Mass, etc. The mean diameter of Jupiter is 139,700 km (86,800 miles), but on account of its rapid rotation it is markedly flattened at the poles. The polar diameter is 133,400 km (82,900 miles) and the equatorial diameter 142,900 km (88,800 miles).

The volume of the planet is approximately 1300 times that of the earth, while its mass is only 318 times the earth's mass. Its mean density is, therefore, only one-fourth that of the earth or 1.4 on the water standard.

Its surface gravity is about 2.5.

299. Albedo, etc. The mean albedo of Jupiter is 0.56, although the different parts of the surface differ considerably from one another. At mean opposition its brightness equals that of a star of magnitude −2.3. This changes to about magnitude −1.5 near conjunction.

In brightness the planet is generally exceeded only by Venus, but Mars will outshine it for a few weeks during a very close approach.

300. Telescopic Appearance. When seen with a small telescope of 3- or 4-in. aperture and a magnifying power of about 100, a number of approximately parallel bands of different widths may be noted. These bands are of a dull-reddish color as seen against the remainder of the surface, which is of a white or yellowish tinge. The use of a larger telescope and a magnification of 200 or more will show much detail in these bands (or belts), and this finer structure, at times, will be found to undergo considerable variation from one night to the next.

Occasionally small spots are seen which may be either dark or bright, but, for the most part, these spots are comparatively short-lived phenomena.   In 1878, however, a large oval spot having a width of about 14,000 km (8700 miles) and a length of about 40,000 km (25,000 miles) became a very conspicuous object on the planet's surface.   It became known as the *Great Red Spot* on account of its size and color.   As the years passed the Great Red Spot lost most of its color, but its outline still remained partially visible.   In 1937 its color was again very pronounced but it has faded considerably since then.   There is some evidence that this spot was seen as early as 1831.

The color of the belts is also subject to change.

FIG. 168. Drawing of Jupiter, Oct. 26, 1916, by Latimer J. Wilson, showing bright and dark spots.   (*Popular Astronomy.*)

301. Rotation Period. Observation of well-marked spots on the surface shows that Jupiter is in rapid rotation.   The various determinations are not wholly in agreement and there is evidence that, while the rotation period from spots at the equator is $9^h50^m.5$, the period given by other spots in higher latitudes is about 9^h55^m.   Whether there is a regular progression from the one value to the other with increasing distance from the equator is not yet certain.

302. Atmosphere. The brightness of Jupiter's surface falls off very noticeably near the limb—an indication of atmospheric absorption.   This phenomenon is particularly marked on photographs of the planet.

The changing belts and the appearance and disappearance of spots are most simply explained by the assumption that we are looking at the upper side of a cloud-laden atmosphere.

The composition of the atmosphere appears to be simple.   Years ago Slipher of the Lowell Observatory detected heavy absorption bands in the spectrum of the planet, which, at the time, could not be identified.   Later

Dunham at Mt. Wilson, using more powerful instruments, definitely identified methane (CH₄) and ammonia (NH₃). Adel and Slipher, on the basis of the strength of the absorption bands in the spectrum, estimate the amount of methane in Jupiter's atmosphere above the cloud layer to be equivalent to a layer 800 m (0.5 mile) thick at atmospheric pressure, and Dunham estimates the amount of ammonia to be equivalent to a layer about 10 m (33 ft) thick. It may be that the clouds are composed of crystals of ammonia.

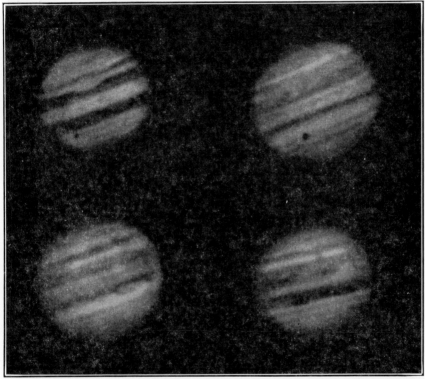

Fig. 169. Jupiter, Mar. 28, 1920; Feb. 12, 1921; Mar. 15, 1921, with Ganymede and shadow; May 29, 1922, 100-in. Hooker reflector. (*Mt. Wilson Observatory.*)

There seems to be no spectroscopic evidence of constituents other than methane and ammonia in any quantity in the atmosphere of Jupiter, although Baum and Code, using the 152-cm (60-in.) reflector at Mt. Wilson to observe the occultation of a star by Jupiter, found that the probable molecular weight of Jupiter's upper atmosphere was of the order of 3.3. They interpret their results as indicating the presence of large amounts of hydrogen and helium in the upper atmosphere of the planet. Theoretically large amounts of free hydrogen should exist in the atmospheres not only of Jupiter but of all the major planets.

303. Physical Conditions on Jupiter. Since the planet is over five times farther from the sun than is the earth, the amount of heat and light falling on equal areas of the two is in the ratio of 1:27. It is therefore evident that if Jupiter is dependent on the sun for its heat, its surface temperature must be low. Radiometric measures at the Lowell and Mt. Wilson Observatories indicate a temperature of the visible surface of about −135°C (−210°F).

Below the cloud-laden atmosphere the surface of the planet must have a low density, probably less than that of water, because the mean density is only 1.4. There is no certainty as to the nature of the surface, whether it is solid or liquid. Since the Great Red Spot has been visible for over a century, it seems necessary to assume it is a solid. In the last 60 years it has apparently shifted by more than 260° in longitude. This can be explained by assuming that it is a great island floating in a sea of liquid of unknown composition.

The change in color of the Great Red Spot may mean that at times the atmosphere may clear so that the true color is seen, and then, as the clouds thicken, the color apparently fades.

In 1938 many highly colored spots appeared on the disk of Jupiter. The color faded rapidly. It has been suggested that these were caused by some internal disturbance which brought up fresh material from lower levels. When this fresh material was exposed to the sunlight in the upper atmosphere, it faded.

It must be remembered that the explanations mentioned are nothing but *guesses*. They have been made by observers in an effort to put the observed phenomena into some sort of order and with the hope that, in the future, it may be possible to put them to the test.

304. The Satellite System. Jupiter has 12 known satellites. The four brightest were the first new bodies discovered by the telescope, as they are bright enough to be seen easily with a good field glass. They were discovered independently by Galileo and by Simon Marius in January, 1610. The diameters of these satellites, in the order of their distances from their primary, are 3950, 3290, 5730, and 5390 km, according to Barnard. Their periods of revolution are 1^d18^h, 3^d13^h, 7^d4^h, and 16^d18^h, respectively. Their orbits are practically in the plane of Jupiter's equator and almost circular. There is evidence that they rotate at such a rate that they present the same face toward the planet and that the two larger ones may have thin atmospheres.

The fifth satellite was discovered by Barnard at the Lick Observatory in 1892. It is probably about 160 km (100 miles) in diameter, its period of revolution is 12 hr, and it is only 182,000 km (113,000 miles) from Jupiter's center.

The other seven satellites were all discovered photographically—the sixth and seventh by Perrine at the Lick Observatory in 1904 and 1905, the eighth by Melotte at Greenwich in 1908, the ninth by Nicholson at the Lick Observatory in 1914, the tenth and eleventh by Nicholson at the Mt. Wilson Observatory in 1938, and the twelfth, also by Nicholson, in 1951.

The sidereal periods of the last seven discovered are 250.6, 259.6, 739, 758, 260.5, 700, and 625 days, respectively. The first seven and the tenth revolve around Jupiter in the same direction as the planet rotates; the four of long period revolve in the opposite direction. These four are so far from Jupiter (their mean distances are of the order of 22,000,000 km) that the sun greatly perturbs their orbits around Jupiter. Nicholson reports that in the cases of the eighth and ninth the eccentricity of the orbits may change from 0.25 to 0.50 and the mean distance from 22,000,-000 to 23,500,000 km during a single revolution around the planet.

All the satellites, except the first four, are comparatively small bodies, ranging from about 20 to 150 km (14 to 100 miles) in diameter. These small bodies are difficult to see at best, and the tenth and twelfth have never been observed except photographically. These two are about as bright as a candle flame at a distance of 5000 km (3000 miles), when Jupiter is nearest the earth.

305. Satellite Transits and Eclipses. In their movements about Jupiter the first three of the brighter satellites pass regularly, and the fourth frequently, between that planet and the earth and can be noted as small bright points at such times, particularly when there is a dark belt of the planet for a background. The shadows of the satellites appear as small black spots on Jupiter's surface (Fig. 170).

When one of these satellites is on the farther side of Jupiter, it also passes into Jupiter's shadow and disappears from view. The eclipse is not instantaneous but requires some minutes. It is an

Fig. 170. Jupiter with one satellite and satellite shadow. (*Hale telescope, Mt. Wilson and Palomar Observatories.*)

interesting observation and easily made when the planet is not too near opposition to prevent following the satellite into the shadow.

306. Jupiter's Satellites and the Velocity of Light. After the four brighter satellites had been observed, so that their mean periods were known with some degree of accuracy, it was found that if eclipses of the satellites were predicted by starting from observed times of eclipse near opposition, the eclipses of the four occurred systematically later and later, until near conjunction they were many minutes behind the predicted times. After conjunction the discrepancy decreased correspondingly, until near opposition the eclipses again occurred on time.

Roemer, a Danish astronomer stationed at Paris at the time, was engaged in the problem of improving the tables of the satellites used to predict the eclipses. He found a maximum discrepancy of 22 min between the observed and computed times and suggested the true explanation, namely, that light does not pass instantaneously from one point of space to another but requires 22 min* to cross the earth's orbit. This was in 1676. His explanation was not generally accepted at the time, but Bradley's discovery of the aberration of light in 1726 proved Roemer's theory to be correct.

An inspection of Fig. 171 shows that if E_1 and J_1 represent the positions of the earth and Jupiter at a certain time, and E_2 and J_2 the corresponding

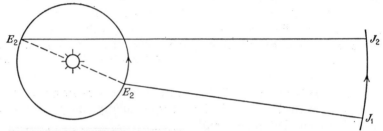

Fig. 171. Phenomena of Jupiter's satellites and the velocity of light.

positions 6 months later, the distance E_2J_2 is practically equal to $E_1J_1 + E_2E_1$. Hence a signal, such as a satellite eclipse or transit, would reach E_2 later than E_1, the difference being the time required for light to travel across the earth's orbit.

SATURN

307. Distance, Orbit, Period. Saturn was the outermost planet known to astronomers, until late in the eighteenth century when Uranus was discovered. Its mean distance from the sun is 9.54 AU.

The orbit has an eccentricity of 0.056 and is inclined 2°29′ to the plane of the ecliptic.

The *sidereal period* is 29.458 years and the *synodic period* is 378 days.

308. Dimensions, Mass, etc. Saturn has a marked oblateness, its polar diameter being 108,200 km (67,250 miles) and the equatorial diameter 120,900 km (75,100 miles). The mean diameter is 116,700 km (72,500 miles). Its volume is therefore about 760 times that of the earth.

* The modern value is 16.6 min.

The mass of the planet is only 95 times the earth's mass. Its mean density is the lowest of all the planets, being only 0.7 that of water. The surface gravity is about equal to that of the earth.

309. Albedo. The mean albedo of the planet is 0.63, but its great distance from the sun makes its actual surface brightness comparatively low. Its stellar magnitude varies from about 0 to 1.5, depending upon its distance from the earth and upon the angle which the rings make with the line of sight.

(a)

(b)

Fig. 172. (a) Saturn with rings open (*Mt. Wilson and Palomar Observatories*); (b) Saturn with rings nearly edgewise (*Lick Observatory*).

310. Rotation. The period of rotation is difficult to determine as few spots are ever seen on its surface. The value obtained by Hall of the U.S. Naval Observatory in 1876 was 10^h14^m for a spot near the equator. In 1903, Barnard obtained 10^h38^m for a spot in latitude $+36°$. If these values are still correct, a spot on the equator gains approximately 30° of longitude over a spot in middle latitudes in 24 hr.

The rapid rotation causes a marked bulging at the equator which is easily seen through the telescope as well as in photographs (Fig. 172).

The plane of Saturn's equator is inclined 28° to the plane of its orbit, so that it must have marked seasonal changes, at least insofar as sunlight is concerned.

311. Telescopic Appearance. When seen through the telescope, the planet shows an almost uniform surface of a slightly yellowish tint with a few poorly defined belts parallel to the equator. The color of the belts changes at times. Near the equator they are at times white. Other belts may acquire bluish tints. There is a decided falling off in brightness near the edge of the disk, which indicates considerable atmospheric absorption.

At irregular intervals, usually of some years' duration, one or more spots may appear on the surface. One of the most recent cases occurred in the summer of 1933 (Fig. 173). Ordinarily these spots are white, but

(a)   (b)

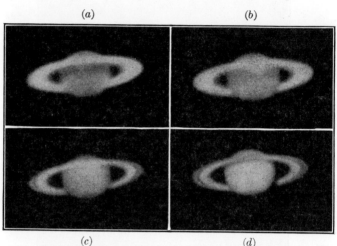

(c)   (d)

FIG. 173. A recent bright spot on Saturn: (a) in ultraviolet light; (b) in violet light; (c) in yellow light. These three taken on Aug. 7, 1933. (d) In yellow light, taken Sept. 13, 1933. (*Lick Observatory.*)

dark ones are not unknown. They are comparatively short-lived phenomena, lasting only a few months at most, and afford the only satisfactory means of determining the period of rotation except the spectrographic method.

312. Atmosphere. The spectrograph shows the atmosphere of Saturn to be similar to that of Jupiter in that it contains large amounts of methane and some ammonia. The methane bands, however, are stronger and the ammonia bands weaker than in the case of Jupiter. From the intensity of the absorption bands of methane Adel and Slipher find the amount equivalent to a layer over 800 m thick if at atmospheric pressure. The amount of ammonia is much less, possibly equivalent to a layer 5 to 8 m thick at atmospheric pressure.

313. Physical Condition. There is great difficulty in coming to any conclusion regarding the physical conditions obtaining on Saturn. Its extremely low mean density seems to preclude much solid or liquid matter as we know it. If there is such a solid or liquid core, it must be enveloped by a very extensive atmosphere, probably filled with clouds, which hide the interior.

The white spots which sometimes are seen have the appearance of an eruption of some substance from beneath the level we ordinarily see, but we have no knowledge of its internal temperature. The spots may be merely especially bright clouds, for sometimes, as in 1876, 1903, and 1933, they lengthen on the preceding side in a direction parallel to the equator.

Figure 173 gives an indication of a disturbance which occurred on Saturn in August, 1933. A great white spot suddenly appeared near the planet's equator. It was best defined in photographs taken in ultraviolet and violet light. In a few days the spot had been drawn out on the preceding side as if blown by a strong wind, and, in the course of a few weeks, the erupted material appeared to have been distributed practically all around the equatorial belt.

It has been thought that Saturn may have considerable internal heat, but radiometric observations indicate a low surface temperature of about $-150°C$ ($-240°F$).

314. The Rings. The most interesting and impressive thing about the planet is its system of rings. There are three[1] of these, usually spoken of as the outer, inner, and crepe or dusky rings. The outer ring has an outer diameter of 277,700 km (172,600 miles) and a width of 17,500 km (10,900 miles); the inner ring has an outer diameter of 235,000 km (146,-000 miles) and a width of 28,800 km (17,900 miles). There is a gap of 3600 km (2300 miles) between the two rings, which is known as the Cassini division. The dusky or crepe ring seems to touch the inner ring and extends inward 17,700 km (11,000 miles). Between the inner edge of the dusky ring and the planet there is a gap of about 9400 km (5900 miles). The thickness of the rings is not easy to determine, but it is probable that they are not over a few, possibly ten, kilometers in thickness.

The inner ring is much brighter than the outer, and the dusky ring must be looked for with some care in order to be seen at all.

315. The Nature of the Rings. Keeler's study of the nature of Saturn's rings by the spectrograph is an excellent illustration of the usefulness of this instrument.

Assume that AB (Fig. 174) represents the slit of the spectrograph attached to the telescope and the telescopic image of the planet falls on the slit as indicated.

---

[1] A fourth ring, sometimes referred to as ring D, has been reported from time to time. This ring, as reported, is narrow, very faint, and just outside the outer ring. It has been seen by very few observers. More observations are needed before it can be accepted as a fully accredited member of the ring system.

If planet and ring system were not rotating, the lines of the spectrum would run across the spectrum at right angles to its length. Let $A'B'$ represent a single line in such a spectrum.

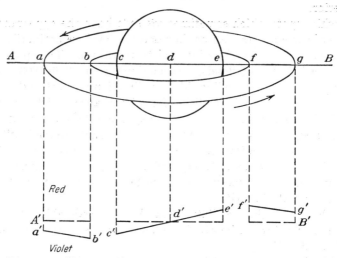

FIG. 174. Diagram to illustrate the shape of the lines in the spectrum of Saturn and its ring system.

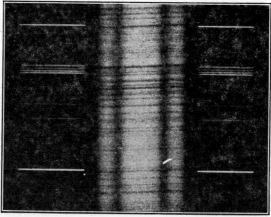

FIG. 175. Spectrum of Saturn and ring system showing tilt of lines caused by rotation. (*Lick Observatory.*)

If the planet rotates as indicated by the arrows, the point c at its equator is approaching the observer, the point e is receding from him, and the point d is moving directly across the line of sight. In consequence of this motion the portion of the spectrum line representing c will be found at c', the portion representing e will be at e', that representing d at d' and other points between c and e will have their corresponding positions between c' and e'.   The spectrum line will therefore be inclined with respect to the line $A'B'$, and the greater the speed of rotation, the greater the inclination.

If the ring system rotated as a unit, then the portions of the spectrum lines representing ab and fg would be inclined to the direction of $A'B'$ and occupy positions approximately parallel to $c'e'$.   But $a'b'$ and $f'g'$ are not parallel to $c'e'$, since a' is displaced less than b' and g' less than f'.   This means that the outer portion of the ring system at a and g is not moving so rapidly as points b and f, or that the ring does not revolve around the planet as a unit.   From the inclination of $a'b'$ and $f'g'$ it is seen that the inner edge of the ring moves fastest and that the velocity decreases the farther the point of the ring is from the planet's center.   Hence it cannot be solid.

Figure 175 is a portion of the spectrum of Saturn and its ring system. It will be seen that each line of the spectrum corresponds to the situation illustrated by Fig. 174.   The most probable constitution is that of myriads of small satellites of various sizes, each pursuing its own orbit about Saturn, but so small that at the earth's distance the individual constituents cannot be seen.   There is evidence that the total mass of the ring system is very small, probably less than 0.00001 that of Saturn. The rings may therefore be merely clouds of fine material like dust or grains of sand, for all of the rings, even the brightest, are sufficiently transparent to allow stars of moderate brightness to be seen through them. According to spectrographic evidence obtained by Kuiper at the Mac-donald Observatory, the light from the rings is similar to that reflected by ice crystals.   The particles of the rings may therefore either be covered with frost or possibly be composed of ice crystals.

The plane of the rings coincides with the plane of the equator of Saturn, which is inclined 28° to the plane of the ecliptic.   When the earth is in the plane of the rings, these disappear from view for all except the largest telescopes.   Such disappearances occur about every 15 years.   The last time was in 1950.   As the rings gradually shift their plane more and more from the direction toward the earth, they become visible again and afford a wonderful spectacle to astronomer and layman alike.

316. Satellites. Saturn has nine known satellites.   Huyghens discovered the first in 1655; Cassini the next four in the period from 1671 to 1684; Sir William Herschel the next two in 1789; Bond of Harvard the eighth[1] in 1848; and W. H. Pickering of Harvard the ninth in 1899.   In 1905, Pickering also found an object on some photographic plates which appeared to be moving about Saturn, and it was announced as a tenth satellite.   It was followed for a few months and then lost, and has not

---

[1] This satellite was also discovered independently by Lassell in England only a few hours after Bond had found it.

been recovered since. In general, the order of discovery of the satellites is their order of brightness. The innermost satellite, Mimas, moves about Saturn at a distance of about 187,000 km (117,000 miles) from the planet's center in a period of approximately 23ʰ, while the outermost, Phoebe, is at a distance of nearly 13,000,000 km (7,300,000 miles) and requires 550 days to complete a single circuit.

FIG. 176. Six satellites of Saturn photographed at the Lowell Observatory, Mar. 2, 1921. From left to right the satellites are Titan, Rhea, Dione, Tethys, Mimas, and Enceladus.

With the exception of the two outer satellites, Japetus and Phoebe, their orbits lie approximately in the plane of the ring. All of them move about Saturn from west to east except Phoebe, which moves in the opposite direction.

A number of the satellites show some variation in brightness. This is particularly true of Japetus, which has the remarkable property of being regularly brighter when west of Saturn than when east of it. The usual explanation of this phenomenon is that Japetus, like the moon, always turns the same face toward its primary, and therefore we see opposite sides of the satellite when it is on opposite sides of Saturn. If this is the case, and if these sides do not have the same mean albedo, then such a variation in its light is a necessary consequence.

From time to time certain observations of Titan, the largest of the satellites of Saturn, were believed to indicate that this satellite had an atmosphere, but it was not until 1944 that Kuiper at the McDonald Observatory was able to get definite proof. His observations show definite absorption lines of methane, and possibly of ammonia, in the spectrum of the satellite, the same gases which have been found in the atmosphere of the planet itself.

URANUS

317. Discovery. In the late winter of 1781, while William Herschel was observing with a 6¼-in. reflector of 7-ft focus of his own make, a small round object came into the field of view of his telescope. His practiced eye immediately noted that it was different from an ordinary star and he determined to watch it with care. It was soon found to be in motion with respect to the stars in the field and he announced that he had discovered a new comet. It was followed diligently, but every effort to calculate an orbit on the assumption of its being a comet near the earth and sun failed. After some months it proved to be in reality a new planet, twice as far from the sun as Saturn.

318. Distance, Orbit, Period. Uranus, as the new planet came to be named, has a mean distance of 19.19 AU from the sun. The eccentricity of the orbit is 0.047 and its plane is inclined 0°46′ to the plane of the ecliptic. This is the smallest inclination of any planet orbit.

Its *sidereal period* is 84.0 years and its *synodic period* 369.7 days.

319. Diameter, etc. The diameter is not easily determined for two reasons: (1) its small apparent diameter, about 3″.8, and (2) its somewhat indefinite outline. For these reasons the measures of various observers differ considerably. A value of 49,750 km (30,900 miles) is the mean of several determinations. This makes the volume 59.3 times that of the earth.

320. Mass, Density, etc. The mass of Uranus is 14.6 times the earth's mass and its density about 1.3 times that of water. The surface gravity is a little over 0.9.

321. Albedo, etc. The albedo is 0.63, the same as for Saturn. Under favorable conditions the planet can be seen with the unaided eye as a star of the sixth magnitude.

322. Rotation. The absence of definite surface markings prevents a determination of the rotation period by direct visual measures, but photometric measures by L. Campbell (1916–1918) and Calder (1934–1936) of Harvard showed variations in brightness with a period of 10^h49^m. In 1912, Lowell and Slipher determined the period by means of the spectrograph to be $10^h.8$. This was confirmed by Moore and Menzel in 1930. Their value was $10^h.84$. The mean of these four values, 10^h49^m, may be taken as the rotation period. It is probably correct to within one minute.

The direction of rotation, based on the spectrographic observations, is retrograde. The plane of the equator makes an angle of 82° with the plane of the ecliptic.

323. Atmosphere and Physical Conditions. The spectrum of Uranus shows very heavy absorption bands of methane. Adel and Slipher estimate the amount of methane in the atmosphere above the reflecting layer to be equivalent to a layer 6 km (4 miles) thick at atmospheric pressure.

It is probable that we cannot see the actual surface of the planet but only the top of a more or less cloud-laden atmosphere.

Radiometric measures indicate a temperature of about −185°C (−300°F).

324. Satellites. Uranus has five satellites. Two were discovered by Sir William Herschel in 1787, two by Lassell in 1851, and the fifth by Kuiper in 1948. Their periods range from 1.4 to 13.5 days. Their orbits make an angle of 82° with the plane of the ecliptic and the direction of revolution is retrograde.   They revolve in the plane of the planet's equator and in the same direction as the planet rotates.

NEPTUNE

325. Discovery. In 1821, Bouvard of Paris published tables of the motions of a number of planets, including Uranus. In preparing the latter he had found great difficulty in making an orbit calculated on the basis of positions obtained in the years after 1800 agree with one calculated from observations taken in the years immediately following discovery.   He finally disregarded the older observations entirely and based his tables on the newer observations.   In a few years, however, the positions calculated from the tables disagreed with the observed positions of the planet and by 1844 the discrepancy amounted to 2' of arc.   Since all the other known planets agreed in their motions with those calculated for them, the discrepancy in the case of Uranus aroused much discussion.

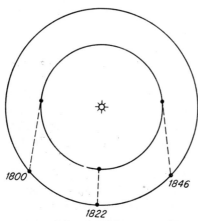

FIG. 177. Relative positions of Uranus and Neptune at various times. It is evident that the perturbations of Uranus by Neptune before 1822 would be different from those after 1822.

In 1845, Leverrier, then a young man, attacked the problem. He checked Bouvard's calculations and found them essentially correct. Thereupon he felt that the only satisfactory explanation of the trouble lay in the presence of a planet somewhere beyond Uranus which was disturbing its motion. By the middle of 1846 he had finished his calculations. In September he wrote to Galle at Berlin and requested the latter to look for a new planet in a certain region of the sky for which some new star charts had just been prepared in Germany but of which Leverrier apparently had not as yet obtained copies. On Sept. 23 Galle started the search and in less than an hour he found an object which was not on the chart. By the next night it had moved appreciably and the new planet, subsequently named Neptune, was discovered within 1° of the predicted place. This discovery ranks among the greatest achievements of mathematical astronomy.

In 1843, J. C. Adams, at that time a student at the University of Cambridge (England), had also attacked the Uranus problem. Two years later he had finished his calculations on the assumption that an undiscovered planet was the cause of the discrepancy in the motion of

Uranus and communicated his results to Airy, the Astronomer Royal at Greenwich. Airy, however, did nothing until the next year when the results of Leverrier's calculations were published. The agreement between the two calculations was so striking that he felt called upon to make an effort to find the predicted planet by requesting Challis of Cambridge to take up the matter with the University telescope. The plan consisted in getting the positions of all the faint stars in a considerable region around the predicted place and then reobserving them to see if any had moved. Challis had gone over the list of stars a second time when word was received of the discovery at Berlin. It was then found that Challis had actually observed the new planet three times, and, had he made the necessary comparison immediately, he would have had the honor of discovery. While Adams' work was therefore barren of results, he must nevertheless be given full credit, along with Leverrier, of having determined independently the data by means of which the actual discovery could be made.

326. Distance, Orbit, Period. Neptune's mean distance from the sun is 30.07 AU. The eccentricity of the orbit is 0.0086 and its inclination to the ecliptic is 1°47′.

The *sidereal period* of the planet is 164.79 years and the *synodic period* 367.5 days.

327. Diameter, etc. As in the case of Uranus, the diameter of Neptune is not easily determined. Barnard's measures give the value 53,000 km (33,000 miles). Its volume is accordingly 72 times that of the earth.

328. Mass, Density, etc. The mass of Neptune is 17 times the earth's mass and its mean density about 1.2 times that of water. The surface gravity is about 0.9.

329. Rotation. Definite surface markings cannot be seen on the planet so that this method has yielded no values of the period of rotation.

In 1928 Moore and Menzel of the Lick Observatory published the results of a series of observations by the spectrographic method from which they determined the period to be about 15^h.8 and the direction of rotation to be direct.

The orientation of the plane of the planet's equator is not easy to determine on account of the entire absence of surface markings. Jackson of Washington studied the problem from a theoretical standpoint, taking as data the perturbations produced by Neptune on the motion of its inner satellite. From these he found that the plane of the equator is inclined about 29° to the plane of the ecliptic. This value cannot be far from the truth, for Moore and Menzel, in working on the spectrographic rotation, found the greatest value for the rotation when the slit of the spectrograph was set for this position, and no rotation when the slit was set at right angles to it.

330. Albedo, etc. The albedo of Neptune is 0.73. Its average stellar magnitude is 8. It is therefore never visible to the naked eye.

331. Telescopic Appearance. In a telescope Neptune appears as a small round disk of 2″.5 diameter, without definite markings and of a faint bluish color. Under ordinary conditions of seeing, the edge is not sharply defined.

332. Atmosphere and Physical Conditions. The spectrum shows the greatest methane absorption bands of any of the planets. Adel and Slipher estimate the observable thickness of methane in the planet's atmosphere to be equivalent to 40 km at atmospheric pressure.

The temperature of the observable surface of Neptune is very low, probably at least −200°C(−330°F). At this temperature most substances would be frozen out of the atmosphere and it is possible that there are fewer clouds than in the atmospheres of the other major planets. The fact that the methane absorption increases as we go from Jupiter to Neptune may merely mean that we can see ever deeper into the atmospheres, and therefore deeper layers of methane can exert their absorbing power.

333. Satellites. Neptune has two known satellites. The first was discovered by Lassell within a few months after the planet was found, and the second was discovered by Kuiper over a century later (1949).

The first satellite has a sidereal period of 5ᵈ.9, its motion is retrograde in an orbit inclined 37° to the plane of the ecliptic, its diameter 3600 km (2240 miles), according to Pickering, and its mass between 0.04 and 0.1 that of the earth on the basis of measures by Nicholson, van Maanen, and Willis of the Mt. Wilson Observatory.

The second satellite has a sidereal period of 359ᵈ, the motion is direct in an orbit inclined 5° to the plane of the ecliptic, and its diameter is of the order of 300 km (200 miles). The eccentricity of its orbit, 0.79, is by far the largest known for any satellite. When nearest the planet, it is only about 1,300,000 km (730,000 miles) from it while at its farthest point it is nearly 11,000,000 km (7,000,000 miles) away. Another peculiarity of this satellite is that, although much farther from its primary, its motion is direct while that of the inner satellite is retrograde. In the cases of Jupiter and Saturn, it is the outer satellites which move in retrograde fashion while the inner ones move directly.

PLUTO

334. Discovery. The question of the possible existence of one or more planets beyond Neptune has engaged the attention of various astronomers such as Forbes, Gaillot, Lau, W. H. Pickering, and Lowell. The last especially made a very extensive investigation of the irregularities in the motion of Uranus, on the assumption that they were caused by the attraction of a distant planet.   He also inaugurated a telescopic search for such a body as early as 1905.   The search was continued intermittently by various members of the Lowell Observatory staff until, in January, 1930, a faint object of the fifteenth magnitude which appeared to satisfy the necessary conditions was found photographically by Tombaugh.   Continued observation confirmed the earlier impressions, and in March, 1930, its discovery was announced.

The method of search may be understood from Fig. 178, which shows portions of the two photographic plates on which Pluto was discovered. The two photographs, taken with a 13-in. star camera, are duplicates of

FIG. 178. Portions of the discovery plates of Pluto.   (A) Jan. 23, 1930; (B) Jan. 29, 1930.   The faint image of the new planet can be located by means of the arrows on the margin.   (*Lowell Observatory.*)

the same region of the sky taken 6 days apart.   The two plates, on being compared, in general showed the same stars, but one of the starlike points on plate A was missing on plate B, and vice versa.   The inference was that the object had moved from the one position to the other in the 6-day interval.   It was then carefully observed for some weeks until its slow motion gradually betrayed its character.

335. The Orbit, etc. After the computation of preliminary orbits, observers elsewhere searched plates taken in earlier years for images of the new planet and several such were found extending back to 1914.   On the basis of these and of later positions, various orbits were computed which are in substantial agreement.   They give the following approximate elements:

$a = 39.5$ AU

$e = 0.25$

$i = 17°$

$\Omega = 110°$

$\pi = 223°$

Period = 248 years

Perihelion passage in 1989

The planet is so small that it shows no appreciable disk. In consequence its diameter cannot be measured by the micrometer. From indirect measures made by Kuiper with the 200-in. Hale reflector the diameter of the planet is 5900 km (3700 miles) and its volume therefore 0.1 that of the earth.

The mass is uncertain. Wylie of Washington, making the assumption that certain irregularities in the motions of Uranus and Neptune could be explained by the presence of Pluto, found a value for the mass approximately equal to that of the earth. If we accept this value of the mass and combine it with the volume given above, the mean density becomes 10 times that of the earth or about 50 times that of water. While such a density is not impossible, it appears very improbable. It may be that the surface of Pluto does not reflect light diffusely like the other planets but more like a smooth surface. If this is the case, then optical measurements cannot give its true diameter. It may also be possible that there are other unknown planets which help produce irregularities in the motions of Uranus and Neptune, and therefore the mass found does not apply to Pluto alone.

Thus far there is no evidence of an atmosphere.

THE ZODIACAL LIGHT

336. In northern latitudes from about the middle of January to the middle of March there may be seen in the west after darkness falls a faint pyramid of light from 20° to 30° wide at the base and rising from 40° to 50° above the horizon. The axis of the light lies nearly in the ecliptic, which at this time of year is most nearly perpendicular to the western horizon in the early evening. The same phenomenon may be seen in the east before dawn during August, September, and October when the ecliptic is most nearly perpendicular to the eastern horizon before dawn. The light is strongest near the horizon and becomes fainter with increasing altitude. It is called the *zodiacal light* (Fig. 179).

In regions where the sky is especially free from dust and haze this light can be seen joining a faint band about 10° wide extending from the usually seen pyramid entirely across the sky. At a point opposite the sun the band increases considerably in brightness and width. This brighter region is known as the *counterglow* or *gegenschein*. Whether the gegenschein is really a part of the zodiacal light or not has not been fully determined, but the prevailing opinion favors the connection.

At certain latitudes, where the sun is just far enough below the northern horizon in the summer at midnight to eliminate twilight effects, the light can be traced along the northern horizon to a distance of 46° from the sun in a direction perpendicular to the ecliptic.

The simplest explanation of the phenomenon is that there is a certain amount of dispersed matter, possibly dust and larger fragments, in a lens-shaped region surrounding the sun.   Its greatest extent is near the plane of the ecliptic; it extends beyond the earth's orbit and its density diminishes with increasing distance from the sun.   This material would reflect some of the sunlight falling on it and present the general appear-

Fig. 179. The zodiacal light with star trails.   (*Yerkes Observatory.*)

ance described above.   This explanation is known as the *meteoric theory of the zodiacal light*.   It is confirmed by the observations of Wright in 1874, who found from 15 to 20 per cent of the light polarized, and by the spectrographic observations of Fath in 1909, who found the spectrum to resemble the spectrum of sunlight.   This has been confirmed by Slipher and by Moore.

No really satisfactory explanation of the gegenschein has been given on this hypothesis of the zodiacal light.   The one usually given is that the particles composing the zodiacal light are in "full" phase when opposite the sun and therefore reflect enough more light to produce the effect of the gegenschein. The problem deserves further study.

EXERCISES

1. What is the value of the solar constant for the planets from Jupiter to Pluto at the planets' mean distance from the sun?　　*Ans.* 0.072, 0.021, 0.005, 0.002, 0.001.

2. If the lag in transits of Jupiter's satellites were 22 min from opposition to conjunction, what would be the velocity of light?　*Ans.* 226,200 km or 140,550 miles per sec.

3. Observe some of the transits and eclipses of Jupiter's satellites through a telescope. Use the *American Ephemeris* data for suitable times.

4. If the inner satellite of Saturn, Mimas, has a period of 23^h and the sixth satellite, Titan, has a period of 15^d23^h, what is the ratio of their mean distances from Saturn?

Ans. 0.153.

5. If a new planet should be discovered with a sidereal period of 350 years, what would be its mean distance from the sun?　　　　　　　　　　　*Ans.* 49.7 AU.

CHAPTER 14

COMETS AND METEORS

COMETS

337. The members of the solar system which we have been considering thus far are characterized by orbits of moderate eccentricity which, for the most part, have small inclinations to the plane of the ecliptic. They are also bodies of spherical or nearly spherical shape and of considerable density.

The comets which occasionally appear are very different from the planets and seem to resemble them only to the extent that they move under the influence of the sun's gravitation.

338. Designation of Comets. The comets discovered in any one year are provisionally designated by letter, *a*, *b*, *c*, etc., in the order of discovery, together with the year number and the name of the discoverer. The comet discovered by Morehouse in September, 1908, was thus first known as "Comet 1908*d* (Morehouse)," as it was the fourth comet discovery of the year. If there are two independent discoverers, both names are used. After the orbits have been computed and the times of perihelion passage determined, they are numbered in the order of the time they came to perihelion. Comet 1908*d* accordingly became 1908III (Morehouse), since it was the third comet to pass perihelion in that year, although the fourth in order of discovery.

The greatest number of comets discovered in any year was 14, in 1947, so that the letters from *a* to *n* were used.

Sometimes it is not possible to determine the discoverer with exactness, and so the name is omitted. At other times the name given is not that of the discoverer but of some investigator who made a careful study of the comet, such as computing the orbit, etc. Thus in Sec. 345 it is stated that Messier discovered a comet in June, 1770, but it is called Lexell's comet, for the latter studied its orbit with care, found where it had been previous to discovery, where it went after it was lost to sight, etc. Other instances of this sort are Halley's comet and Encke's comet.

339. Appearance of Comets. When a comet is visible to the naked eye, there can be distinguished a bright and fairly well-defined head and a tail, which is merely a continuation of the head, whose brightness diminishes with increasing distance from the head.   At times the tail is only a degree or two in length, while at other times it extends to over 100°.

When the head of a large comet is examined with a telescope, it usually

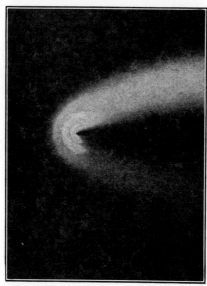

reveals a bright, almost starlike, center which is called the *nucleus*, and a fainter enveloping material which is called the *coma*.   At times the coma is seen to be composed of distinct layers of material, as shown in Fig. 180, which is a copy of one of Bond's drawings of Donati's comet in 1858.

The tail of a large comet is a most unsatisfactory telescopic object, as it is so large that only a small portion is in the field of view at any one time.

The modern method of photographing comets with special cameras of wide field has shown much structure in the tail which is invisible both to the unaided eye and through the telescope.

Fig. 180. The head of Donati's comet of 1858.   (*From a drawing by Bond.*)

The tails of large comets frequently show a dark stripe down the middle, although occasionally this central part is brighter than the adjacent portions of the tail.

340. Dimensions. Comets are the largest units of the solar system. The diameter of the head may vary from 29,000 km (18,000 miles), as in the Comet 1845V, to 1,840,000 km (1,150,000 miles) in the great comet of 1811.   The tails of some comets have exceeded 160,000,000 km (100,000,-000 miles) in length and in the great comet of 1843 the tail at one time measured 320,000,000 km (200,000,000 miles).

The nuclei of comets vary greatly in size.   In the case of two faint comets, 1927c (Pons-Winnecke) and 1930d (Schwassmann-Wachmann), which came near the earth, Baldet of the Meudon Observatory noted faint stellar nuclei.   On the assumption that their light was reflected sunlight and that their albedo was 0.1, he found the nuclei of these two comets to be only about 400 m (440 yd) in diameter.   At the other extreme is the nucleus of Comet 1845III which measured 13,000 km (8000 miles) in diameter, but in this case it is doubtful whether the object measured was the true nucleus.

341. General Changes in Comets. One of the most conspicuous changes which most comets undergo is the development of a tail. When at a considerable distance from the sun and visible only in the telescope, a comet does not appear to have a tail. As it approaches the sun, the tail[1] begins to form and increases in size until about the time of perihelion passage. Thereafter it becomes smaller and smaller until it disappears from view.

A second change occurs in the dimensions of the head. In this instance the head diminishes in size as perihelion is approached and increases in size after perihelion passage. The head of Encke's comet in 1838 had a diameter of about 450,000 km (280,000 miles) when about 200,000,000 km from the sun. Near perihelion, when its distance from the sun was a little over 50,000,000 km, the head shrank to a diameter of 5000 km. Other comets besides Encke's show similar changes in the dimensions of the head, although the changes may not be so great.

A third change occurs in the nucleus. This frequently varies in brightness in an irregular manner. Often a nucleus is not visible until the comet is near the sun, but this is not an invariable rule.

342. The Direction of the Tail. For the most part the tail of a comet is pointed away from the sun so that on approaching this body the tail follows the nucleus while on receding from the sun the tail precedes the nucleus. Occasionally, a comet may have more than one tail and the supplementary tails may make a considerable angle with the line pointing away from the sun. In Comets 1880VII, 1910I, and some others, one tail pointed toward the sun.

The general rule that a comet's tail is directed away from the sun indicates some influence which resides in the sun.

343. Orbits. Kepler supposed that comets move in practically straight lines and wander through space from star to star. Somewhat later it was assumed that the orbits were parabolic, and Doerfel showed this to be the case for the comet of 1681. After the announcement of Newton's law of gravitation and his development of a method to determine the elements of comet orbits, his friend, Halley, calculated the parabolic orbits of all comets whose observations were known to him. He found that at intervals of about 75 years a brilliant comet had appeared and the computed orbits were essentially alike. This led him to conclude that, in reality, he had to do with the same comet which moved in a long ellipse instead of a parabola and predicted that it would reappear in 1759. It came as predicted and has also been observed at the subsequent returns in 1835 and 1910. Halley therefore has the credit of being the first to find an elliptic orbit for a comet which has since then been known as Halley's.

[1] Some small comets never develop tails.

Since Halley's time many other elliptic orbits have been found and it has been shown that the number of elliptic orbits is roughly proportional to the length of time the comets have been observed, so that it is very probable that practically all orbits are elliptical. The periods thus far known range from 3.3 to over 1000 years.

A few comets have had hyperbolic orbits in the neighborhood of the sun, but calculations by Strömgren and others have shown that they were originally ellipses and had been changed to hyperbolas by the perturbations of the larger planets. Comet Morehouse (Sec. 360) belongs to this class. While under observation in 1908, its orbit was hyperbolic; but calculations by van Biesbroeck show that when it was beyond Pluto's orbit on its way to the sun, the orbit was a very eccentric ellipse.

We therefore conclude that comets are really members of the solar system just as much as the planets, except that, in general, their orbits are very elongated ellipses.

The reason for the difficulty in determining the exact orbital elements of comets lies in their great eccentricity. Most comets are not discovered until they are near both the sun and the earth, and after perihelion passage they cannot often be followed very much beyond the earth's orbit unless they happen to be favorably situated. The small portion of their total path which lies within the earth's orbit may be very much alike for a long ellipse, a parabola, or a hyperbola, and very exact observations extending over some months may be necessary to decide the type definitely. If such observations are not available, the difficulty is nearly insurmountable.

Short-period ellipses are comparatively easy to determine, but when the period extends beyond a few hundred years a real difficulty usually exists.

The perihelion distances of known comets range from about 5.51 AU for Comet 1925II (Schwassmann-Wachmann) to 0.005 for Comets 1843I and 1880I. Very few have perihelion distances exceeding 1.5.

The inclinations of the orbits have all values, but the number having inclinations of 90° or less is somewhat greater than those having inclinations between 90° and 180°.

Physical Considerations

344. Density. The fact that stars can be seen practically undimmed through the tail of a comet 1,000,000 km in diameter is strong evidence of the extreme tenuity of the material. Ten kilometers (6 miles) of air at sea-level density will show marked absorption effects; hence it is evident that the mean density of the tail is less than 0.00001 that of air at sea level. The denser portions of the coma are also quite transparent to starlight, and only the nucleus seems dense enough to obstruct much light. In 1910, when the head of Halley's comet passed between earth and sun, nothing could be seen projected against the sun's disk. In view of these considerations it is evident that the mean density of the average comet is extremely low. The only portion which may have an appreciable density is the nucleus, but no method of determining it has been devised.

345. Mass. At present we are compelled to attack this problem in a negative manner.

1. No effect of the presence of a comet has ever been detected by any perturbations in the movements of the planets. Biela's comet, Lexell's comet of 1770,* and some others have passed sufficiently near the earth to have their periods changed by some weeks, but the year was not affected in a measurable amount, that is, not even by as much as a second. Had their mass been as much as 0.00001 that of the earth, they would have produced appreciable effects on the earth's period.

2. The comet discovered by Messier in June, 1770, but since known as Lexell's comet, came very close to Jupiter in 1779, and Comet 1889V (Brooks) passed through the satellite system of Jupiter in 1886 without changing the satellite periods by a measurable amount. Lexell's comet was so strongly affected that it has never been observed since, and the orbit of Brooks' comet was greatly changed. The masses of these comets must, therefore, have been exceedingly small.

346. Spectrum. The spectrum is not simple. First there is a continuous background of two types, according to Bobrovnikoff. When near the sun, reflected sunlight with absorption lines is the dominant one of the two, while when at a distance of more than 0.7 AU from the sun, another type of continuous background, which may be due to the comet itself, is the more important.

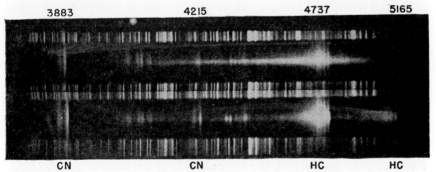

Fig. 181. (Top) spectrum of Comet 1915a (Mellish), May 9, 1915. (Bottom) spectrum of Comet 1914b (Zlatinsky), May 25, 1914. These show the usual bright bands of CN, HC, and some others yet unidentified. The CN bands are normal in Comet Zlatinsky but peculiarly narrow in Comet Mellish. (*Lick Observatory.*)

* This comet came within 1,500,000 miles of the earth, the closest approach on record.

Secondly, superposed on this background, is a spectrum of bright bands, one in the yellow, one in the green, and one in the blue (Fig. 181). This spectrum is identical with that of the blue flame of a bunsen burner. These bands appear to be due to carbon monoxide. Besides these there are some bands due to OH, NH, CN, CH, C_2, and other molecules. Occa-

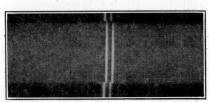

FIG. 182. Bright sodium lines in the spectrum of Skjellerup's comet, Dec. 19, 1927. The displacement of the lines corresponds to a positive velocity of 90 km per sec. (*Lowell Observatory.*)

sionally, bright sodium (Fig. 182) and magnesium lines are seen, and on one occasion there were thought to be some bright iron lines.

In general, the bright bands are much more intense when the comet is near the sun, and metallic lines are visible only near the time of perihelion. The brightness of the spectrum is subject to considerable variation. This variation may be caused by variation in the discharge of electrified particles from the sun as well as by variation in the amount of ultraviolet light given off by the sun.

347. Internal Motions. The layers of the coma as shown in Fig. 180 are not stationary. They appear to come from the sunward side of the nucleus as puffs of matter, possibly gaseous, directed toward the sun, which are then driven backward into the tail. Sometimes several of these puffs may be seen enveloping the nucleus and they are known as *envelopes*.

In other cases, as shown in Fig. 183 of Comet Morehouse, a very large amount of material is emitted from the nucleus to form a dense portion of the tail. This eruptive material then moves outward toward the end of the tail and finally is lost to view. Sometimes secondary tails develop and then disappear, only to be replaced by others.

The nucleus itself undergoes changes of shape and has been known to divide into a number of parts, as in Comet 1882II, and into two parts, as in Biela's comet in 1846. The latter comet actually divided into two complete individuals.

348. The Light of Comets. As stated in Sec. 346, some of the light of comets is merely sunlight reflected by solid particles, mostly dust, ejected from the nucleus, but the bright bands and lines in the spectrum come from self-luminous material likewise ejected from the nucleus. As the comet approaches the sun, the sunward side of the nucleus absorbs heat, and gaseous material within the nucleus is liberated. This gaseous material is then not only illuminated by the sun but absorbs solar energy, which is then reradiated in the cometary spectrum as bright lines and bands. The spectrum varies not only in different comets but also in different parts of the same comet.

349. Tail Formation. Many years ago Clerk-Maxwell predicted that light waves would exert pressure when they fell on a surface. This pressure was first observed by Lebedew in 1900, and a little later Nichols and Hull in this country were able not only to observe but also to measure it. Their measurements showed values agreeing very closely with the pressures calculated on theoretical grounds.

Light-pressure effects vary with the area of the particles involved while gravitational effects depend on the mass and therefore vary as the volume.

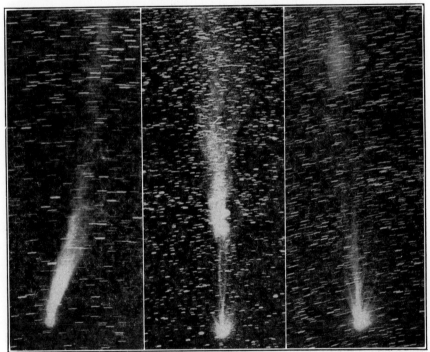

FIG. 183. Comet Morehouse, Sept. 30, Oct. 1 and 2, 1908, showing material being driven away from head of comet. (*Yerkes Observatory.*)

As particles get progressively smaller, the sun's light pressure decreases less rapidly than its gravitational effect until, at certain values for the diameter, the light pressure greatly exceeds gravitation. This does not continue indefinitely, however, for, if the particles are smaller than the wavelength of light, gravitation again assumes control. Particles the size of atoms and molecules are within the limits where light pressure predominates and, therefore, if released from the nucleus of a comet, will be driven away from the sun.

There is one other factor which must also be considered. Whenever the tail shows structure and individual parts can be recognized in a series of photographs, the motion of these parts away from the head is not uniform and the velocity is often much greater than could be produced wholly by light pressure. We seem compelled, therefore, to assume that other forces coming from the sun, possibly electromagnetic in character, play a part in tail formation and structure.

350. What Becomes of the Tail? From the way in which the material of the tail is driven away from the nucleus it is evident that it is finally lost to the comet. The tail of a comet may therefore be likened to the smoke from a locomotive which is continuously left behind. In consequence, the comet must be diminishing in mass and we would expect that a periodic comet, coming repeatedly into the neighborhood of the sun, would ultimately waste away. This has occurred in the case of some periodic comets.

351. The Nature of a Comet. The evidence presented thus far leads to the tentative conclusion that at least the coma and tail consist of very small particles, dust, and gases. The source of this material is the nucleus which could be a solid.

Whipple has developed a theory of the structure of a comet which may be summarized as follows: The nucleus of a comet is a mass of solidified gases such as CH_4, CO_2, NH_3, and H_2O, and meteoric material amounting to possibly one-third of the total mass. When this nucleus approaches perihelion, it absorbs solar energy which vaporizes the solidified gases on the surface. Under the action of the sun's light the gases dissociate into the substances found by the spectrograph (Sec. 346). Meteoric material is also released, but the mechanism is not clear. The nucleus is probably in slow rotation.

The loss of material from the nucleus at each perihelion passage reduces the mass until practically nothing is left and the comet disappears. Whipple estimates that the life of a short-period comet ranges from 3000 to 60,000 years and that the complete disintegration is at the rate of about three comets per century.

352. Comet Families. An investigation of the location of the orbits of the short-period comets shows a curious relationship to the orbit of Jupiter (see Fig. 184). In each instance the aphelion point of the orbit lies close to Jupiter's orbit. About 30 comets of this group are known, but authorities differ in their opinions in the cases of some comets which either have been observed only once or which apparently have been lost. Such a group of comets is referred to as a *comet family*.

Saturn, Uranus, and Neptune also possess comet families of one, two, and six members, respectively, if we accept Flammarion's grouping.

The usual explanation for the existence of such families is the so-called "capture" theory, which is as follows:

The usual orbit of a comet is a long ellipse. At one or more of its

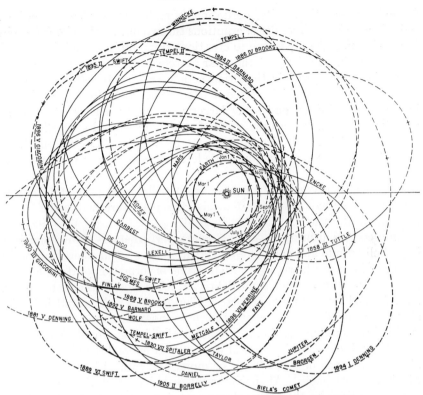

FIG. 184. Jupiter's comet family.   (*Popular Astronomy.*)

approaches to the sun it passed so near the planet that its motion was retarded and the orbit altered into a short-period ellipse.   Whether or not this explanation is the true one may still be a question.

353. Comet Groups. There are a number of instances on record where the orbits of several comets are so nearly alike that one may be justified in saying that several comets are moving in a single orbit.   These are called *comet groups.*

It is possible that the members of a group were once portions of a single comet which has been broken up by repeated approaches to the sun. Such a division has been seen to occur in the case of several small comets, but later the companion comets have either disappeared or the entire comet has been lost, so that the explanation remains merely a working hypothesis.

354. Origin of Comets. It is evident, from the material so far presented, that our knowledge of comets is almost as hazy as their general appearance.   The problem of their origin is still unsolved, but several theories have been suggested which may be summarized as follows:

1. Comets are the results of eruptions of matter thrown out by the sun.

2. Comets are the results of eruptions thrown out by the planets—thus Jupiter's comet family is due to eruptions from Jupiter, etc.

3. Some time in the past the solar system passed through a nebulous region in space—possibly the Orion nebula (Sec. 476). Here there is a considerable amount of dispersed matter, some in the form of gas, some in the form of dust, and some larger and denser masses. The sun's gravitational power captured some of this material and compelled it to revolve about the sun. From this material our comets were formed.

4. Comets represent certain debris left over after the formation of the planetary system.

This last theory seems to be the best available at present. In considering it we shall follow Oort in his Halley Lecture before the Royal Astronomical Society of London in 1951.

Since comets disintegrate and planetary perturbations throw some into hyperbolic orbits and therefore out of the solar system, there must be a source to keep up the supply. At the time of formation of the solar system there must have been some debris left after most of the material had been formed into sun and planets. The debris which moved in orbits about the sun of the same general form as those of the planets would be gradually swept up by them. Some of the debris would have highly eccentric orbits, and this material went out far beyond the planets, possibly to a distance of 100,000 AU or more, and formed into small units, which are our comets. At such extreme distances they would be subject to perturbations by the nearer stars; some would be turned outward and lost to the solar system and some would be turned back into even more eccentric orbits and returned to the sun. The picture as given by Oort is that there may be a swarm of about 10^{11} comets in a spherical space of about 150,000 AU radius about the sun. Most of these move in orbits about the sun which have such great perihelion distances that they are never observed, but a few come near enough to the sun that they can be seen from the earth and keep up the supply of observable comets. At present there is an approximate equilibrium between the number lost by disintegration and planetary perturbations and those influenced by stellar perturbations to come in from the swarm and pass near enough to the sun to be observed.

The great swarm or cloud of comets is estimated to have a total mass of only $\frac{1}{10}$ that of the earth so that the average comet has a mass of but $\frac{1}{10}^{12}$ that of the earth.[1]

[1] This may seem very small, but it still amounts to 6×10^9 metric tons. If the nucleus (which contains practically all the mass) is spherical and its density equal to the earth's mean density, its diameter is 1.3 km (0.8 mile). If the density is only about two times that of water, the diameter would be 1.8 km.

SOME REMARKABLE COMETS

355. Halley's Comet. As stated in Sec. 343, this comet is the first for which an elliptic orbit was calculated. After the publication of Newton's "Principia," in 1687, Halley was so impressed with the truth of the law of gravitation and its possibilities that he collected all available observations of comets and calculated parabolic orbits for 24 of them. This represented a great deal of labor, especially when we consider the relatively crude methods he had at his disposal. Upon comparing the ele-

FIG. 185. Halley's comet as photographed at the Lowell Observatory, May 13, 1910. The bright object near the head of the comet is the planet Venus.

ments obtained, he was struck with the similarity between those of the great comets of 1531, 1607, and 1682. He likewise found references to bright comets appearing in 1305, 1380, and 1456. With this material in hand he felt quite certain that in reality it was the same comet returning to the vicinity of the sun at intervals of about 75.5 years. He accordingly predicted the next return for late in 1758 or early in 1759. It was discovered on Christmas Day in 1758 and passed perihelion some months later. Since then it has been seen at the returns of 1835 and 1910.

While calculating the return for 1910, Cowell and Crommelin examined many ancient records and were able to trace back the comet's history with reasonable certainty to 240 B.C., and it is probable that it was also seen in 467 and 625 B.C. The interval between successive returns of the comet to the sun varies from 74.5 to 79 years owing to planetary perturbations, but it has not differed much from 75.5 years.

At perihelion the head of the comet is at a distance of 0.59 AU from the sun, but at aphelion the distance becomes 35.3, over five units beyond the orbit of Neptune.

The appearance of the comet, as seen by the author about the middle of May, 1910, in California, was as follows:

Shortly before dawn the head of the comet was just above the eastern horizon. Its diameter was about one-fourth of a degree. The tail was practically straight and stretched across the sky a distance of at least 130°, ending in the southwest quadrant. The tail gradually widened as its distance from the head increased until at the end it was about 12° in width. Near the head the tail was very bright (Fig. 185) but became fainter with increasing distance, until near the extremity it was about as bright as the fainter parts of the Milky Way.

356. The Great Comet of 1744. This comet was seen in the morning sky near the rising sun. Late in February two tails were noted, but after a week of cloudy weather in Europe there became visible a wonderful comet of six tails, each over 30° long. During this portion of the apparition the head was below the eastern horizon, so that the comet could not be seen as a whole, but even so the meager reports available show clearly that this must have been one of the most spectacular comets of all time.

357. The Great Comet of 1811. This comet was discovered in March, 1811, and last seen in August, 1812, an exceptionally long period for any comet. In the autumn of 1811 it was visible practically all night in northern latitudes because of its position far north of the celestial equator. The greatest length of tail was about 25° and its breadth about 6°. The actual maximum length of its tail was about 160,000,000 km (100,000,000 miles) and the diameter nearly 25,000,000 km (15,000,000 miles). The orbit computed by Argelander gave a period of slightly over 3000 years with an aphelion distance of about 65×10^9 km (40×10^9 miles), or 14 times the distance of Neptune.

358. The Great Comet of 1843.* This comet was first seen in the southern hemisphere late in February and became visible in North Temperate latitudes about the middle of March. The tail was about 40° in length, about 1° in width, and practically straight. The perihelion distance of this comet is the smallest on record, about 800,000 km (500,000 miles), so that the head was only a little over 100,000 km from the sun's surface as it swung round this body.

359. Biela's Comet. This comet should be classed as remarkable not on account of its size but because of its history. An Austrian officer named Biela discovered a faint comet on Feb. 27, 1826, which had a period of about 6.7 years and which soon proved to be one seen also in 1772 and 1805. A calculation showed that in 1832 the comet would pass within 30,000 km (20,000 miles) of the earth's orbit about a month before the earth reached the same point. The comet was seen on its return in 1832 but not the next time, in 1839, because its position was too near the sun as seen from the earth. On the next return it was first seen in November, 1845. In January, 1846, it began its remarkable changes by dividing into two parts, a brighter and a fainter comet. By March they had separated to a distance of 300,000 km. The fainter one could be followed for over 2 months and the brighter 3 months. In 1852 both comets were again seen, but then about 2,500,000 km apart. The return of 1859 was unfavorable like the one in 1839, so that special efforts were made to see them in 1866, but in vain. In 1872 the comets should have been most favorably situated for observation, but again the search was unrewarded, and they have never been seen since. On Nov. 27, 1872, when the comets should have been very near the earth, a shower of meteors was observed coming from the region of the sky where the comets should have appeared. Possibly these were the remnants of the disintegrating comet. The matter will be considered again in a later section.

360. Comet 1908III (Morehouse). This comet was discovered photographically by Morehouse at the Yerkes Observatory on Sept. 1, 1908. It presented many features which distinguished it from the ordinary comet. It was very bright photographically, although faint visually, as its light was predominantly from the blue region of the spectrum. The tail showed many changes and was often markedly different in the course of a few hours. Sometimes the tail was of the ordinary type and then an eruption of substances from the head would furnish material for a number

---

* The appearance of this comet aroused great interest in astronomy and led a group of public-spirited citizens of Boston and vicinity to raise a fund to purchase and house a 15-in. refractor for the Harvard Observatory. This telescope, although over a century old, is still in active use.

of streamerlike tails which appeared to have curves and twists. At other times a puff of material would leave the head and be driven backward along the tail. Changes of this character were frequent and of extraordinary interest as showing the complexity of cometary phenomena (Fig. 183).

FIG. 186. Comet 1910I as photographed at the Lowell Observatory, Jan. 28, 1910.

361. Comet 1910I. In January, 1910, a comet of exceptional brightness was discovered simultaneously by a number of persons in South Africa. It was so bright that for a short time it could be seen in full daylight near the sun with the unaided eye. A few days after discovery it became visible in the evening in the northern hemisphere and was a wonderful sight in the western sky (Fig. 186). It presented a broad and moderately curved tail nearly 40° in length, a shorter, narrower tail pointing in nearly the same direction as the main tail, and a very short tail, about a quarter of a degree in length, pointing directly toward the sun. Within a few weeks it became too faint to be seen with the unaided eye, but it could be followed telescopically until July of that year.

362. Comet 1925II. This comet was discovered photographically by Schwassmann and Wachmann of the Hamburg Observatory in November, 1927, over 2 years after it had passed perihelion. Its perihelion distance of 5.51 AU is the greatest known. The period is 16.2 years. Its entire orbit lies between the orbits of Jupiter and Saturn. Thus far the comet has been seen each year since discovery. Since aphelion occurred in 1933 it is the first case of observation at aphelion, and also of a comet which has been followed entirely around its orbit.

The comet is faint but shows remarkable fluctuations in brightness and appearance. Thus it has several times changed from 2- to 15-fold in brightness within a few days and Van Biesbroeck reports that it changed from a "very small and starlike object to a diffuse round coma 20″ in diameter with little indication of any nucleus" in 3 days.   In January, 1933, it increased in brightness from the seventeenth to the twelfth magnitude (an increase of 100-fold) in 2 weeks.

Since these peculiar changes have occurred when the comet was approximately 8 astronomical units from the sun, it seems probable that they are determined by causes residing in the comet rather than by any solar action.

METEORS

363. General Appearance. On any clear moonless night an observer may see an occasional swiftly moving point of light which remains visible

Fig. 187. A meteor photographed at the Yerkes Observatory, June 7, 1899.

for 1 or 2 sec and then vanishes (Fig. 187).   These vary in brightness from that of the full moon to the limit of visibility in a telescope.   They vary in color from a bluish white through white to yellow, green, and reddish.   The fastest moving are bluish white and the slowest are reddish.   Occasionally, they leave trains which endure from a second or two to an hour.   Such objects in general are known as shooting stars or *meteors*.

Occasionally, much larger bodies, often called *fireballs*, are seen, fragments of which reach the earth's surface.   There is reason for believing these to be different from the ordinary meteor or shooting star and they will be considered later under Meteorites.

364. Altitude and Velocity. If two observers, stationed from 15 to 50 km apart, observe the same meteor with reasonable accuracy, it is possible to determine the height and velocity in accordance with the principle illustrated in Fig. 188, where A and B are the observers and CD the path of the meteor. Observations of this character have been carried out many times. The altitude of the beginning of the meteor path varies from about 100 to 135 km (60 to 85 miles), of the end from about 60 to 80 km (40 to 50 miles). The paths are of the order of 100 km (60 miles) in length, and the velocity with respect to the earth ranges from about 25 to 70 km (15 to 45 miles) per sec.

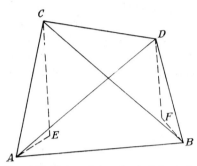

FIG. 188. Determining the height and velocity of a meteor by observers at A and B. Each determines the direction of the beginning and end of the meteor path and the time during which it is visible. From these data, and using the triangles involved, the heights CE and DF, the length of path CD, and the velocity are determined.

In the last few years Whipple has developed this method still further by substituting high-speed cameras for the two visual observers and photographing the meteor's path against the background of stars in the night sky. This method gives more accurate values of the positions of beginning and ending of the path. In addition the light from the meteor is interrupted by means of a rotating sector at the rate of about 20 times a second so that the photographed path consists of a series of short segments. By counting the number of breaks in the path the duration of the flight can be determined with far greater accuracy than by means of stopwatch or chronograph. Combining this time with the length of path gives the velocity with respect to the earth.

365. Luminosity. The high velocity of meteors explains their luminosity. When a small particle moving with high velocity strikes our upper atmosphere, great friction and air pressure result. This heats the surface to incandescence and the molten and vaporized material is stripped off as soon as formed. The degree of heat depends upon the initial velocity, the fastest ones becoming white-hot, while the slowest attain only a red heat.

The luminosity of the meteor train has been the subject of much study. Millman finds, from a study of meteor spectrograms, that air and meteor particles are ionized by the intense heat, and, when a recombination of the ions takes place, the energy released is radiated as light.

366. Mass. The disappearance of almost all meteors at considerable heights above the earth's surface indicates that they must be comparatively small particles of matter. All determinations of their mass rest upon certain assumptions which are difficult of proof, but it appears reasonable to assume that the largest of those ordinarily seen are not likely to weigh much over 1 g ($\frac{1}{30}$ oz) and the smallest must be mere grains of sand or specks of dust.

367. Probable Number. The number of meteors striking the earth's atmosphere daily is very great. A single observer may average about 10 per hour. Owing to the curvature of the earth's surface, the height at which they are observed, atmospheric absorption, and their brightness, it is not likely that any are visible to the unaided eye at distances over 500 km. Some years ago H. A. Newton of Yale estimated that from 15,000,000 to 20,000,000 bright enough to be seen with the naked eye enter the earth's atmosphere daily. Evidence is now accumulating that this number is too small. Poulter, of the Byrd Second Antarctic Expedition, 1934–1935, raises the number to one billion.

368. Radiants. Meteors may be seen at the rate of about 6 to 10 per hour on almost any good night in various parts of the sky, but at times a

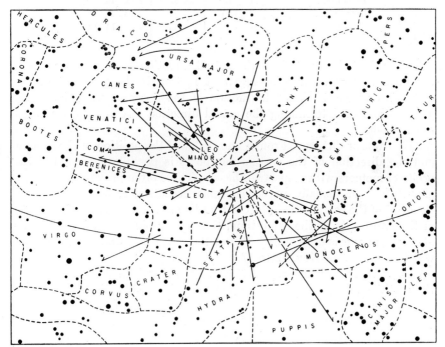

FIG. 189. Meteors observed at the Goodsell Observatory, Nov. 15, 1900. About two-thirds of them are seen to radiate from a small area in Leo.

much larger number may be observed. Such an increased number is designated a *meteor shower*. When the paths of the individual meteors of a shower are traced backward, it will be found that they intersect in a small area in the sky.   Such an area is known as a *radiant* and may be only a degree or two in diameter (Fig. 189).

Meteors are named according to the location of their radiants.   The Leonids come from a radiant in Leo, the Perseids from Perseus, etc.

Most of the meteor paths appear as straight lines coming from the radiant. The explanation of this appearance is that they are moving in parallel lines for which the radiant is merely the vanishing point. A few of the best-known radiants with the dates when they are most active, according to Denning, are the following:

TABLE V

| Name | Radiant | | Date |
	R.A.	Dec.	
Lyrids.............	270°	+33°	Apr. 20
Perseids............	45	+57	Aug. 11
Leonids.............	150	+22	Nov. 14–15
Geminids...........	111	+33	Dec. 11–12

The radiant does not show the actual direction in space from which the meteors come, since the apparent motion is the resultant of the meteor's own motion and the motion of the observer with the earth. The method of determining the actual direction lies beyond the scope of this book.

369. Meteor Orbits.   From a knowledge of the position of the radiant and the direction of the earth's motion it is possible to compute the orbits of meteors with respect to the sun. These often prove to be ellipses about the sun, usually of considerable eccentricity, and intersecting the orbit of the earth. When the earth and a meteor are at the intersection of the two orbits at the same time, the meteor plunges into the earth's atmosphere and is destroyed.   Figure 190 shows the orbit of the Leonids which appear from Nov. 12 to 17.

370. Meteor Velocities.   The velocity with which a meteor strikes the earth's atmosphere depends upon several factors which will now be considered. From Fig. 190 it is obvious that since earth and swarm are going in opposite directions around the sun the speed of the meteor with respect to the earth will be the *sum* of the orbital velocities. If, on the other hand, a meteor went around the sun in the same direction as the earth, then it would strike the earth only if it were moving faster than the earth and its speed with respect to the earth would be the *difference* between the orbital velocities. Head-on collisions occur on the morning side of the earth, overtaking collisions on the evening side.

The velocity of the meteor in its orbit depends upon the character of the orbit (Sec. 161). If the orbit is an ellipse, the greatest possible speed, at the earth's distance from the sun, is less than 42 km per sec; if it is equal to 42 km per sec, the orbit is a parabola, while if it is greater than this, it is a hyperbola. If the orbit is an ellipse, the meteor evidently belongs to the solar system, while if it is either parabola or hyperbola, it would be a visitor from outer space.

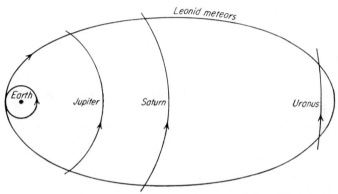

Fig. 190. The orbit of the Leonid meteors. The plane of the orbit is inclined 17° to the plane of the ecliptic.

Since 1946 the great radar station of the University of Manchester, England, has been adapted to a study of meteors. The pulses sent out from the transmitting station are reflected by the ions in the meteor path. By means of appropriate auxiliary apparatus not only the direction and distance of the meteor but also its velocity can be determined. An analysis of the radar velocities of nearly 12,000 meteors by McKinley does not show a single case of a definite hyperbolic velocity. We may therefore conclude that the meteors we see have been members of the solar system and are not coming in from interstellar space.

The radar method has a distinct advantage over the visual or photographic methods in that observations can be made by day as well as by night. This more than doubles the time available for observations.

371. Meteor Showers. When a swarm of meteors travels about the sun, each meteor has its own orbit, those nearer the sun moving faster than those farther away. The path of the densest portion of the swarm is the one to which the term "orbit of the swarm" is applied.

If the meteors are distributed quite evenly around the orbit, and if this orbit intersects the earth's orbit, a shower may be expected each year when the earth reaches the intersection of the two orbits; but if the meteors are grouped in a swarm, then a shower is possible only when both earth and swarm reach the intersection at the same time.

The best-known case of a swarm is that of the Leonid meteors. These were first especially noted on the night of Nov. 11 to 12, 1799, when many thousands were seen in the course of about 4 hr. In 1833 they again appeared, especially to North American observers. One observer states that during the height of the shower the meteors appeared "like a snow fall to the earth," and another estimates the rate after the maximum was past as about 10,000 per hour. In 1866, European observers saw a splendid display, although it was by no means equal to that of 1833. At Greenwich eight observers covered the sky and counted a total of 8000, with a maximum of 4860, between 1 and 2 o'clock in the morning. Great expectations were therefore aroused for the expected return in 1899, but the results were rather disappointing, as only comparatively few were seen. Better displays occurred in 1900 and 1901, but they were not remarkable. Perturbations by the larger planets seem to account for this.

Each year a few Leonids are seen, so that there must be some scattered all the way around the orbit in addition to the main swarm which completes its circuit in 33 years.

One of the most remarkable showers of meteors for nearly a century occurred on the evening of Oct. 9, 1933, for European observers. It lasted about 4 hr. During maximum activity Potsdam observers counted 5700 in 30 min, a group of four observers at Hamburg-Bergedorf counted 345 in 1 min, and Forbes-Bentley on the island of Malta reported 480 per minute. The range of brightness was from that of Venus down to the limit of visibility. By the time the radiant was above the horizon for American observers the shower was over.

Another very fine shower occurred on Oct. 9, 1946. It was known that the Pons-Winnecke comet would pass very near the earth about that time and observers were alerted to be on the lookout for a meteor shower. They were not disappointed, for, in spite of a full moon, many thousands were seen in a few hours.

372. Relation between Comets and Meteors. In 1866, Schiaparelli computed the orbit of the August meteors, the Perseids, and compared the elements with those of the bright comet seen 4 years previously, Comet 1862III. The similarity was striking. Shortly thereafter Leverrier found a marked similarity between the orbit elements of the Leonids and Comet 1866I. In 1867, Weiss found a third case in that of the Andromedes and Biela's comet, and a fourth in that of the Lyrids and Comet 1861I; various observers and computers from 1868 to 1910 gradually established a fifth for the Aquariids and Halley's comet; in 1916, Olivier and Denning independently found a sixth between the meteors from a radiant near η Ursae Majoris and the Pons-Winnecke comet; and the meteor shower of Oct. 9, 1933, has been connected with Comet 1900III.

Since that time several other cases have been found where the connection is reasonably certain. This connection may be stated as follows: In a number of cases comets and meteor swarms travel in essentially the same orbits about the sun. This indicates an intimate connection between the two which may throw considerable light on the nature of comets.

Biela's comet was seen in 1846 to break into two parts, which had separated about 2,500,000 km by 1852. The comet should have been seen in 1872 but was not, and has never been seen since. At about the time of closest approach in 1872, and again in 1892 when the comet should have been near the earth, fine meteor displays were observed coming from the region where the comet should have been. It therefore appears possible that the comet was broken up and the remnants appeared as meteors.

The numerous instances of the connection between comets and metors is gradually being accepted as the rule rather than the exception. It may be that all meteor swarms were originally constituent parts of comets, and, as in the case of the Leonids, comets of long ago still reveal themselves by their disintegration products.

METEORITES

373. Definition. From time to time large meteors are noted which strike the earth. They are sometimes called fireballs when seen in the sky. The portions which reach the earth's surface are called *meteorites*.

374. Phenomena of Fall. The usual events when such a large meteor is seen are as follows: First there is a brilliant flash of light which lasts as long as the meteor is visible but which may fluctuate in brightness. Sometimes it breaks into several parts. Frequently a luminous train is left which may persist upward of an hour and which will become bent and broken by the air currents encountered. If the fall occurs in the daytime, the train looks like smoke. Sounds like rolling thunder or the crackling of rifle fire, accompanied by explosions which may be violent enough to shake buildings, are usually heard. The color varies, like that of shooting stars, from a bluish white to a dull red.

The velocity with which the meteorite plunges into the outer atmosphere averages about 40 km (25 miles) per sec. Friction and air pressure against the forward part rapidly reduce the velocity so that luminous effects are not seen below an altitude of 15 km (10 miles). Sometimes the meteorites reach the earth's surface with sufficient velocity to bury themselves several feet in the earth,[1] while at other times they hardly dent the ground.

375. Meteorite Showers. In some instances only a single meteorite is found, while in others the number of individual pieces runs into the thousands. In the latter case most of the pieces are small. When the number is large, they are usually found over an elliptical area, the longer axis of which is in the direction of motion. This area was 16 miles long and 3 miles wide in the Khairpur fall of Sept. 23, 1873, in India. It is not impossible that the individuals of such a fall were separated before

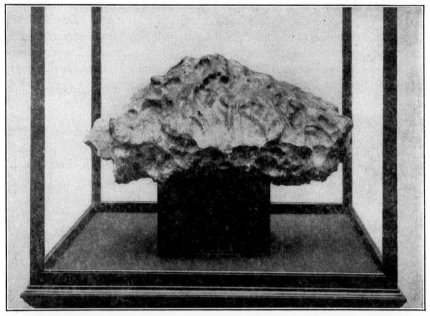

Fig. 191. A large iron meteorite from Quinn Canyon, near Tonopah, Nev., and now in the collection of the Field Museum, Chicago. Weight 1486 kg (3276 lb). Note the pitted surface and conical form which is characteristic of meteorites. (*Field Museum.*)

striking the earth's atmosphere, but in the light of our present knowledge it seems probable that in the majority of cases the disintegration occurred within the atmosphere.

376. Temperature. The temperature of the meteorite before it strikes the earth's atmosphere must be very low, possibly not far from absolute zero. The intense heating while passing through the air appears to be confined to the outer layers, the thin molten and vaporized layer being continuously stripped off by the rush of air. In the cases of many which

---

[1] The largest mass of the Estherville, Iowa, meteorite shower weighing over 180 kg (400 lb) buried itself 8 ft in a stiff clay soil. A depth of 11 ft was recorded in another fall.

were seen to fall and were immediately found, they could be handled easily. Other instances are known where they have fallen into stacks of hay or other inflammable materials without setting them on fire. Young states that one which fell in India in 1860 was found in moist earth, half an hour after its fall, coated with ice. If the passage through the atmosphere lasts but a few seconds, we would expect to find them comparatively cold, but if the duration of fall lasts for some minutes, the heat undoubtedly penetrates the mass.

377. Size and Weight of Meteorites. Meteorites vary in size from those of practically microscopic dimensions to those of the largest of the Cape York group of irons whose dimensions are about 1.5 × 2 × 3.3 m (5 × 7 × 11 ft) and of the Grootfontein (Southwest Africa) iron which measures 1.2 × 2.8 × 3.2 m (4 × 9 × 10 ft).

In weight they vary from a small fraction of a gram to 60,000 kg (66 tons) for the largest of the Cape York masses and the Grootfontein mass.

The largest meteorite seen to fall was the Norton County, Kans., stony mass which weighs about 900 kg (2000 lb). It fell on the afternoon of Feb. 18, 1948.

These weights are those of the recovered masses. The weight before encountering the atmosphere must have been considerably greater. The amount of matter stripped off in the case of a friable stony mass would be much greater than from an iron mass. Such material sometimes remains suspended in the air in the form of a cloud many cubic kilometers in volume. The cloud is no doubt composed of very fine dust.

378. Length of Path in Atmosphere. If the mass comes through the air practically perpendicularly to the surface of the earth, the path noted may be only about 100 km in length. If it comes in at an angle, however, the path may be much longer. The longest path on record is that of a group of meteorites which were first noted near Regina, Saskatchewan, at an altitude of 57 km (35 miles) and which were last seen from a ship in latitude −3°, longitude 32°.5 west, at a height of 23 km (14 miles). This path measured 9100 km (5650 miles).[1] The average velocity over the entire path was about 8 km (5 miles) per sec.

Some authorities have expressed doubts concerning the long path. The contention is that such a conspicuous group should have been seen by many more observers. Since observations are very few, it may be that the meteorites seen in Saskatchewan were not the same ones seen in the South Atlantic. If the objection is valid, the length of path may have to be reduced to less than half.

[1] See reports on this remarkable group of meteorites in *Journal Royal Astronomical Society Canada*, vol. 7, p. 145 (1913); and *Popular Astronomy*, vol. 30, p. 632 (1922); vol. 31, pp. 96, 443, 501 (1923).

379. Classification. Meteorites may be roughly divided into three classes: the iron meteorites, the stony-iron meteorites, and the stone meteorites. The one kind gradually merges into the other, but for practical purposes this simple division into three classes will answer. About 1500 meteorite falls are now known. Of this number less than one-half were seen to fall, the others being recognized by their general characteristics. Only a few of the approximately 500 meteorites seen to fall have been irons.

380. Composition and Structure. About 50 elements have thus far been detected in meteorites. Iron is the most important. This is

FIG. 192. Widmanstätten figures of the Shrewsbury, Pa., iron meteorite. (*Field Museum.*)

always alloyed with nickel and sometimes with other metals. In no case has a new chemical element been found, but minerals not known on the earth are found in many meteorites.

According to Merrill, the three classes have the following general composition:

Iron Meteorites. These consist essentially of an alloy of nickel-iron with iron phosphides and sulfides. When these meteorites are etched with dilute acid, they show a peculiar crystalline structure known as Widmanstätten figures (Fig. 192).

Stony-iron Meteorites. These consist of an extremely variable network or sponge of nickel-iron, the interstices of which are filled with silicate mineral (Fig. 193).

Stony Meteorites. These consist essentially of silicate minerals with minor amounts of metallic alloys and sulfides.

Fig. 193. Section of a portion of the Admire, Kans., stony-iron meteorite from the Goodsell Observatory collection. The light part is nickel-iron. Embedded in this are the dark crystalline masses. Illustration about one-half size of original.

Figure 194 shows an enlargement of a portion of the Homestead meteorite. The material is seen to be fragmented and the fragments cemented together. This type of structure is characteristic of most stony meteorites.

When a fragment of a meteorite is heated, it gives off a number of gases. Those commonly found are hydrogen, nitrogen, carbon monoxide, carbon dioxide, and methane.

381. Meteor Craters. In central Arizona there is a crater formation having a diameter of over 1 km and a depth of about 170 m (Fig. 195). The rim rises from 40 to 50 m above the level of the plateau. In the vicinity of this crater thousands of masses of meteoric iron have been found. They range in weight from a fraction of a gram to 460 kg (1000 lb). From all the evidence available it seems reasonably

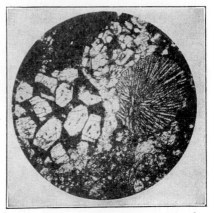

Fig. 194. An enlargement ($\times 44$) of a portion of the Homestead, Iowa, stony meteorite. The material is seen to be fragmented and the fragments cemented together. This type of structure is characteristic of many stony meteorites. (*Field Museum.*)

ably certain that the crater was formed by the impact of a meteoric mass possibly 150 m in diameter. This mass is believed to be buried under the southern wall, and attempts are being made to reach it. The fragments found around the crater are probably fragments of the main mass.

On June 30, 1908, some meteoric masses probably fell in central Siberia forming craters from 10 to 50 m in diameter and causing serious devastation over an area of 60 km (40 miles) radius. No meteoritic matter has been recovered as yet.

FIG. 195. An airplane view of Meteor Crater in Arizona taken from the west. *(Official photograph, U.S. Army Air Corps.)*

Meteoritic iron has been found near a craterlike formation near Odessa, Texas, and near a series of craters in central Australia. There is also a series of craters on the island of Oesel in Esthonia bearing a marked resemblance to these others.

Another large crater has been found in northern Quebec. It is about 3 km (2 miles) in diameter and 435 m (1350 ft) in depth. An expedition in 1951 found evidence, by geophysical prospecting techniques, of a heavy mass underneath the rim. No meteoritic material was found, but, from the evidence submitted, it appears probable that this crater, named Ungava Crater, should be added to the list of meteor craters.

From the evidence we must conclude that at times quite large masses of meteoritic material fall to the earth and cause some destruction. The only fall which can be dated is the one in Siberia. The others may have occurred from hundreds to many thousands of years ago.

382. Age of Meteorites. The age of meteorites has been the subject of study by Paneth, Evans, and others. The methods used, which need not be described here, are similar to those used to determine the age of rocks on the earth. From all the evidence available, meteorites range in age as do the earth's oldest rocks. None have been found whose age exceeds 3×10^9 years, the generally accepted value for the approximate age of the earth. We are probably not far from the truth when we assert that meteorites are of about the same age as the earth.

It has been assumed that the age of iron meteorites could be computed from the amount of helium, uranium, and thorium they contain. Large helium content appears only in small meteorites while large meteorites have only small helium content. This is contrary to what would be expected if appreciable leakage had occurred. The more promising explanation as advocated by C. A. Bauer is that the helium is the result of bombardment of the meteorite while still in interplanetary space by cosmic rays (Sec. 490) producing disintegrations of which alpha particles (helium nuclei) are a product. Comparing helium content with mass of meteorite shows that cosmic radiation is sufficient to account for all helium.

383. Origin of Meteorites. This problem is still far from solution. Analyses show clearly that, however formed, they were formed where there was neither free oxygen nor water. The simplest theory is as follows:

Asteroids of appreciable size have approximately the same structure as the earth, namely, rocky surface layers, deeper layers containing mixtures of rocky material and metals, and finally a central core consisting largely of metallic material. If two asteroids, in following their orbits around the sun, should collide, they might easily be broken into fragments. These fragments would be the meteorites—the stony ones coming from the surface layers, the stony-iron ones from the intermediate layers, and the iron ones from the central parts.

Nininger does not object to the theory as a start but argues that a collision would produce so much heat that the fragments would be reduced to a molten, or at least to a semimolten condition. These would cool rapidly and begin their separate journeys around the sun. Any of them having perihelion distances near that of Mercury or less would be subject to reheating and gradual change from merely solidified material to a crystalline structure such as shown by most meteorites. One perihelion passage might produce slight change, but many such trips could produce the present structure.

Harrison Brown has attacked the problem of origin by the application of thermodynamics to the distribution of the chemical elements in meteorites. His conclusion is that our meteorites were at one time part of a planet, roughly the size of Mars, disrupted by an unknown course of events.

The fact that meteorites are the only materials to reach us from regions beyond the earth is ample reason to justify our making every possible effort to learn more about them.

EXERCISES

1. If a comet had a period of 1000 years and its orbit had an eccentricity of 0.9, what would be its perihelion and aphelion distances from the sun?

Ans. 10 and 190 AU.

2. If the total number of meteors seen by a group of observers at a single station averaged 30 per hour, and they saw all meteors within a radius of 300 km, how many meteors would probably fall over the entire earth in 24 hr? *Ans.* 1,300,000.

3. If the field of vision for European observers of the meteor shower of Oct. 9, 1933, had a radius of 100 km, and, at the maximum of the shower 500 meteors per minute could be counted at a single station, what would be the average separation of the meteors if the earth cut across the swarm so that the velocity of the meteors with respect to the earth was 40 km per sec? *Ans.* Approximately 50 km (30 miles).

CHAPTER 15

THE STARS

384. The Constellations. It is evident to anyone observing the night sky that the brighter stars can be formed into groups which facilitate the identification of the individual stars. The ancients did this, too, many thousands of years ago, associating various groups of stars with their deities and heroes. Such groups of stars are called *constellations*.

At the present time about 88 constellations are recognized. Of this number 48 have come down to us from the time of Ptolemy (second century A.D.). The remaining 40 are largely modern and are found, for the most part, in the southern heavens, which were below the horizon of Alexandria where Ptolemy lived.

A knowledge of the constellations, including the names of the brightest stars, is desirable on the part of every student of astronomy. It is also a source of great pleasure to many who may not otherwise be interested in the subject.

385. The Zodiacal Constellations. These constellations are the principal ones crossed by the zodiac. In order, they are Aries, Taurus, Gemini, Cancer, Leo, Virgo, Libra, Scorpius, Sagittarius, Capricornus, Aquarius, and Pisces. Sun, moon, and planets are therefore usually found within the borders of these 12 constellations.

386. Designation of Stars. The ancients, in general, designated stars by their positions in the constellation figures, such as "the star in the head of the preceding of the twins," "the star in the heart of the lion," etc. Besides this, they gave special names to hundreds of stars, the same star sometimes having more than one name. At the present time three methods are used: names, Bayer's letters and Flamsteed's numbers, and catalog numbers.

387. Star Names. From 25 to 30 names of stars are in common use. These as well as others only infrequently used have come down to us from the Greeks, Romans, and Arabs. For the most part these names refer to the brightest stars, such as Sirius, Canopus, Vega, Arcturus, but in a few instances they refer to relatively faint stars which are of special interest, such as Alcor and Merope.

388. The Bayer and Flamsteed Systems of Star Designation. In 1603, Bayer of Augsburg published what is usually considered as the first star atlas of general value. He arranged the stars in each constellation roughly in the order of brightness, and assigned to them the various letters of the Greek alphabet. Thus α Arietis is the brightest star of Aries, β Arietis the second brightest, etc. In some cases this arrangement was not followed, as, for example, in Ursa Major, where the letters were assigned in the order of the stars beginning at the front of the bowl of the Big Dipper

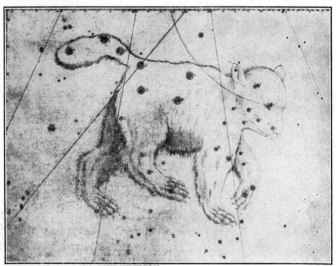

FIG. 196. The constellation of Ursa Major from Bayer's Uranometria.

and out along the handle (Fig. 196). Then the other stars in the constellation were lettered. When the Greek alphabet did not suffice, he used the letters of the Roman alphabet in order.

About a century later, Flamsteed, England's first Astronomer Royal at Greenwich, numbered the approximately 3000 stars he had observed according to constellations. At the present time we combine the two systems in that we use the Bayer letter when possible. If a star has no Bayer letter but has a Flamsteed number, the number is used.

The letter or number of the star is combined with the genitive form of the constellation name in order to designate the star completely. Thus, α Orionis means α of Orion, etc.

389. Catalog Number. Many catalogs of stars are now in existence, the stars being numbered according to the plan on which the catalog is constructed. Thus Boss 1234 is the star numbered 1234 in Boss's Preliminary General Catalog, and A. G. Washington 673 is the star numbered 673 in the portion of the catalog of the Astronomische Gesellschaft observed at the Naval Observatory, Washington, D.C.

The brighter stars occur in many catalogs, in Bayer's atlas, and also have special names.   One star may therefore have quite a variety of designations.   The one to be chosen in any instance will depend upon the conditions involved.

390. Star Atlases and Charts. Following the atlas of Bayer there have been many others.   Some give only the brighter stars, while others give all of them to the limit of naked-eye visibility.   Atlases, in general, are for constellation study and the identification of naked-eye (sometimes

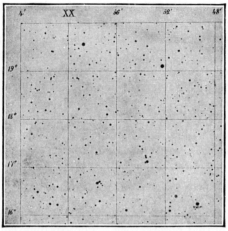

Fig. 197. Small portion of one of the Bonn Durchmusterung charts.   Scale two-thirds original scale.   (*Bonn Observatory.*)

called *lucid*) stars.   Among the best of the modern ones may be mentioned those of Klein, Norton, Schurig, and Upton.

Star charts, in general, are for the observing astronomer and show telescopic as well as the brighter stars.   Some cover only portions of the sky, such as the Paris or Peters' Ecliptic Charts; others give only small isolated regions, like Hagen's Variable Star Charts; while others cover a large portion of the sky, such as the Bonn Durchmusterung Charts, or the complete sky, such as the Franklin-Adams Charts, or the great project of the Astrographic Chart (Carte du Ciel).

Bonn Durchmusterung Charts. These charts, 40 in number, show all stars to the ninth magnitude, and many still fainter, from the north celestial pole to 2°S of the celestial equator on a scale of 1° to 2 cm ($\frac{3}{4}$ in.). They were published by Argelander of Bonn from 1857 to 1863.   Over 300,000 stars are shown.   The star positions were first obtained by visual observations with a small telescope and the charts engraved afterward. The charts (Fig. 197) represent an enormous amount of work and are still of great value.

Some years later Schoenfeld continued the series of charts to declination 23°S, so that the BD[1] covers practically all the sky visible at latitude 45°N.

Franklin-Adams Charts. These charts, 206 in number, are photographic reproductions, on a scale of 1° to 15 mm (0.6 in.), of photographs covering the entire sky taken by the late Franklin-Adams of England. Each chart is a little over 15° square and shows stars down to the seventeenth magnitude, about the limit of visibility in the great Lick and Yerkes refractors. The photographs were taken with a 25-cm (10-in.) lens, especially designed for the purpose, with exposures of about 2 hr.

Astrographic Charts. In 1887, an international astronomical conference was called at Paris to consider photographing the entire heavens on a most elaborate scale. It was decided to use photographic refractors of about 34-cm (13.5-in.) aperture and 3.4 m (11.2 ft) focal length. The work was divided among 18 observatories scattered over most of the world. Each was to photograph about 1200 regions of the sky, each region being photographed twice, and then have charts made showing the stars thus photographed. The great project is not yet complete, although it has been pushed with considerable vigor and most of the plates have been taken. There is a possibility that the great chart with its millions of stars may never be completed because of the great expense involved in its publication.

Mt. Wilson–Palomar Charts. In 1954 there was completed a survey of the heavens which could be reached from Mt. Palomar with the 48-in. Schmidt camera of that observatory. Photographic copies of this survey will be available soon. The limiting magnitude will be considerably beyond that of the Franklin-Adams Charts. It is hoped that in time the survey will be completed to the south celestial pole. This will require the removal of the camera to a suitable location in the Southern Hemisphere.

391. Star Catalogs. A star catalog is a list of stars together with their positions, usually in right ascension and declination, their magnitudes and such other information as may be desired. Some catalogs contain approximate positions of many stars, while others give accurate positions of a relatively small number. A few of the important catalogs with brief descriptions follow:

The Almagest. This is the earliest star catalog of which we have copies. It was made by Ptolemy of Alexandria about A.D. 138 and contains the longitudes and latitudes of 1028 stars together with the constellations in which they are located.

The Bonn Durchmusterung. The charts made from this catalog were mentioned in the preceding section. The catalog itself is printed in four volumes and gives the approximate positions of nearly 460,000 stars between the north celestial pole and declination 23°S.

[1] The Bonn Durchmusterung is abbreviated either to BD or DM.

The Cape Photographic Durchmusterung. The purpose of this undertaking was to continue the work of Argelander and Schoenfeld to the south celestial pole. Instead of making visual observations, however, Gill, the director of the Cape Observatory at Capetown, South Africa, elected to photograph the sky with a camera of large size, 15-cm (6-in.) aperture, and then determine the star positions by measuring the plates. The plates were actually measured by Kapteyn of the University of Groningen, Holland, so that the work represents a cooperative enterprise. Work was begun in 1885 and the final results published in 1899. The catalog, in three large volumes, gives the approximate right ascensions and declinations of nearly 455,000 stars between declination 18°S and the south celestial pole.

Rutherfurd of New York had demonstrated the value of photography in the study of star groups as early as 1865, but Gill's work, 20 years later, marked the beginning of stellar photography on an extensive scale.

Astrographic Catalog. This catalog is a part of the international undertaking referred to in the preceding section, being undertaken after Gill had shown the success of the photographic method. In addition to the plates taken for the chart, others of shorter exposure were to be taken on which the positions of the stars were to be measured with accuracy and a great catalog of stars provided. This catalog will ultimately be completed and give accurate positions and magnitudes of between eight and ten million stars over the entire sky.

392. Stellar Spectra. Various classifications of stellar spectra have been used. The first was the work of Secchi at Rome who observed visually. Another system resembling Secchi's was developed by Vogel of Potsdam. The system now used almost exclusively was developed at Harvard by E. C. Pickering and his assistants while studying the photographic spectra of over 10,000 stars. The results of this study were published in 1890 under the title "The Draper Catalog of Stellar Spectra." In this work the spectra were grouped according to their appearance and letters from A to Q were assigned to the various groups. Further study has shown that some of the groups were not necessary and certain considerations to be stated later led to some change in the order of the letters.

Over 99 per cent of all stars classified according to spectral type fall into six classes as follows: B, A, F, G, K, and M. The six classes grade continuously one into another. This fact is reflected in the further division of each spectral type into 10 subdivisions numbered 0 through 9. The characteristics of these various classes will be stated briefly; and one star named whose spectrum may be considered typical for the class.

B. Helium stars. Continuous background with most prominent absorption lines belonging to helium and hydrogen. It is important to realize that the term "helium star" means that the helium lines are prominent, but not necessarily that helium is an abnormally abundant element in the star. The class differences arise primarily from temperature differences, not differences of composition (δ Orionis).

A. Hydrogen stars. Most prominent absorption lines belong to hydrogen (Sirius).

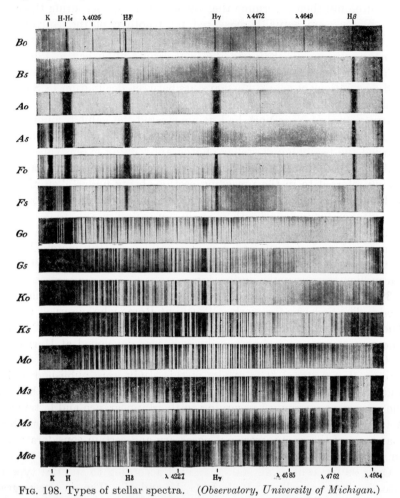

Fig. 198. Types of stellar spectra. (*Observatory, University of Michigan.*)

F. Calcium stars. H and K lines of calcium most prominent. Hydrogen lines next in prominence (δ Aquilae).

G. Solar stars. H and K lines of calcium most prominent. Hydrogen lines no longer prominent. Many metallic lines (sun).

K. Calcium lines still very prominent. Many metallic lines. Intensity of continuous spectrum decreases rapidly toward violet end (Arcturus).

M. Calcium lines remain prominent. Absorption bands appear in green and blue regions. Violet end very weak (α Orionis).

Figure 198 shows the appearance of these types of spectra, with subdivisions listed for many cases.

Additional spectral classes are frequently used, such as class O. O-type stars, which are very rare, precede the B-type stars in the above listing, and fall into two groups: the one shows bright bands due to hydrogen, helium, and some other elements; and the other shows absorption lines of the same substances. The stars of the first group are often called Wolf-Rayet stars, because the first examples were discovered by Wolf and Rayet. The second group are known as the *absorption* O-type stars (γ Velorum, ι Orionis).

Astronomers also recognize today R-type and N-type stars, but they do not fit into a continuous gradation with the principal stars, and they

Fig. 199. Spectrum of B-type star, ζ Tauri, showing a remarkably fine series of hydrogen absorption lines. (*Observatory, University of Michigan.*)

occur in negligible proportion among the naked-eye stars. Even within the sequence from B through M, stars are frequently found whose spectra show abnormalities peculiar to themselves. For example, the last of the M-type stars shown in Fig. 198, M6e, has the added letter e. This indicates that there are bright emission lines in the spectrum. These can be seen at Hδ and Hγ.

393. Stellar Temperatures. The colors of the stars, from the O-type and B-type through the M-type, grade continuously from blue-white through reddish stars. With the color changes go gradual changes in temperature from very hot stars at the beginning of the sequence to relatively cool stars at the end. Obviously the order of a spectral classification scheme is physically important since it divides stars into a series with a continuous graduation of temperature and, as we shall see, of other physical characteristics.

Table VI gives the approximate surface temperatures and visual colors corresponding to the various types of stars.

Some stars of even lower surface temperature are known. N-type stars, for example, are sometimes no hotter than 2000°. The faint companion of ε Aurigae has a surface temperature estimated at only 1700°. Stars like this cease to be visible to the eye and can be detected only by means of infrared detectors. It is thus quite possible that substantial numbers of invisible low-temperature stars exist.

Not only are color and temperature directly related to spectral type, but so also is the intrinsic luminosity of the stars. The brightest stars are those at the top of the sequence, and the faintest those at the bottom, with some important and interesting exceptions. Furthermore, it is quite likely that spectral type has an important bearing on the evolution of stars.

TABLE VI

Type	Degrees K	Apparent color
O	25,000–50,000	Blue-white
B	25,000	Blue-white
A	11,000	White
F	7,500	Yellow-white
G	6,000	Yellow
K	4,500	Orange
M	3,500	Red

Deep down in the stellar interiors, theoretical research indicates, the temperatures of stars rise to very high values. The surface temperature, though closely related to spectral type, tells us little about the internal temperature of stars.

394. The Distances of the Stars. It had been the dream of Sir William Herschel and of astronomers before him to determine the distances of some of the stars, but all their efforts were in vain. About 1838, however, Bessel at Koenigsberg, Struve at Dorpat, and Henderson at the Cape of Good Hope succeeded in determining the distances of 61 Cygni, Vega, and α Centauri, respectively.

The principle underlying the method employed by Bessel and Struve is still in use and will now be considered. On the average, the fainter

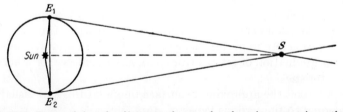

FIG. 200. Determining the distance of a star by the trigonometric method.

stars are farther away than the brighter ones. As a consequence of the earth's revolution about the sun, a star which is comparatively near us would appear to change its position in the sky with reference to fainter and more distant stars. Thus, in Fig. 200, the star S would shift its position by the angle $E_1 S E_2$ with respect to very distant stars lying in the same general direction, as the earth moved from E_1 to E_2 in the course of 6 months. This displacement would give the value of the angle E_1SE_2 and, knowing the distance E_1E_2 to be 300,000,000 km, the distance from sun to star can be determined.

Bessel, Struve, and their successors used an instrument called a *heliometer* for the measurement of the angular displacement of the star under consideration with respect to faint stars in the same field of view. The modern method consists in taking photographs of the star field at about 6-month intervals and measuring the displacement with respect to the faintest stars on the plate.

395. Stellar Parallax. In Fig. 200 the angle E_1S-*Sun*, the angle subtended at the star by the radius of the earth's orbit, is called the *parallax* of the star. The largest parallax known, $0''.76$, belongs to an eleventh-magnitude star about $2°.2$ distant from α Centauri. There is some evidence that the two stars are physically connected.

Parallaxes determined by the displacement method are called *trigonometric parallaxes*. It should be noted that these parallaxes are always relative to much fainter stars of unknown but presumably much greater distance. The parallaxes thus found are always too small by the amount of the mean parallax of the reference stars, but thus far no wholly satisfactory method has been devised to correct for this.

396. Units of Distance. If a star were 206,265 times the sun's distance from us, its parallax would be exactly $1''$. The distance has come to be used as a unit of distance and has been given the name of *parsec*.

Another unit in common use is the *light-year*, the distance light travels in 1 year in a vacuum. This is equal approximately to 6×10^{12} miles. One parsec is equal to 3.26 light-years.

397. Values of Stellar Distances. Table VII gives a list of stars, compiled by van de Kamp, whose distances from the sun do not exceed 5 parsecs. Various other data concerning these stars are also included.

398. Stellar Rotation. The lines in the spectra of some stars are found to be very sharp; in others they are very broad. The spectra of most stars have lines between these extremes. The width of a spectral line which is determined by various causes involved in the physical conditions under which the line is produced need not be considered here, but the effect of rotation and the application of Doppler's principle to line width is of great interest.

Fig. 201. A rotating star with rotation axis pointing toward observer.

Let us assume a star to be rotating about an axis which is directed toward the observer (Fig. 201). The various parts of the surface move across the line of sight, they maintain the same distance, and therefore

TABLE VII

STARS NEARER THAN 5 PARSECS

No.	Name	Visual magnitude	Spectrum	Distance in light-years	Abs. vis. mag.	Visual luminosity
1	Sun	−26.9	G0		4.7	1.0
2	α Centauri A	0.3	G0	4.29	4.7	1.0
3	α Centauri B	1.7	K5	4.29	6.1	0.28
4	α Centauri C	11	M	4.29	15.4	0.000052
5	Barnard's star	9.5	M5	5.98	13.2	0.0004
6	Wolf 359	13.5	M8	7.74	16.6	0.000017
7	Luyten 726-8 A	12.5	M6	7.9	15.6	0.00004
8	Luyten 726-8 B	13.0	M6	7.9	16.1	0.00003
9	Lalande 21185	7.5	M2	8.2	10.5	0.0048
10	Sirius A	−1.6	A0	8.7	1.3	23
11	Sirius B	7.1	A5	8.7	10.0	0.008
12	Ross 154	10.6	M6	9.3	13.3	0.00036
13	Ross 248	12.2	M6	10.3	14.7	0.0001
14	ε Eridani	3.8	K2	10.8	6.2	0.25
15	Ross 128	11.1	M5	10.9	13.5	0.0003
16	61 Cygni A	5.6	K3	11.1	7.9	0.052
17	61 Cygni B	6.3	K5	11.1	8.6	0.028
18	Luyten 789-6	12.2	M7	11.2	14.5	0.00012
19	Procyon A	0.5	F5	11.3	2.8	5.8
20	Procyon B	10.8	. . .	11.3	13.1	0.00044
21	ε Indi	4.7	K5	11.4	7.0	0.12
22	Σ 2398 A	8.9	M4	11.6	11.1	0.0028
23	Σ 2398 B	9.7	M4	11.6	11.9	0.0013
24	Groombridge 34 A	8.1	M2	11.7	10.3	0.0058
25	Groombridge 34 B	10.9	M5	11.7	13.1	0.00044
26	τ Ceti	3.6	K0	11.8	5.8	0.36
27	Lacaille 9352	7.2	M0	11.9	9.4	0.013
28	BD + 5°1688	10.1	M4	12.4	12.2	0.001
29	Lacaille 8760	6.6	M0	12.8	8.6	0.028
30	Kapteyn's star	9.2	M0	13.0	11.2	0.0025
31	Krüger 60 A	9.9	M4	13.1	11.9	0.0013
32	Krüger 60 B	11.4	M6	13.1	13.4	0.00033
33	Ross 614	10.9	M7	13.1	12.9	0.00052
34	BD − 12° 4523	10.0	M5	13.4	11.9	0.0013
35	van Maanen's star	12.3	G	13.8	14.2	0.00016
36	Wolf 424 A	12.6	M4	14.6	14.3	0.00014
37	Wolf 424 B	12.6	M4	14.6	14.3	0.00014
38	Groombridge 1618	6.8	K6	14.7	8.5	0.03
39	CD − 37° 15492	8.6	M4	14.9	10.3	0.0058
40	CD − 46° 11540	9.7	M4	15.3	11.3	0.0023
41	BD + 20° 2465	9.5	M5	15.4	11.1	0.0028
42	CD − 44° 11909	11.2	M5	15.6	12.8	0.00058
43	CD − 49° 13515	9.0	M3	15.6	10.6	0.0044
44	AOe 17415-6	9.1	M4	15.8	10.7	0.004
45	Ross 780	10.2	M5	15.8	11.8	0.0014
46	Lalande 25372	8.6	M1	15.9	10.2	0.0063
47	CC 658	11.0	. . .	16.0	12.5	0.0008
48	o² Eridani A	4.5	G5	16.3	6.0	0.3
49	o² Eridani B	9.2	A	16.3	10.7	0.004
50	o² Eridani C	11.0	M6	16.3	12.5	0.0008
51	70 Ophiuchi A	4.2	K1	16.4	5.7	0.4
52	70 Ophiuchi B	5.9	K5	16.4	7.4	0.083
53	Altair	0.9	A5	16.5	2.4	8.3
54	BD + 43° 4305	10.2	M5	16.5	11.7	0.0016
55	AC + 79° 3888	11.0	M5	16.6	12.5	0.0008

have no effect on a spectral line because of motion. The lines in the spectrum will be narrow.

Let us now consider the case of a star rotating about an axis perpendicular to the line of sight and in the direction indicated by the arrow (Fig. 202). Consider now three small equal areas of the surface along the equator at a, b, and c. The area a will be approaching the observer, and any part of a particular absorption line which it forms will be shifted toward the blue, a', the part depending on c will be shifted toward the red, c', while the part depending on b will occupy the central undeviated part of the line b'. Other parts of the surface will be responsible for other parts of the line. Integrating the effects over the entire surface of the star will produce a spectral line with the outline shown by the dotted line. It is evident that the greater the rotational velocity, the greater will be the shift of a' and c' from the center of the line, or the greater the rotational velocity, the wider the line. The width of the line will be proportional to the equatorial velocity and therefore a measure of this velocity. Equatorial velocities as high as 500 km per sec (300 miles per sec) have been observed.

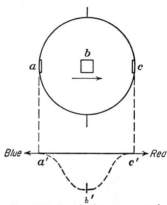

Fig. 202. A rotating star seen in a direction perpendicular to the rotation axis. Equal areas of star's surface, a, b, and c, and their part in forming a single absorption line of the star's spectrum.

399. Star Magnitudes. In Ptolemy's Almagest the stars were divided into six groups according to their brightness. The brightest stars, like Sirius, Aldebaran, and Altair, were called first-magnitude stars and the faintest stars seen with the naked eye were classed as of the sixth magnitude. Stars of intermediate brightness were given as of the second, third, fourth, and fifth magnitudes. Ptolemy's magnitudes were used for more than 1500 years.

The great revival of observational astronomy at the time of Sir William Herschel resulted in considerable confusion as regards star magnitudes, each observer having his own magnitude scale which adhered more or less closely to the general scheme of Ptolemy for naked-eye stars, but which became greatly confused when applied to telescopic stars. Various observers of the nineteenth century, among whom may be mentioned Heis and Argelander of Germany, Pogson and Pritchard of England, and Gould of this country, helped to bring some order out of this chaos. The most important work, however, was done by Pickering at Harvard and the observers at Potsdam. By means of carefully made instruments and observations, these two institutions established scales of magnitude of high precision. The Harvard scale is now universally used for visual work, and, with some necessary modifications, for photographic magnitudes as well.

The magnitude of a star as seen in the sky is known as its *apparent visual magnitude*.

400. Relation between Brightness and Magnitude. Experiments on the part of several observers about the middle of the nineteenth century showed that the magnitude scale was not an arithmetical but a geometrical series of brightness. Observers had somewhat different values for the ratio of the brightness of one magnitude to the next but all were found to be using a ratio not far from 2.5. Pogson thereupon suggested that this ratio be taken as 2.512, so that a first-magnitude star would be precisely 100 times brighter than a sixth-magnitude star for $(2.512)^5 = 100$. This suggestion was adopted. Hence when we say that a certain star is one magnitude brighter than another, we mean it is 2.512 times brighter, while if it is two magnitudes brighter, it is $(2.512)^2$ times brighter, etc. This value of 2.512 is called the *magnitude ratio* or *light ratio*.

401. Fractional Magnitudes. Most stars do not fall at exactly integral values on the magnitude scale. It is therefore necessary to recognize

TABLE VIII

Magnitude difference	Ratio of brightness	Magnitude difference	Ratio of brightness
0.5	1.6	4	39.8
1.0	2.5	5	100
1.5	4.0	10	10,000
2.0	6.3	15	1,000,000
3.0	15.8	20	100,000,000

fractional magnitudes as well. Thus, if a star appears to be halfway between a second- and a third-magnitude star in brightness, it is said to be of magnitude 2.5. If somewhat nearer the second-magnitude star, it may be of magnitude 2.2 or 2.3, while if nearer the fainter star, it may be of magnitude 2.7 or 2.8. A tenth of a magnitude is a difference just perceptible to a trained observer. By means of visual photometers it is possible to measure a difference of about one-tenth of a magnitude, while with the photoelectric photometer even one one-hundredth of a magnitude difference can be determined.

In Table VIII difference of magnitude and ratio of brightness are compared.

402. Negative Magnitudes. On the Harvard scale Altair has a magnitude of 0.9, Aldebaran 1.1, Castor 2.0, Alpha Ursae Majoris 2.0, Delta

Ursae Majoris 3.4. These stars may be used as standards for visual comparisons. There are, however, stars, such as Vega and Sirius, which are brighter than Altair. In order to have the magnitude scale continuous, it is necessary to recognize both zero and negative values. Thus Vega, which is 0.8 magnitude brighter than Altair, has a magnitude of 0.1, and Sirius, which is 2.5 magnitudes brighter than Altair, is of magnitude -1.6. Continuing the scale to still brighter objects, it is found that the sun has a magnitude of about -26.9.

403. Relation between Apparent Magnitude and Distance. According to a well-known law of physics, the brightness of a light varies inversely as the square of the distance. Thus, a light moved to double its original distance appears only one-fourth as bright, to 5 times the distance one twenty-fifth as bright, to 10 times the distance one one-hundredth as bright, etc. This law may be expressed by a simple formula,

$$I = \frac{1}{d^2}$$

where I is the intensity in terms of the brightness at unit distance and d the distance to which it may be removed. Solving the equation for d, we find $d = 1/\sqrt{I}$.

Let us now determine the necessary change in the distance of a star in order to reduce its brightness by one magnitude. If B_1 and D_1 represent original brightness and distance, while B_2 and D_2 represent the new values, respectively, then, since $B_1 = 2.512B_2$, we may write

$$\frac{B_1}{B_2} = \frac{2.512B_2}{B_2} = \frac{D_2{}^2}{D_1{}^2}$$

whence

$$D_2{}^2 = 2.512D_1{}^2$$

or

$$D_2 = 1.585D_1$$

Therefore, in order to decrease the brightness of a star by one magnitude, its distance must be increased to 1.585 times its original distance.

To reduce its brightness two magnitudes it would have to be removed to $(1.585)^2$ times its original distance, and to reduce it five magnitudes it would have to be removed to $(1.585)^5 = 10$ times the distance. This last result may also be stated thus: To make a star appear five magnitudes fainter requires its removal to 10 times its original distance. At 10 times the distance it would be only one one-hundredth as bright, which agrees with the table of Sec. 401, which says that a star of any magnitude is 100 times as bright as one five magnitudes fainter.

In general

$$\frac{D_{m+n}}{D_m} = (1.585)^n$$

where D_m is the distance when the star's magnitude is m and D_{m+n} is the distance when the brightness has been changed n magnitudes because of change in distance.

404. Photographic Magnitude. When photography was applied to the stars, it soon became evident that stars like α Orionis or α Scorpii, which appear to the eye to be among the brightest in the sky, appeared relatively much fainter on the photographs, while others, in turn, which appeared comparatively faint to the eye, were much brighter photographically. The reason for this lies in the fact that the eye measures brightness largely in the yellow-green region of the spectrum, while the ordinary photographic plate is most sensitive to light in the deep blue.

It became necessary, therefore, to establish a system of magnitudes based on photographic results which are known as *photographic magnitudes*. The same light ratio of 2.512 was kept. By agreement the visual and photographic magnitude scales were assumed to agree for stars of spectral class A0 and visual magnitude 6.0.

405. Photoelectric Magnitudes. The photoelectric cell, and its modern astronomical successor the photomultiplier tube, are electronic devices which, when used with the appropriate accessories, convert the light from stars into electric currents. The currents, in turn, can be accurately measured. Modern photoelectric photometers permit the most highly refined determinations of stellar magnitudes. Photoelectric photometers are often used with different color filters. From such measures star colors can be computed.

406. Color Index. Stars of B type are brighter photographically than visually while stars from A1 to M are brighter visually than photographically. The difference between the visual and photographic magnitudes of a star is called its *color index* and is taken in the sense

$$C.I. = Ph. - V.$$

The B-type stars, accordingly, have negative color indexes while those from A1 to M have positive values.

The color index varies from -0.3 for a B0 star to $+1.5$ for a late M star.

407. Photovisual Magnitudes. It has been found possible to photograph the stars and obtain quite closely their relative visual magnitudes by the use of photographic emulsions sensitive to yellow and green light, whose blue sensitivity has been reduced by appropriate color filters. Magnitudes obtained in this manner are called *photovisual* magnitudes.

408. Absolute Magnitude. The apparent magnitudes of the stars vary from -1.6 for Sirius to about $+22.5$ for the faintest stars which have been photographed. The apparent magnitude of a star depends upon its intrinsic brightness and upon its distance. For many investigations a knowledge of the intrinsic brightness is of importance and the term *absolute magnitude* has been introduced to denote it. The absolute magnitude of a star is defined as its apparent magnitude if at a distance of 10 parsecs. On this basis the absolute magnitude of the sun is $+4.7$ and a star of absolute magnitude -0.3 is $(2.512)^5 = 100$ times as bright as the sun, while one of absolute magnitude $+9.7$ would be only one one-hundredth as bright as our luminary.

Some stars are known of absolute magnitude brighter than -5, while the faintest at present known has an absolute magnitude of $+19.5$. This range in brightness represents intensities exceeding the ratio 6,000,000,000 : 1.

409. Spectroscopic Parallaxes. A careful study of the relative intensities of certain pairs of lines in the spectra of many stars has shown that the relative intensity varies with the absolute magnitude of the star. The relation thus established was so close that it is now being used with marked success as a measure of the absolute magnitude. Knowing also the apparent magnitude of the star, its parallax follows (Sec. 410).

The spectroscopic parallax method was developed at the Mt. Wilson Observatory by Adams and Kohlschütter. It is now being used at several other observatories as well and is by far the most rapid method of parallax determination. Already several thousand parallaxes determined by this method have been published.

410. Modulus of Distance. If we know the apparent magnitude and the distance of a star, it is evident that we can calculate its absolute magnitude. A formula frequently used is

$$5 \log \pi = M - m - 5$$

where π is the parallax of the star, M its absolute, and m its apparent magnitude.

If we wish to employ the distance instead of its reciprocal (parallax), we can use the formula

$$\text{Distance in parsecs} = 10(1.585)^{m-M}$$

The exponent $(m - M)$ is called the *modulus of the distance* or *distance modulus*. We shall have occasion to use it from time to time in later chapters.

411. The Hertzsprung-Russell Diagram. In about 1910 H. N. Russell and E. Hertzsprung independently noticed an interesting trend in the absolute magnitudes of stars of different colors. Shortly later, Russell presented a series of diagrams that showed the essential features of what we now call the Hertzsprung-Russell diagram, or simply the H-R diagram. In the diagram, which plots the absolute magnitudes of stars against their temperature (or spectral class), there are two main concentrations

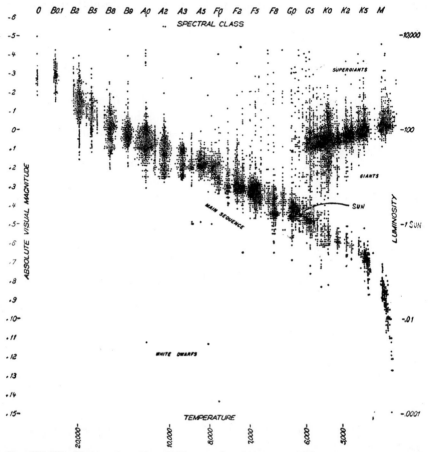

Fig. 203. The Hertzsprung-Russell diagram for 6700 stars within easy range of modern telescopes. (*Lund Observatory, Sweden.*)

of stars, as shown in Fig. 203. The thinner band, running from the upper left of the diagram to the lower right, is known as the main or dwarf sequence; the compact swarm above the main sequence on the right is the giant branch. At the lower left are a few dots corresponding to remarkable white-dwarf stars. These white dwarfs are small, dense, and hot stars like the companion of Sirius, whose mass is only 15 per cent less than that of the sun, even though it is only 1/400 as luminous.

412. Stellar Populations. The H-R diagram as shown in Fig. 203 is a mixture of stars from all possible sources. Baade has shown that if we plot the diagram and pay attention to the various sources, two kinds of diagram emerge. If we take the stars in the neighborhood of the sun or the stars in the spiral arms of distant galaxies (Chap. 21), we derive a diagram like the dotted parts of Fig. 204, while if we take the stars of the

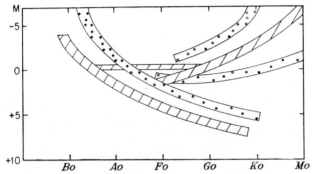

Fig. 204. The H-R diagram showing the regions occupied by stars of populations I (dotted) and II (shaded), according to Pecker.

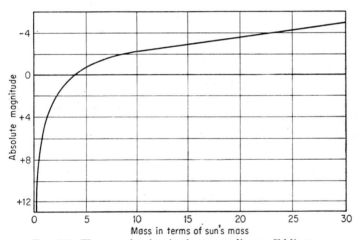

Fig. 205. The mass-luminosity law according to Eddington.

globular clusters (Secs. 463ff.) or the central parts of distant galaxies, we have an H-R diagram like the shaded sections of Fig. 204. The first group is called *population I* and the second group *population II*. We shall have occasion to consider some characteristics of the two populations later.

413. The Mass-luminosity Law. A second important relationship involving the absolute magnitudes of the stars was presented in 1924 when Eddington published a curve relating the mass of a star to the amount of energy radiated by it. The relationship covers a range of absolute magnitude between −4 and +13 and a range of mass from about $\frac{1}{6}$ to 30 times the sun's mass. A comparison of the curve (Fig. 205), which was based on theoretical considerations, with the absolute magnitudes and masses of known stars shows the difference between the observed and the calculated values to be very small. We therefore appear to have a definite physical relationship established between the mass of a star and its luminosity which will enable us to calculate the one if the other is known. From the curve we read the following absolute magnitudes: 10, 5, 0, −4. These correspond to the masses 0.3, 0.7, 3.4, 23, respectively, times the sun's mass.

The most remarkable thing about this relationship is that the same curve applies not only to the giant branch but also to the dwarf branch. The white dwarfs alone violate the rule. The relationship, coupled with the H-R diagram shows that the stars that slip down the main sequence and become red dwarfs must do so with a corresponding loss of mass, whereas stars in the giant branch must maintain a reasonably constant mass. These facts are of greatest significance in theoretical understanding of the internal physics of stars.

The star of least mass known is Krüger 60B, with a mass 0.14 that of the sun. No stars are known whose mass is as great as 100 times the sun's mass. The total range in mass is therefore very small, possibly of the order of 500 to 1. If we disregard a very few exceptional stars, the range is more nearly 50 to 1.

414. Total Number and Light of the Stars. An investigation by Sears and van Rhijn shows that the total number of stars to the twenty-first magnitude is approximately one billion. They found no satisfactory way of determining the limiting magnitude of the stars or their total number, but a theoretical investigation indicates the latter to be of the order of 3×10^{10}.

The same investigators also find the total light of all the stars in the sky is equivalent to 1076 stars of magnitude 1.0. The uncertainty in the total number does not affect this value greatly, as the stars to magnitude 21 furnish 98 per cent of the total light.

415. Diameters of Stars. For many years the only knowledge we had of the dimensions of stars, except the sun, was obtained from the eclipsing variable stars (Sec. 439). These binary systems gave values ranging from about 0.8 to 10 times the sun's diameter for the diameters of the components. Direct visual observation of stellar diameters seemed forever hopeless, for the angular diameter of the spurious disk of a star in the great 254-cm (100-in.) telescope of the Mt. Wilson Observatory is between $0''.04$ and $0''.05$ and a star would have to show a disk nearly double this value to be certainly recognizable, and no star is near enough to do this.

The realization that there are giant stars had led Eddington, Russell, and Wilsing to calculate the diameters of some of these from theoretical considerations. Their computed values for Betelgeuse were 0″.051, 0″.031, and 0″.039, respectively.

Long ago Michelson had suggested a method of determining the diameters of Jupiter's satellites by interference methods and he had tried this as an experiment at the Lick Observatory in 1891. When the predictions mentioned above were made, Michelson believed it possible to try the same method on the stars. After some experimenting at the Yerkes Observatory he went to Mt. Wilson, and, with the help available there, an interferometer[1] 6 m (20 ft) long was built to be used with the 254-cm telescope. In December, 1920, Pease of this observatory was successful in measuring the diameter of Betelgeuse. His result was 0″.046, in remarkable agreement with the predicted values, considering the difficulties of the problem. Using the mean of the measured parallaxes for this star, the diameter becomes 420,000,000 km (260,000,000 miles). The diameter has since been found to vary between the limits given in the table. The diameters of several other giant stars have been measured. These are given in Table IX.

TABLE IX

Star	Diameter (in millions)		Diameter (sun = 1)
	Kilometers	Miles	
Arcturus...........	38	23	27
Aldebaran..........	53	33	38
β Pegasi...........	56	35	40
Betelgeuse..........	290–420	180–260	210–300
Mira..............	350	220	250
α Herculis..........	550	350	400
Antares............	630	390	450
ε Aurigae..........	3900	2400	2800[1]

[1] This value for ε Aurigae was not obtained by the interferometer but by a study of the light and velocity curves.

This great achievement naturally led to a desire to measure the diameters of other stars, but the difficulties were great. A larger instrument (Fig. 206) was consequently built at Mt. Wilson Observatory.

The greatest number of estimates of stellar diameters come, however, from the method of comparing the star's total luminosity with its lumi-

[1] The theory of instrument and method is too complicated for this book. A simple explanation will be found in *Popular Astronomy*, vol. 29, p. 189, and a more elaborate one in the *Astrophysical Journal*, vol. 51, p. 257.

nosity per unit area, which in turn comes from estimation of the star's effective temperature from its observed color.   The method is not very accurate but can be applied to a great many stars for which other methods are unavailable.

FIG. 206. The 50-ft interferometer of the Mt. Wilson Observatory for measuring diameters of stars.   It might be called a special telescope of 18 ft focal length and 50 ft in diameter.

STELLAR MOTIONS

416. Radial Motions. In the study of stellar spectra it is found that the star lines are usually displaced with reference to those of the comparison spectrum, either toward the red or toward the blue.   According to the Doppler principle, this implies motion between the observer and the star in the line of sight.   We know, of course, that the observer with his instrument is moving with the earth around the sun at an average velocity of 30 km (18.5 miles) per sec.   By allowing for the component of the earth's motion which is in the direction of the star (this is called the *reduction to the sun*), the remainder of the motion indicated by the displacement of the lines in the spectrum of the star represents the motion of the star with respect to the sun.   This velocity in the line of sight is called *radial velocity* and is usually referred to the sun.

Radial velocity is given a positive sign if the distance from the sun is increasing and a negative sign if the distance is decreasing.   Radial velocities of stars from $+339$ km to -309 km ($+211$ to -192 miles) per sec have been observed. The spectrograph, however, shows only that component of a star's real motion which is in the line of sight. It gives no information whatever concerning any crosswise component.

417. Proper Motion. As stated in Sec. 391, Ptolemy's Almagest contained the longitudes and latitudes of over 1000 stars. The date of this

FIG. 207. Proper motions of stars in Ursa Major. At the end of 100,000 years the stars will have moved to the points of the arrows.

catalog was about A.D. 138. In 1718, Halley found that, after allowing for the change in longitude caused by the precession of the equinoxes, there were some stars whose longitudes and latitudes differed from those given by Ptolemy. This meant that they had changed their positions with respect to the stars as a whole. Such a motion, which is *across* the line of sight, is known as *proper motion*.

Since Halley's time a great deal of work has been done on the positions of stars and we now know the proper motions of thousands of stars with some degree of accuracy.

If we could again live on the earth 100,000 years hence and look toward that portion of the sky in which we are now accustomed to see the Big Dipper, the well-known figure would be gone. Figure 207 shows it as it appears now, while 100,000 years hence the stars, because of proper motion, will occupy the positions of the heads of the arrows to which they are connected. Other stars would also be found to have changed their

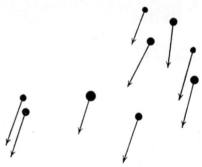

FIG. 208. Proper motions of stars in the Pleiades. At the end of 20,000 years the stars will have moved to the points of the arrows.

relative positions, but the little group of the Pleiades (Fig. 208) would still appear as it does now, for the stars of this group are moving together along practically parallel lines. Groups like the Pleiades are said to have common proper motion.

418. Methods of Determining Proper Motion. If we know the right ascension and declination of a star for two dates, such as 1850 and 1950, the two positions will not be the same because of precession, nutation, aberration, and proper motion. By computing the corrections due to the first three and applying them to the position for 1850, we obtain the "1850 position reduced to 1950." The amount by which the reduced position differs from observed position for 1950 will be the proper motion in the 100-year interval.

Another method of finding the larger proper motions is also available since celestial photography has become general. If we compare two plates taken of the same region with a considerable interval of time between them, it is possible to determine which stars have moved with respect to the entire group photographed (Fig. 209).

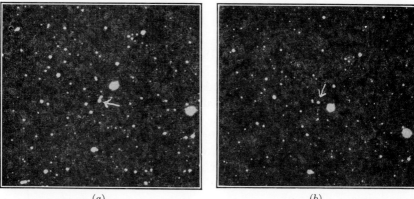

(a)   (b)

Fig. 209. Barnard's proper-motion star. (a) Aug. 24, 1894; (b) May 30, 1916. (*Lick and Yerkes Observatories, respectively.*)

419. Amount of Proper Motion. Proper motion is usually expressed in seconds of arc per year or per century. For most of the stars it is exceedingly small. Only one star with a proper motion of more than 10″ per year is known (Fig. 209). It was discovered by Barnard at the Yerkes Observatory in 1916 in the constellation Ophiuchus. In this case the motion amounts to 10″.3 a year. The vast majority of stars showing any proper motion move less than 1″ a year.

In general, the brighter the star, the greater its proper motion, because the brighter stars as a class are nearer than the fainter ones and would therefore betray their motion most readily.

If Newton's law of gravitation holds throughout the universe, then every star is subject to the gravitational attraction of every other. Since it is highly improbable that for any star the resultant of the attraction of all the stars should have been zero at the beginning, and continued so up to the present time, we would expect all stars to be moving more or less with respect to the others. Theoretically, therefore, stars, in general,

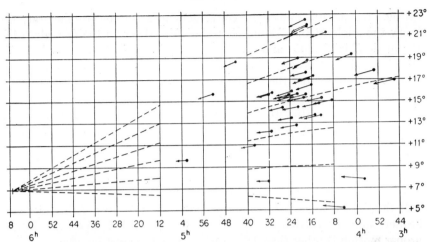

FIG. 210. Moving cluster in Taurus. The arrows indicate the proper motions for 50,000 years. (*Astronomical Journal.*)

should show some proper motion (and radial motion as well), but since most of them are very remote, the proper motions of only the nearer ones have been detected in the comparatively short time since accurate observations have been possible.

420. The Moving Cluster in Taurus. In 1909, Lewis Boss announced the discovery of a group of stars in Taurus which had common proper motions. Figure 210 is a copy of his diagram. He found 39 stars distributed over an area about 15° square, whose proper motions, when projected forward, converged toward a single point in the sky. The explanation is that the stars are moving in parallel lines and the convergent is the vanishing point of the parallel lines.

In such a cluster there is a method of determining its distance if we can get the radial velocity of one or more of its stars. The method is as follows:

In Fig. 211 let O be the observer, who, for the sake of simplifying the problem, is assumed stationary in space; S the star of the group whose radial motion has been determined; SA the direction and amount of the star's motion in space; and OC a line drawn to the convergent of the group. Since the convergent is the vanishing point for parallel lines, OC will be parallel to SA. Resolve the motion SA into two components, BA parallel to the line of sight, and SB perpendicular to it. BA will give the radial velocity and SB will give the proper motion,

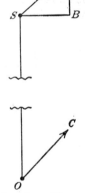

FIG. 211. Diagram illustrating principle of determining the distance of a star in a moving cluster if proper motion, radial velocity, and convergent are known.

Since OC points toward the convergent and OS toward the star, we know the angle SOC. Assume it to be 45°. Then in the triangle SAB the angle S is also 45° and AB is equal to SB. After determining the radial velocity, we know the velocity along SB will be equal to it.

Assume further that the proper motion in the direction SB amounts to $1''$ a year. Then the distance SO will be 206,265 times the annual motion in the direction SB. By multiplying the observed radial velocity, expressed in kilometers per second, by the number of seconds in a year and this product by 206,265, we have the distance in kilometers.

When the distance to one star of the cluster has been determined, the distances of the others follow easily since these are approximately inversely proportional to the proper motions of the stars.

If the right triangle SAB is not isosceles, the relations of the sides can be determined by trigonometry, since the angle S is known.[1] If the proper motion is other than $1''$, a different factor must be used.

By a process analogous to this, and using more recent values for the radial velocities than Boss had available, H. C. Wilson found the center of the Taurus cluster to be at a distance of 131 light-years and the diameter of the cluster to be 54 light-years. The luminosities of its stars vary from 5 to 100 times the luminosity of the sun.

A number of clusters of a similar character are known.

421. The Sun's Motion. 1. *The Proper-motion Method.* Since our sun is one of the stars, we would expect it to be in motion like the others. If we are in a grove of trees and move toward some part of the grove, the trees in that direction appear to be moving *apart*, those on either side to move in a direction opposite to our own, and those behind us to move closer *together*.

In a similar manner the analysis of the proper motions of the stars has shown that in one part of the sky their general tendency is to move *apart*, in the opposite part of the sky to move closer *together*, while in the region between they appear to be streaming past. The simplest explanation of this phenomenon is that the sun is moving toward that part of the heavens where the stars are separating. From the investigations of Lewis Boss on the proper motions of over 5000 stars, the sun is moving toward a point in the sky whose position is R.A. = 18^h02^m, Dec. = $+34°.3$, not far from the bright star Vega.

2. *The Radial-velocity Method.* Let us return to the illustration of the grove of trees. The trees toward which we are moving would be *approaching* us, those behind would be *receding*, while those on the sides would be neither approaching nor receding. An investigation by Campbell and Moore of the Lick Observatory on the radial velocities of over 2100 stars shows precisely this general effect. In one part of the sky the stars on

---

[1] Angle $S = 90°$ − angle SOC.

the whole are approaching, in the opposite part they are receding, while in the region between they are, on the average, doing neither. The point toward which the sun is moving as determined by the Lick observers is in R.A. = 18^{h}02^m, Dec. = +29°.2, in good agreement with the position determined by Boss from the proper motions.

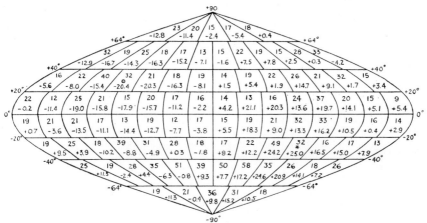

FIG. 212. Distribution of radial velocities. (*Lick Observatory.*)

The sun's motion through space is called the *sun's way* and the point toward which it is moving is termed the *apex of the sun's way.* The velocity of the sun's motion as determined by Campbell and Moore is 19.6 km (12.2 miles) per sec.

Figure 212 shows this material in graphical form. The figure represents the entire sky. Each area has two numbers in it; the upper is the number of stars in the area and the lower the mean radial velocity. It is readily seen that the large negative velocities cluster around the apex of the sun's way and the large positive velocities cluster around the antapex.

422. Parallactic and Peculiar Motions. Since the sun is moving among the stars, it is evident that a part of the proper motion as observed must be caused by the sun's motion. We must therefore separate the component due to the sun from the observed proper motions in order to study

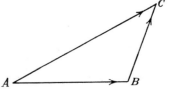

FIG. 213. Relation of proper motion, *AC*, parallactic motion, *AB*, and peculiar motion, *BC.*

the motions of the stars among themselves. That component of the proper motion which results from the sun's motion is called the *parallactic motion,* and the component which represents the star's own motion is called its *peculiar motion.*

The relation of the three kinds of motion is shown in Fig. 213. If *AC* represents the direction and amount of the proper motion and AB the parallactic motion, then BC will represent the direction and amount of the peculiar motion. To reduce the peculiar motion to velocity it is necessary to know the star's distance.

423. Radial Motions and Spectral Class. Campbell and Moore found that after subtracting the effect of the solar motion from the observed radial velocities of over 2100 stars, a most interesting relationship existed between these velocities and the spectral type of the stars. This result in tabular form is as shown in Table X.

TABLE X

Spectral class	Number of stars	Average radial velocity, km per sec
B	284	8.7
A	500	9.9
F	199	12.5
G	244	14.8
K	687	15.3
M	234	16.1

424. Proper Motions and Spectral Class. On the basis of the material in the Preliminary General Catalog, after excluding all stars having proper motions exceeding 20″ per century, Boss published a table showing the relation between proper motions and spectral class. This table in abridged form is as shown in Table XI.

TABLE XI

Spectral class	Number of stars	Average proper motion per century
O and B	707	2″.8
A	1552	5.0
F	492	7.9
G	444	5.2
K	1227	5.7
M	222	5.0

There is evidence that the average stars of the O and B types are farther away than the average of the others, and this greater distance would, in general, result in smaller proper motions, but even this does not seem to be the complete explanation. Boss was led to conclude that even when allowing for distance, there is still evidence that, on the whole, the relative velocities of the groups O-B, A, and F-M are in the ratio of 6.3,

10.2, and 16.6, respectively. This is in general agreement with the results obtained from the radial velocities as given in the preceding section, so that there is good reason to believe we are dealing with one of the fundamental facts of stellar motion.

It is known that the B stars are more massive than the average of the other spectral types, so that we may assume the following to be a statement which is in accord with fact: *The more massive stars have smaller space velocities than the less massive.* We need additional facts before we shall have an adequate explanation.

425. Solar Motion and Absolute Magnitude. A number of investigations have been made which show that both the direction and the amount of the sun's motion depend upon the magnitudes of the stars involved as well as on their spectral class. Thus Stromberg has shown that with reference to 800 stars of absolute magnitude averaging zero the sun's velocity is 19 km per sec, while with reference to 415 stars of about +4.6 absolute magnitude the velocity is nearly 32 km per sec. The stars used were of spectral types ranging from F to M.

The computed position of the apex of the sun's way also changes as stars of various spectral types are used for a reference system. A great deal of new material is being published from time to time, but no definitive statement can be made concerning its bearing on the sun's motion or on the larger question of the structure of the stellar system. Enough has been said, however, to show something of the complexity of the problem and some of the factors which have to be considered.

426. Star Drifts. In 1904, Kapteyn announced the results of a study of the proper motions of 2400 stars. After eliminating the parallactic motion, the peculiar motions showed a decided tendency to separate themselves into two groups, the one group indicating motion toward a point in R.A. 6^h04^m, Dec. $+13°$, and the other a motion toward R.A. 18^h04^m, Dec. $-13°$. This distribution of peculiar motions was explained by Kapteyn as due to two groups of stars moving through each other in opposite directions. He referred to these as two star *streams*, but the term star *drifts*, suggested by Eddington, is now more generally used. The relative velocity of the two drifts is about 40 km (25 miles) per sec.

The two points toward which the star drifts are moving both lie in the Milky Way. These two points are called the *vertices* of the corresponding drifts.

There is also some evidence of the existence of a third group of stars practically at rest with respect to the two drifts. This third group is usually called Drift O. The other two drifts are referred to as Drifts A and B. Drifts A and B contain stars of spectral types A to M, but no B-type stars. Drift O, however, contains all the B-type stars as well as some others. The B-type stars thus seem to be a special group.

The motions of the stars in any drift are not along parallel lines as in the Taurus group. There is considerable variation both in the direction and in the velocity of the individual stars, but when the group is taken as a whole, it shows a decided group motion toward its vertex.

The work on star drifts depends on proper motions. Since we know the proper motions of relatively near stars only, we must not assume that distant stars will have the same vertices as Drifts A and B.

Work by Schwarzschild, Stromberg, and others casts some doubt on the simple physical explanation of two drifts as given by Kapteyn, but more material is necessary before a reasonably complete discussion of the space velocities of the stars and their relationships can be made. In the meantime we can accept Kapteyn's work as a first approximation which may be modified when we have more nearly complete knowledge of the factors involved in the problem. This matter will be considered again in Sec. 498.

EXERCISES

1. If the apparent magnitude of Polaris is 2.1 and its absolute magnitude is -2.4, what is its distance?   *Ans.* 80 parsecs.

2. What is the probable mass of Polaris if its absolute magnitude is -2.4?
                                                    Ans. About 10 times sun's mass.

3. If the radial velocity of a star with respect to the sun is zero, devise a method of determining the distance from earth to sun by means of measured radial velocities of the star.

4. What distance does the sun move annually toward the apex of the sun's way?
                                                                   Ans. 4.1 AU.

CHAPTER 16

THE STARS (*Continued*)

427. Double and Multiple Stars. There are in the sky a number of stars which appear single to the ordinary eye but which may be separated into two components by a keen eye. A good example of such a star is ε Lyrae. When the telescope is used, many thousands of close pairs are found. Star pairs of this kind are called *double stars*.

In some cases the two components are of approximately the same brightness, while in others there is a difference of many magnitudes. An example of the first kind is γ Virginis, with components of magnitudes 3.6 and 3.7, while one of the second kind is Sirius, with components of magnitudes −1.6 and 7.1.

Occasionally, a star is found which on examination proves to have more than two components. Such stars are called *multiple stars*. An example of this is θ Orionis, in which four stars can be detected with a telescope of ordinary size.

428. Optical and Physical Double Stars. Some double stars are such only because two stars are seen nearly in line, whereas, in reality, they are far apart in space and have no physical connection. Such a pair is called an *optical double star*. Stars of this kind will, in general, ultimately betray their true character because their proper motions will finally separate them.

Other double stars are not only apparently but actually close together, bound to one another by their mutual gravitation. They show this connection either by having a common proper motion or by showing orbital motion around their center of mass. Such pairs are called *physical double stars*. Stars which show orbital motion are known as *binary stars*.

429. Binary Stars. The first binary stars were discovered by Sir William Herschel. In 1781 he had presented before the Royal Society a paper "On the Parallaxes of the Fixed Stars," in which he called attention to the value of the displacement method (trigonometric) in parallaxes and stated that very close double stars offered the greatest promise of success. (At this time he seems to have assumed them to be optical doubles only.) The next year he presented a catalog of 269 double stars,

and a second list of 434 additional ones followed 2 years later.   He failed
to find the parallaxes he sought, but in 1797 he began remeasuring his
double stars, and by 1803 he was able to present evidence that "many of
them are not merely double in appearance, but must be allowed to be real
binary combinations of two stars, intimately held together by the bonds
of mutual attraction."

430. Designation of Double Stars. While practically all stars which
occur in the lists of double stars have their customary constellation letter
or catalog number, it has nevertheless been found convenient to designate
them by a letter and number, the letter signifying the discoverer and the
number the order in which the star stands in his list of discoveries.   Thus
Σ 554 means the star ordinarily known as 80 Tauri, but which is No. 554
in F. G. W. Struve's Catalogus Novus, and in his famous Mensurae
Micrometricae, β 491 is δ Andromedae and is No. 491 in Burnham's list of
discoveries, while A 2900 similarly represents Aitken's twenty-nine-
hundredth discovery.

Aitken, in succession to Burnham and Doolittle, had completed a list
of all double stars known to 1927 from the north celestial pole to declination −31° including a record of the measurements.   This large two-
volume work was published by the Carnegie Institution in 1932 and contains data for 17,180 double stars.   A convenient designation is the number of the double star in this catalog by Aitken.

431. Measurement of Double Stars. The measurement of a double
star has for its purpose the determination of the position of one component, called the *companion*, with respect to the other, called the *primary*.
When the stars are of unequal magnitude, the brighter is termed the
primary, but when they are equal in magnitude, one must be selected
arbitrarily as the primary.

The two quantities that it is possible to measure are the direction of the
line joining the two stars and the angular distance between them.   This
measurement is accomplished by means of the
micrometer attached to the telescope, which is
usually provided with but two parallel spider
threads, one fixed and the other movable by
means of a fine screw.   After the direction of
the north-and-south line in the field has been
determined and the circle reading obtained, the
threads are placed parallel to the line joining the
stars and the circle read again.   The difference
in the circle readings gives the angle which
the line joining the primary to the companion

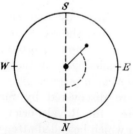

Fig. 214. Position angle of
a double star.

makes with the north-and-south line through the primary.   This angle
is called the *position angle* and is measured around the circle from the

north through the east. In Fig. 214 the position angle is about 135°. The micrometer is then rotated 90° and the angular separation of the two stars measured by means of the micrometer threads. This angular separation is called *distance*. Figure 215 shows the change in position angle in the faint companion of the star known as Krüger 60. The period for a complete revolution of Krüger 60 is 55 years.

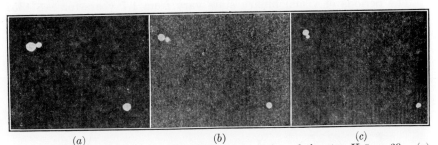

(a)   (b)   (c)

FIG. 215. Change in position angle of faint companion of the star Krüger 60. (a) 1908; (b) 1915; (c) 1920. (*Yerkes Observatory.*)

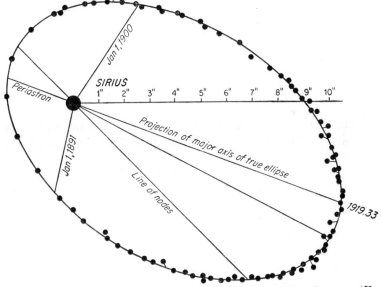

FIG. 216. Apparent orbit of the companion of Sirius around its primary. (*Howard, Popular Astronomy*, 1922.)

432. The Orbit of a Visual Binary. If a series of measures of position angle and distance have been made covering one complete revolution of the stars around their center of mass, it is possible to plot the apparent orbit of the one about the other. For a well-observed pair this is always an ellipse, but unless the orbit plane makes an angle of 90° with the line of sight, it is not the true orbit.   It is then the work of the computer to determine the real orbit of the one with respect to the other.   Figure 216 shows the *apparent* orbit of the companion of Sirius while Fig. 217 shows their true relative orbits.

The point of the orbit nearest the primary is termed *periastron* and the opposite point *apastron.*

The periods of visual binary stars vary from 1.7 years for $-8°4352$ upward, but, since those of long period have not completed an entire revolution since discovery, definite values cannot be obtained.

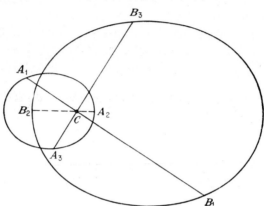

Fig. 217. The true relative orbits of Sirius A and B about their common center of gravity, C.   When Sirius A is at A_1 Sirius B is at B_1, etc.

The lengths of the semimajor axes of visual binary-star orbits listed in Aitken's book "The Binary Stars" vary from $0''.16$ for β 524 to $17''.65$ for α Centauri.

The eccentricities vary from 0.134 for Σ 518 to 0.96 for Σ 1865.

433. Colors of Double Stars. When there is but little difference in brightness in the components of a double star, they are generally of the same color, but when there is a considerable difference in brightness, the color of the fainter star is usually bluer.   This peculiarity has been demonstrated to be largely a subjective effect, and, judging from the varying descriptions of the colors by different observers, is also dependent upon peculiarities of vision of some observers.   There are, however, some cases where there is a real difference in color.   A good example of this is β Cygni.

In some cases the binary consists of a blue-white giant star and a main-sequence dwarf star.   Cases like this present serious theoretical problems, for we know that the blue-white giant is so prodigal with its energy that it must be young.   It could not keep up such a rate of energy generation for long.   Yet its companion is already a stable older star.   The binary, thus, appears to represent stars of two ages. This shows, contrary to earlier theories of binaries, that the two stars cannot have had a common origin. The problem is yet unsolved, and it goes to the very heart of cosmogony.

434. Spectroscopic Binary Stars. In 1889, E. C. Pickering announced that the star Mizar, ζ Ursae Majoris, showed a very peculiar spectrum in that at times the lines appeared double, at other times single, and at still

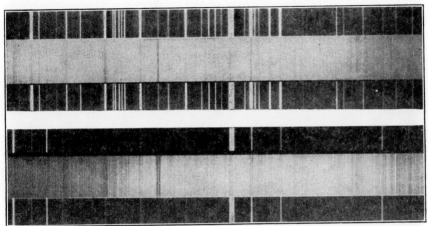

Fig. 218. Portion of spectrum of ζ Ursae Majoris (Mizar) showing single lines (above) and double lines (below). (*Yerkes Observatory.*)

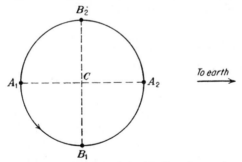

Fig. 219. Explanation of single and double lines in spectrum of Mizar.

other times they were merely broadened (Fig. 218). His explanation was that the star really consisted of two components of the same spectral type and of approximately equal brightness which are revolving around their common center of mass. When the stars are in the positions A_1, A_2 (Fig. 219), they are moving across the line of sight and the combined spectrum would show single lines. When they are in the positions B_1, B_2, however, the lines in the spectrum of B_2 would be shifted toward the red while those of B_1 would be shifted toward the violet and the lines of the combined spectrum would be double, one set belonging to star 1 and the other to star 2. The period of revolution of the two stars is about 20.5 days. A star of this kind is called a *spectroscopic binary star*. If the plane of the orbit passes very near the earth, it will also be an eclipsing variable star (Sec. 439).

If the components of a spectroscopic binary star are of about equal magnitude, both spectra will be visible, but when there is a difference of several magnitudes, the spectrum of the brighter one alone is visible on the photographic plate. Since the spectra are superposed on the plate, no increase of exposure will bring out the fainter spectrum.

435. Variable Radial-velocity Stars. When the spectrum of only one component of a spectroscopic binary is visible, the binary character is shown by the shifting of the lines (Fig. 220) of the spectrum—toward the

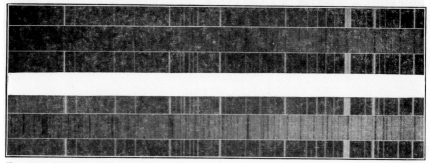

Fɪɢ. 220. Shifting of the position of the lines in the spectrum of μ Orionis due to change in radial velocity. (*Yerkes Observatory.*)

red when this component is moving away from and toward the violet when moving toward the earth. In such a case a series of spectrograms will give values of the velocity which show definite periods corresponding to the period of revolution of the binary. When these values[1] are plotted with reference to the period, a curve, known as the velocity curve, is formed. Figure 221 shows the velocity curve of μ Orionis as determined at the Yerkes Observatory. From this curve the computer can determine the elements of the orbit. These elements are the radial velocity of the center of mass of the binary, the period, the eccentricity of the orbit, and other quantities which correspond more or less to like quantities in the orbit elements of a planet (Sec. 248).

The range in velocity as shown by the velocity curve is often great. In the case of δ Pictoris this amounts to 342 km.

When both spectra are visible, it is possible to determine the orbit of one component with respect to the other, as in a visual binary. Their relative masses may also be obtained as well as minimum values of the

[1] After reduction to the sun.

masses.   For TT Aurigae, Adams and Joy have found a relative velocity
of the two components amounting to 450 km per sec.

It is evident that every visual binary star whose orbit plane is not
accurately perpendicular to the line of sight is a potential spectroscopic
binary star.

The orbits of over 300 spectroscopic binary stars have been computed.
Their periods range from about 2.5 hr for γ Ursae Minoris to many years.

436. Number of Double Stars. Undoubtedly, there are many double
stars still undiscovered, but the Lick Observatory survey by Aitken and

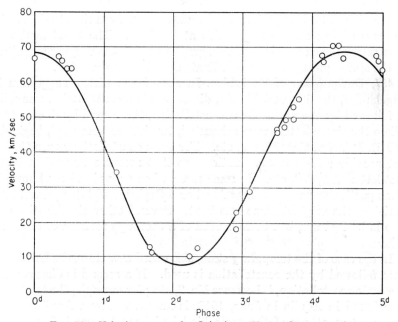

Fig. 221. Velocity curve of μ Orionis.   (*Yerkes Observatory.*)

Hussey is an extraordinarily valuable piece of observational work.   This
survey involved a careful scrutiny of all stars of magnitude 9.0 or brighter
listed in the BD from the north celestial pole to −23° declination to see
if they were single or double.   In his book on binary stars, Aitken has
given the results of the work for the northern hemisphere of the sky.   A
total of 100,979 stars was involved, and of these, 5400 were double stars.
The discoveries were as follows: W. Struve 1053, O. Struve 296, Burnham
551, Hough 237, Hussey 766, Aitken 2057, all others 440.   We thus see
that about one star in every 18 as bright as magnitude 9.0 in the northern
sky is a visual double star as seen with the 36-in. Lick refractor.

Recent researches give us even higher proportions of binaries, when
spectroscopic binaries are included.   Observations reveal that nearly one

star in six is a binary, and there are great numbers of triplets and more complex multiple stars. It is evident that twinning among the stars is a common process. Kuiper has estimated that, if all the multiple stars could be detected, we would find that perhaps 80 per cent of all stars are binaries or multiples. One of the most intriguing problems of modern astrophysics is to answer the question of why there are so many multiples. Its answer will tell us much about stellar evolution.

VARIABLE STARS

A variable star is one whose brightness changes from time to time owing to causes lying outside the earth's atmosphere. The usual method of illustrating the change is to draw a graph in which the varying magnitude of the star is plotted as one coordinate and time as the other.

437. Designation of Variables. In accordance with a suggestion by Argelander, the first variable star discovered in a constellation was called R followed by the name of the constellation, the second by S, etc., to Z. When the single letters were exhausted, two letters were used, beginning at RR, RS, etc., then SS, ST, etc. For some constellations even this did not provide sufficient combinations, so that recourse was taken to the first letters AA, AB, etc. In some cases, when a star has been known by some particular name, such as Algol or δ Cephei, and later proved to be variable, the original name was kept. Several other classifications are also in limited use, but there is need of a thorough revision of the entire scheme.

In the case of the temporary stars, also called new stars, the Latin word *nova* followed by the constellation is used. If a second is discovered in the same constellation, it becomes No. 2, etc.; for example, the temporary star found in Aquila in June, 1918, is known as Nova Aquilae No. 3, because two others of the same kind had been known before in that constellation.

438. Classification. Variable stars are generally divided into two principal categories, known as the *extrinsic* and *intrinsic* variables. The separation attests our belief about the causes of the variability. The *extrinsic* variables, we believe, are actually stable stars which do not vary in light output but whose light is, in one way or another, periodically obscured by some means outside the earth's atmosphere. The *intrinsic* variables, on the other hand, are stars whose light output varies appreciably.

The extrinsic variables consist entirely of eclipsing binaries. They are actually double stars of various types, but with orbits so inclined to the line of sight that they alternately eclipse each other.

The intrinsic variables, according to Gaposchkin and Gaposchkin, are subdivided into five principal types, as follows:

1. Cluster-type variables
2. Cepheid variables
3. RV Tauri stars
4. Semiregular variables
5. Long-period variables

These five types make up what is known as the *Great Sequence*. They show a general progression of physical characteristics.

There is another pair of related types of variable stars that conventionally are not designated as variables, although their variations are the most spectacular of all variables: the *novae* and *supernovae*.

439. Eclipsing Variables. The classical illustration of this type is Algol (β Persei). For over 2 days this star appears to be of almost constant brightness with a magnitude of 2.3. It then begins to decrease in brightness and in about 5 hr it reaches magnitude 3.5. In another 5 hours it has recovered its former brightness and remains so for the next 2.5 days. This variation has continued with great regularity ever since its discovery by Montanari in 1667.

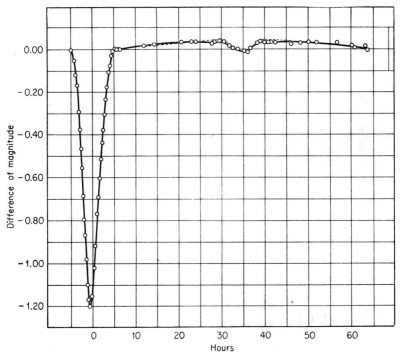

FIG. 222. Light curve of Algol. (*According to Stebbins.*)

The simplest explanation of the variation is that the star is not a single but a double star, one component being darker than the other, and the two moving around their common center of gravity.   The plane of the orbit is turned so nearly edgewise to the line of sight that at each revolution the darker body eclipses the brighter one, cutting off most of its light.

This explanation is confirmed by spectrographic observation.   Before eclipse the brighter star is found to be moving away from us, and after eclipse it is moving toward us.

The most exact study of the light variation of Algol has been made by Stebbins.   His light curve is given in Fig. 222.   The relative orbit is shown in Fig. 223.

Fig. 223. Apparent orbit and relative sizes of the components of Algol.

It will be noted that the light curve is not flat at the top.   A secondary minimum occurs halfway between the principal minima.   This is due to the eclipse of the darker by the brighter component and shows that the darker radiates some light.   The curve also slopes upward from primary to secondary minimum and downward from secondary to primary.   This is an indication that the side of the darker companion which faces the brighter star is somewhat brighter than the other side and after the principal eclipse we see more and more of the brighter side of the darker companion.

From the radial velocities of Algol it is possible to determine the size of its orbit, and since the light curve gives the duration of eclipse it is clear that we have a possibility of determining the diameters of the components. Stebbins's latest results are shown in Table XII.

TABLE XII

Ratio of radii	0.85
Area of bright body obscured at minimum	0.700
Light of bright body	0.925
Light of bright side of faint body	0.075
Light of faint side of faint body	0.045
Radius of bright body (orbit radius = 1)	0.207
Radius of faint body	0.244
Angle between plane of orbit and line of sight	8°.2
Mean density of system (sun = 1.0)	0.07
Duration of eclipse	9^h.66

A second example of this class of variable stars is β Lyrae.   Its light curve is given in Fig. 224.   This curve is explained by assuming two bright stars of unequal size practically in contact and alternately eclipsing one another.

There are at present over 300 stars of the eclipsing type known. Their periods vary from 6^h for RW Com. Ber. to 29 years for ϵ Aurigae. From the abundant information gleaned about β Persei and shown in Table XII, it is easy to understand why Payne-Gaposchkin has stated that "eclipsing variables are our most important direct source of information about the physical properties of the stars."

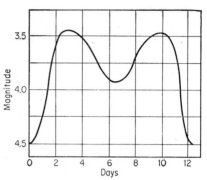

FIG. 224. Light curve of β Lyrae.

440. Classification of Great Sequence Variables by Physical Properties. The intrinsic variables that make up the Great Sequence show a progression of physical properties. In the order listed in Sec. 438 they form a series with decreasing temperatures and decreasing densities from one end to the other. They also, for the most part, form a series with increasing period, though there are large fluctuations within each class, and larger in some classes than others. Most Great Sequence stars also lie in the upper part of the H-R diagram (Sec. 411) at or brighter than absolute magnitude 0, rather than on the Main Sequence.

441. Cluster-type Variables. The cluster-type variables are the shortest-period variables of the Great Sequence. They generally vary in a semiregular fashion with periods of about 0.5 day. They are called cluster-type variables because they are found in great abundance in the globular clusters (Secs. 463ff.). The globular cluster, Messier 3, for example, has 166 known cluster-type variables. They are also numerous in our galaxy and increase in abundance toward the center, nearly 2000 being known. Their absolute magnitudes at maximum are about 0, and their spectral classes range from A to F. Their light curves resemble Fig. 225.

Some have periods shorter than 0.1 day. Within any given globular cluster these variables show a relationship between period of variation and the shape of the light curve, with an abrupt change of shape at some period, and with abrupt changes in period not uncommon in individual stars.

Little is known about their internal physics. They are suspected of relationship to the cepheid variables.

442. The Cepheid Variables. This group takes its name from the first one discovered, δ Cephei. All are known to be giant suns, much larger than our own.   Their periods vary from less than one day to about 50 days, but the period and the light curve of any one are quite constant.   A light curve of δ Cephei is given in Fig. 225.

About 500 cepheids are known in our galaxy.   However, most knowledge of cepheids comes from the Magellanic Clouds.   They are very luminous stars, and mostly of spectral class from F to G, but their spectra present serious classification troubles because they tend to be abnormal.

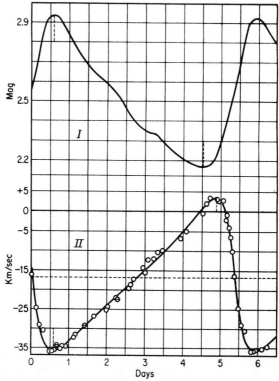

Fɪɢ. 225. The light (*I*) and velocity (*II*) curves of δ Cephei.   (*Lick Observatory.*)

443. The Period-luminosity Law. In 1908, Miss Leavitt of the Harvard College Observatory called attention to a peculiar relationship which existed among a number of variable stars in the smaller Magellanic Cloud, a mass of stars and nebulae in the southern heavens which looks like a detached part of the Milky Way.   This relationship may be stated thus: The period of variation of these stars depends upon their brightness in such a way that the longer the period of variation, the brighter the star. Since these stars undoubtedly belong to the smaller Magellanic Cloud, they are at approximately equal distances from us.   The relationship could be stated more specifically as follows: The periods of this group of variables depend upon their absolute magnitudes.

The next great advance was made by Shapley, who showed, among other things, that the relationship between period of variation and absolute magnitude held for cepheid variables wherever found. This relationship is usually called the period-luminosity law of cepheid variation. The law was published by Shapley in the form of a curve which, for the purposes of this book, has been redrawn in a modified form and is given in Fig. 226 (full line).

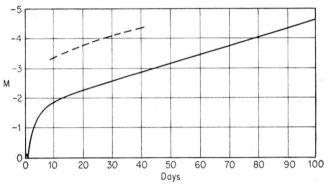

FIG. 226. The period-luminosity curve. Solid line is the original Shapley curve which applies to stars of population II. Broken line is approximate position of curve for stars of population I.

This remarkable relationship cannot be fully explained as yet. There is evidence that the cepheids are all giant stars and it does not seem improbable that at certain periods of their development the internal forces tending to disrupt the star are practically in balance with the gravitative force which works toward condensation. With different masses and temperatures the balance would be attained under different conditions and the pulsations therefore would have different periods.

The application of the period-luminosity law will be illustrated by an example. Let us suppose that we observe a cepheid variable having a period of 30 days and an apparent mean magnitude[1] of +7.4. Using this period, the curve (full line) shows that the absolute magnitude of the star is approximately −2.6. The difference between apparent and absolute magnitude is 10. According to the relation between change of magnitude and distance (Sec. 403), a change of five magnitudes corresponds to a tenfold change in distance and therefore a change of 10 magnitudes corresponds to a change of $10 \times 10 = 100$-fold change in distance. Since, by definition, the absolute magnitude equals the apparent magnitude at

[1] The mean magnitude used is the arithmetic mean of the magnitudes at maximum and minimum light.

a distance of 10 parsecs, the star under consideration would be at a distance of 1000 parsecs.

Further applications of this law will be made when we study the globular star clusters and the distant galaxies. From time to time, however, certain applications of the period-luminosity law led to results which did not appear to be entirely acceptable. These discrepancies were brought out most definitely by Baade in 1952. According to his work the cepheids should be grouped into two types, type I being associated with stars of population I and type II with stars of population II (Sec. 412). On this basis the period-luminosity law is no longer a single curve but two curves separated by approximately 1.5 magnitudes. Type I cepheids are about 1.5 magnitudes brighter (broken curve, Fig. 226) than type II cepheids of the same period. This in turn leads to distances about twice as great for a type I cepheid as compared with one of type II of the same period.

The exact difference in magnitude and slope between the period-luminosity curves of the two types of cepheids is not known with any precision. Kron finds the difference about $1^m.3$, while Shapley obtains $1^m.7$. Iwanowska presents some evidence that the two curves intersect at periods of about 8 hours. Some years of work will be required before definitive curves can be obtained. For the present we may use a difference of $1^m.5$. In the example above the value of $m - M$, is 11.5 magnitudes and the distance 2000 parsecs if we use the broken curve.

444. Physical Nature of Cepheids. Spectroscopic observations of cepheids reveal a remarkable result. For many years it was believed that the cepheid variables were spectroscopic binary stars because the lines in their spectra showed periodic shifts in conformity with their period of light variation. One peculiarity, however, seemed to place them in a special class, for the maximum light occurred at the time of maximum velocity of approach, and minimum light at maximum velocity of recession. Various theories were proposed to explain this peculiarity but none appeared entirely satisfactory.

Shapley then advanced the theory known as the *pulsation* theory. This assumes that a cepheid variable is a giant star of low density which alternately expands and contracts, and explains the shift in the spectral lines by this motion. The pulsation theory so far fails to account in detail for the rather complicated relationships that usually exist in cepheids among spectral class, surface velocity of pulsation, and light variation.

The relation between the light and velocity curves of δ Cephei is shown in Fig. 225. The two curves are seen to be practically mirror images of each other. Minimum light occurs at the time of maximum velocity (greatest velocity of recession) and maximum light occurs at minimum velocity (greatest velocity of approach). In terms of the pulsation theory, this means that maximum light occurs at the time of the most rapid expansion of the star, and minimum light at the time of the most rapid contraction.

445. RV Tauri Stars. The RV Tauri stars are a group of variables taking their name from their prototype RV Tauri. The stars include a wide range of properties. Their periods range from about 19 days to 150 days. They tend to alternate between deep and shallow minima, and have less regular curves than the cluster variables or the cepheids (Fig. 227). Their spectral classes at maxima range from F to nearly to K, and they often show bright lines. They are very luminous.

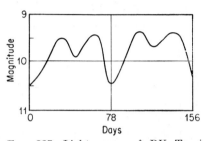

FIG. 227. Light curve of RV Tauri showing unequal maxima and unequal minima.

Many different sorts of physical behavior are represented among these stars, and in all probability, when more is known of them, we shall find them to consist of many different separable types requiring differing theories.

446. Semiregular Variables. The semiregular stars are redder than the preceding classes. Their spectra generally fall in class M and in the rarer classes of very red stars R, N, and S. Practically all red stars exhibit some variability; most in this class exhibit a relatively small range of luminosity variation. There is, however, a great range in luminosity at maximum for these variables. They probably do not represent a homogeneous physical class.

447. Long-period Variable Stars. These variables form a rather clear-cut group with periods ranging from 90 days for T Centauri to 709 days for AH Scorpii. They have large amplitudes of variation. There is a pronounced tendency for the periods to fall near either 260 days or 340 days, with the former far the more abundant. Apparently there are two main classes of physical types in this category.

The spectral class is generally M, and the stars, of course, are therefore reddish. Often the spectra are of the even redder classes R and N. Because of the low temperatures there are usually *band spectra* of compounds in the stars.

A typical star of this class is o Ceti, sometimes called Mira, the wonderful, the first variable discovered. In August, 1596, an amateur astronomer, D. Fabricius, saw in the constellation Cetus a second-magnitude star which he had never seen before. It soon faded from view. He saw it again for a few weeks beginning in February, 1609, but does not appear to have given it much further attention. In 1638 it was independently discovered by Holwarda, and later seen by others. Hevelius followed it with sufficient energy to detect its variability in the interval 1648 to 1662.

During most of the time the star is below naked-eye visibility, but about every 11 months it is visible for some weeks. At maximum it may almost reach the second magnitude, but sometimes it rises only to the fifth. The time between succes-sive maxima is not constant but averages approximately 11 months. At minimum, it sinks to about the ninth magnitude. The rise to max-imum is more rapid than the decline and there are some fluctuations throughout. Figure 228 is an aver-age light curve.

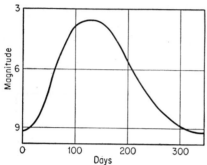

FIG. 228. An average light curve of Mira.

Mt. Wilson Observatory stud-ies assign to this star the enor-mous diameter of 350,000,000 km (220,000,000 miles.) Thus *o* Ceti is a red giant vastly larger than the sun. There is also evidence from recent work that the long period varia-bles are pulsating stars.

448. Novae and Supernovae. Stars of this group are the most spectacu-lar of all variables. They are frequently referred to as *new stars* or *novae*. The latter name in this technical sense is not objectionable but the word "new" seems to imply a star not previously existing and therefore should not be used, as the evidence clearly shows that the phenomenon is nothing more than a sudden increase in brightness of a faint star.

The common type of nova may be divided into two principal subdivi-sions, the *fast* and the *slow*. An example of the fast type is Nova Aquilae No. 3 (Fig. 229). Its history is as follows:

On the night of June 7 to 8, 1918, a new star of the first magnitude was noted in the constellation Aquila. By the next night its magnitude rose to −1.2. Thereafter it slowly waned, being of magnitude 4 by the end of June and of magnitude 6 by the middle of November. From the last of June on it fluctuated more or less, with some evidence of a 12-day period. The fluctuations continued but the star gradually became fainter, until in October, 1921, it had reached the tenth magnitude. In the meantime a search of photographs of that region of the sky taken before the out-burst showed that the star had been for some time of about magnitude 10.5 and was still that faint on the night of June 5. Between this date and June 9 it rose from magnitude 10.5 to −1.2, a difference of nearly 12 magnitudes, which meant an increase in brightness of about 60,000-fold. Some extraordinary thing must have occurred to cause such an outburst in so short a time. At maximum light this star had an absolute magnitude of approximately −9.2, thus exceeding the sun nearly 400,000-fold in brightness.

The slow novae appear to be similar to the fast ones in the first rapid rise, but the final increase in brightness to the maximum and the decline thereafter are much slower.

About 85 stars may be considered as having shown nova characteristics according to McLaughlin. The earliest in his list is the nova of 1572. All but five of these were seen in the last 100 years.

Most novae appear to rise to an absolute magnitude of the order of −5, but once in a great while one appears with an absolute magnitude of about

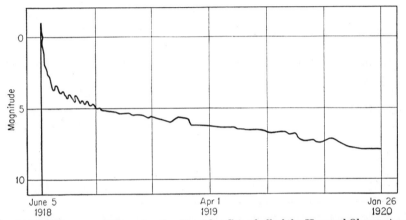

FIG. 229. Light curve of Nova Aquilae No. 3 by Campbell of the Harvard Observatory.

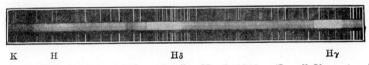

FIG. 230. The spectrum of Nova Aquilae No. 3, 1918. (*Lowell Observatory.*)

−15. These extraordinarily bright stars thus outshine the sun about one hundred million times at maximum. They are recognized as a special class and are called *supernovae*. One such star at a distance of 10 parsecs (33 light-years) would give us approximately 10 times the light of the full moon.

The spectra of novae are more or less alike. If caught before reaching maximum brightness, there is a strong continuous spectrum with a few absorption lines, so that it appears to be somewhat like that of a B- or A-type star. At maximum brightness and for a few days thereafter strong bright bands of hydrogen and other elements appear (Fig. 230) together with absorption lines corresponding, the latter being displaced to the violet. These displacements correspond to a motion up to 2000 km per sec.   Then more complicated changes occur until after a time the spectrum resembles that of a planetary nebula (Sec. 477).   After a lapse of several years the spectrum gradually changes until it is that of an O-type star.   So far as known, this is the last stage of the nova spectrum.

There has been no entirely satisfactory theory to account for the novae. From the spectroscopic evidence it seems clear that the outer layers of the star are suddenly blasted outward from the body of the star with velocities measured in thousands of kilometers per second.   This bares to view the excessively hot interior of the star and accounts for the sudden increase in brightness.   As the new surface cools off, the light of the star decreases, and, after the lapse of a few years, it returns to its former brightness.

Gamow and others have given novel theories of novae and supernovae, but further work must be done to test whether the spectacular processes proposed can actually occur.   Novation is probably a one-time-only event in the life of a star, though some few stars appear to be able to repeat the process.

449. Other Variable Stars. Finally we must recognize that many variable stars fall clearly into none of the categories listed.   As an example consider the star R Coronae Borealis (Fig. 231).   For a year or more

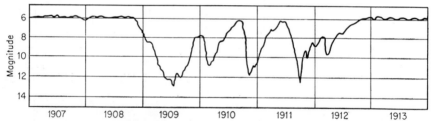

FIG. 231. Part of the light curve of R Coronae Borealis.   (*Harvard Observatory.*)

it may remain at about sixth magnitude.   Then, during several years, it varies irregularly with a range up to seven magnitudes but finally returns to the sixth magnitude.   No satisfactory explanation of the erratic behavior of this star and many others has been offered.

Study of these stars is of great interest.   Their range of properties is enormous.   The intrinsic variables offer one of the most complex of all modern fields of astrophysical investigation.

450. Study of Variable Stars. The careful study of variable stars is engaging the attention of an increasing number of observers.   Over 20,000 variable stars are known at the present time and more are being discovered.   It is likely that all stars vary in brightness to some extent and that only those whose variations are rapid, in terms of the life history of a star, can be detected by means now at our disposal.

Hagen has issued a series of charts of great value for the study of these stars.   The Harvard Observatory also has issued many photographic charts for this purpose and is headquarters for the general collection of variable-star observations in this country.

The variable-star field is one in which amateur astronomers can be of great aid to the science, as the number of variables is so great that the regular observatories cannot follow them adequately.   The American Association of Variable Star Observers and the Variable Star section of the British Astronomical Association are composed largely of amateurs who are producing valuable results.

EXERCISES

1. If the semimajor axis of the orbit of the double star α Centauri is $17''.65$ and its parallax is $0''.76$, what is the mean separation of the two components?

Ans. 23.2 AU.

2. If the maximum separation of the double lines of the spectrum of ζ Ursae Majoris is 0.5 A for the hydrogen line $H\gamma$ (λ 4341), what is the orbital velocity of the components of the star?   *Ans.* Approximately 17 km per sec.

3. If the period of ζ Germinorum is 10 days and its mean apparent magnitude is 4.0, what is its distance?   (Use solid line, Fig. 226.)   *Ans.* 144 parsecs.

4. If the components of an eclipsing binary star have different diameters but the same mass and the plane of the orbit passes through the observer, show that the linear diameters of the stars can be determined if we have the light curve of the pair and the radial velocity curve of the brighter component.

CHAPTER 17

NUMBER AND ARRANGEMENT OF THE STARS

451. Naked-eye versus Telescopic Observations. There is a general impression that the number of stars within reach of the naked eye is without limit, but an exact count of various regions of the sky will soon convince anyone that the actual number that can be seen at any one time is quite limited. It is doubtful if there are at any time, even with a clear sky and in the absence of the moon and of artificial illumination, as many as 2500 stars in the visible hemisphere. A telescope, however, will bring out many thousands.

It is estimated that with the 91-cm (36-in.) Lick refractor about 100,-000,000 stars could be seen in the entire sky, while with the large reflectors available today many times this number could be photographed.

452. The Milky Way. One of the most conspicuous objects in the heavens on a clear summer night is the *Milky Way*, or *galaxy*. If observed carefully through the summer, fall, and winter, it will be seen to encircle the sky and divide it into two approximately equal parts. As soon as a telescope is used, it is found to consist of many stars, and photographs of the denser regions show literally great clouds of stars (Fig. 232).

453. Galactic Coordinates. For reasons which will soon appear it has been found convenient to take the central line of the galaxy as a fundamental circle for a system of coordinates called *galactic latitude* and *longitude*. The north pole of this circle is at R.A. 12^{h}40^m, Dec. +28°. Galactic latitude is measured north and south from the galactic equator and galactic longitude is measured eastward from the intersection of the galactic circle with the celestial equator in Aquila at R.A. 18^{h}40^m, Dec. 0°.

454. The Herschel Star Gages. The first one to investigate the Milky Way with care was Sir William Herschel. He made counts, over the northern sky, of the number of stars that could be seen in the 15' field of view of one of his telescopes, a 45-cm (18-in.) reflector, and his son, Sir John Herschel, using the same instrument, made similar counts in the southern sky. The results of these thousands of "star gages" showed a most remarkable relation between the average number of stars seen in the field of the telescope and the location of the field with respect to the

Milky Way.   The following table is a brief résumé of these gages, the values being taken from Herschel's "Outlines of Astronomy."

TABLE XIII

Galactic latitude	Average number of stars in field 15′ diameter
90°	4.2
75	4.7
60	6.5
45	10.4
30	17.7
15	30.3
0	122.0

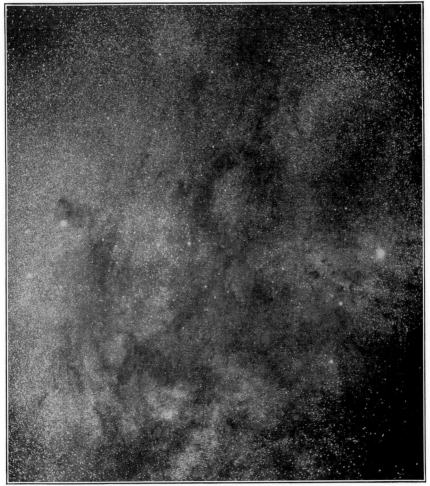

FIG. 232. Milky Way north of θ Ophiuchi.   (*Yerkes Observatory.*)

From these figures it is evident that the Milky Way is of fundamental importance in any general consideration of the arrangement of the stars.

455. Recent Star Counts. In 1925, Seares and van Rhijn published an extensive table, based upon star counts on plates taken at Harvard, Göttingen, Greenwich, Mt. Wilson, and Oxford, which gave the average values for the number of stars per square degree for 14 galactic latitudes from 0° to 90° from the brightest down to magnitude 18.5.   From the

TABLE XIV

NUMBER OF STARS PER SQUARE DEGREE FROM THE BRIGHTEST TO MAGNITUDE m

m	Galactic latitude				
	0°	15°	30°	60°	90°
4.0	0.016	0.011	0.007	0.005	0.005
5.0	0.045	0.032	0.021	0.015	0.013
6.0	0.129	0.093	0.062	0.042	0.037
7.0	0.363	0.263	0.174	0.117	0.102
8.0	1.0	0.724	0.479	0.324	0.275
9.0	2.82	1.95	1.32	0.871	0.724
10.0	7.77	5.25	3.47	2.24	1.82
....	....	....	....	....	....
15.0	912	513	275	123	87.1
....	....	....	....	....	....
20.0	39,800	19,500	5620	1820	1170
21.0	74,100	34,700	8710	2630	1660

regularity with which the numbers changed, they continued the table to magnitude 21.   The entire table is too long to be reproduced but enough is given in Table XIV to show the character of the results.

Two facts are clearly brought out by these figures.

1. Stars of all magnitudes, within the limits given, increase in number as the galactic latitude decreases.

2. This concentration is more marked for the fainter than for the brighter stars.

Two terms will now be defined which we shall need in a consideration of the structure of the galactic system, namely, *star density* and *star ratio*.

456. Star Density. This term means the number of stars in unit volume, or, to be specific, the number of stars per cubic parsec.   Since the stars, on the average, are more than 1 parsec apart, there will be less than one star in each cubic parsec—in other words, the star density will be less than 1.   Thus, if the star density is 0.1 in any particular region, this means that there is one star for every 10 cubic parsecs, or an average of one-tenth of a star for each cubic parsec.   The star density in the neighborhood of the sun is approximately 0.105 on the basis of the material in Table VII, page 252.

457. Star Ratio. Let us consider a certain volume of space, O-$ABCD$ (Fig. 233), the observer being at O.   Within this volume the faintest average star will have a certain magnitude, let us assume the tenth, and be at the boundary $ABCD$.   Let us then penetrate space still farther so that the volume included will be O-$EFGH$, and so that the faintest average star in the added volume between $ABCD$ and $EFGH$ will be of the eleventh magnitude.   If the star density is the same throughout the volume of

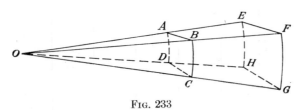

FIG. 233

space under consideration, then the average star of the eleventh magnitude will be 1.585 times as far away as the average star of the tenth magnitude (Sec. 403).   This means that the distance from O to the boundary $EFGH$ will be 1.585 times the distance from O to the boundary $ABCD$. From solid geometry we know that the volumes of similar solids are proportional to the cubes of homologous lines of the solids.   Therefore the volume O-$EFGH$ will be to the volume O-$ABCD$ as $(1.585)^3 : 1^3$, or as $3.98 : 1$.   For convenience let us call this ratio $4 : 1$.

By penetrating space far enough to include the average star of the eleventh magnitude, we have therefore quadrupled the volume of space under consideration.   If the star density is constant, we should therefore expect that the number of all the stars in the region down to the eleventh magnitude would be four times the number of stars down to the tenth magnitude.   This argument holds as well for any two consecutive magnitudes.   We can say therefore that, assuming uniform star density, the number of stars seen in any given area of the sky down to any magnitude m should be four times the number down to magnitude $m - 1$.   This ratio of $4 : 1$ will be called the *theoretical star ratio*.

The *actual star ratio* is obtained by dividing the total number of stars found in any given area of the sky down to any magnitude m by the number of stars in the same region down to magnitude $m - 1$.

Let us now compare the results of actual star counts with the theoretical ratio, using the table of Sec. 455.   Dividing each number by the one above it, we obtain the following results given in Table XV, below. We thus see that the star ratio is nowhere equal to 4, the theoretical value; that it decreases, in general, as we include fainter and fainter stars; and that the decrease is more rapid toward the poles of the Milky Way than in its plane.

TABLE XV
STAR RATIOS

Magnitudes	Galactic latitude				
	0°	15°	30°	60°	90°
5: 4	2.8	2.9	2.9	3.0	2.6
6: 5	2.9	2.9	2.9	2.8	2.8
7: 6	2.8	2.8	2.8	2.8	2.8
8: 7	2.8	2.8	2.8	2.8	2.7
9: 8	2.8	2.7	2.8	2.7	2.6
10: 9	2.8	2.7	2.6	2.6	2.5
. . . . .	. . .	. . .	. . .	. . .	. . .
15:14	2.5	2.3	2.2	2.0	1.9
. . . . .	. . .	. . .	. . .	. . .	. . .
21:20	1.9	1.8	1.5	1.4	1.4

458. Results of Star Counts. From the material of the preceding section we are led to the following interesting results: (1) The star density decreases with increasing distance from the sun.[1] (2) The decrease is more rapid in a direction at right angles to the Milky Way than in its plane. (3) Unless the star ratio increases again at some point not yet accessible to observation, we should finally reach portions of space with practically no stars in them as we went ever farther from the sun—in other words, *the stellar system is limited in extent.*

The values of the star ratio for the stars brighter than the seventh magnitude in the table are not far from the theoretical value 4, so that for the region immediately surrounding the sun the actual and theoretical values are in fair agreement. Analysis of star counts in restricted regions sometimes shows values beyond the theoretical amount, which indicates that the sun is not in the densest part of the system—in other words, it is not at the center.

The total number of stars in the system cannot be determined very exactly as some assumptions which underlie all estimates cannot be proved. From the best available evidence the total number is of the order of 10^{11}.

This system of stars together with other objects found in their midst is called the *galactic system.*

[1] Either sun or earth. The relatively small distance between the two is negligible.

459. Dimensions of the Galactic System. On the basis of the star-ratio argument it is concluded that the stars and most other members of the galactic system are found within a region having approximately the shape of a thin convex lens.

Various estimates of the dimensions of this lens-shaped space have been made from time to time. It is a rather difficult problem, as large parts of the system are not accessible to observation. Probably the best values attainable at the present time are a diameter of 30,000 parsecs (100,000 light-years) and a thickness of not over 3000 parsecs (10,000 light-years).

Fig. 234. The galactic cluster, NGC 6705. (*Lick Observatory.*)

460. The Sun's Position. As stated in Sec. 458, there is evidence to show that the sun is not at the center of the stellar system, but authorities disagree as to its distance from the center. Since the Milky Way is practically a great circle in the sky, the sun must lie close to its plane. Its distance from this plane is estimated as 33 parsecs by Gerasimovic and Luyten. The center, as seen from the sun, would therefore be in the Milky Way, that is, in galactic latitude 0°, provided the sun is at some distance from the center. The longitude is not so definite, but the evidence favors the Scorpius-Sagittarius region.

The distance of the sun from this center is a problem of great difficulty.

The best estimate at present puts the sun about 9000 parsecs (30,000 light-years) from the center.

461. Galactic Clusters. Embedded in the great masses of stars which form the galactic system are certain clusters of stars which have been called *galactic clusters.* One well-known example is the Pleiades cluster (Fig. 245) which consists of stars having common space velocities and which are predominantly of one spectral class. The diameter of the Pleiades cluster is approximately 33 light-years and its mean distance 500 light-years.

Another example is NGC 6705* (Fig. 234) which has a diameter of 16 light-years and is at a distance of 4400 light-years from the sun.

These clusters all lie in or near the galactic plane. In the list of 334 objects of this class recently published by Trumpler nearly two-thirds are within 100 parsecs (330 light-years) of this plane, and only nine are farther from it than 500 parsecs (1650 light-years). In so far as their distances can be measured or estimated, Trumpler finds only nine that lie farther than 5000 parsecs (16,500 light-years) from the sun and most of them are much nearer than that limit.

The diameters of the galactic clusters range from 1.6 to 15 parsecs (5 to 50 light-years), but fully three-fourths of them lie within the range of 2 to 6 parsecs (7 to 20 light-years).

462. The Local Cluster. A study of photographs of the Milky Way shows that the stars are not uniformly distributed. In some instances this lack of uniformity is caused by clouds of dust (Sec. 485), but in others there seems to be simply a greater star density. There is evidence that the sun belongs to such an aggregation of stars which is called the *local cluster* or *local star cloud.* According to Charlier, this cloud is more or less lens-shaped with a diameter of about 2000 light-years and a thickness of about one-third this amount. Seares finds the Charlier cloud to be merely the central part of a larger unit with dimensions about ten times greater.

EXERCISES

1. (*a*) Select a limited area of sky such as the square of Pegasus or the bowl of the Big Dipper and count the number of stars visible to the unaided eye within its boundaries. (*b*) Make a similar count using an opera glass or field glass.

2. Note the central line of the Milky Way with reference to the stars and trace this line on a star chart.

* NGC refers to Dreyer's New General Catalog of Nebulae and Clusters.

CHAPTER 18

OTHER MEMBERS OF THE GALACTIC SYSTEM

THE GLOBULAR CLUSTERS

463. The Hercules Cluster. In the summer and fall the constellation Hercules is above the horizon in the early hours of the night. Between the stars η and ζ Herculis and about one-third of the way from the former to the latter a moderately good eye will detect an object looking like a faint hazy star. Examination with a small telescope of about 3-in. aperture and with moderate magnification will show a bright disk with hazy edges. A 5-in. telescope will begin to resolve this into a mass of stars, and telescopes of larger aperture will show correspondingly more and fainter stars. In order to appreciate the wonderful beauty of this object, however, we must resort to photographic telescopes of the largest size. These reveal to us the object shown in Fig. 235. Counts of the stars made at the Mt. Wilson Observatory show that there are at least 50,000 stars in this one cluster and it is believed that very long exposures would reveal at least 100,000.

464. Number and Shape of Globular Clusters. There are now about 100 objects of this character known to astronomers. They are called *globular clusters* because there is evidence which shows that they are all approximately spherical in shape. In some cases Shapley has shown that the outline is slightly elliptical instead of circular. The Hercules cluster is the finest of all its class in the northern sky; in the southern heavens only a few such as the ω Centauri cluster exceed it in apparent size.

465. Distance and Dimensions of Globular Clusters. The distance and dimensions of the globular clusters are questions which were often discussed from the time of their discovery up to the present time. One question in particular was considered most frequently: Are these clusters within the limits of our own system of stars or are they beyond it? No particularly good arguments could be advanced for either side until Shapley published his remarkable series of papers on the globular clusters in 1914 to 1918. He found three methods of determining their distances.

466. First Method. Bailey of the Harvard Observatory had discovered some years ago that in certain globular clusters there were many variable stars; thus in NGC 5272 there were 132 and in NGC 7078 there were 51 variables. Other clusters had fewer variables and in some clusters none were found. Some of these variables were of the ordinary δ Cephei type and others of the so-called *cluster* type, but there seemed to be no valid reason for differentiating between the δ Cephei variables having periods

Fig. 235. The great globular star cluster in Hercules (NGC 6205). (*Mt. Wilson Observatory.*)

longer than one day and the cluster-type variables having periods of about half a day. Shapley therefore assumed that they were essentially alike and used these as well as some cepheids not in the clusters, and the variables of this type found by Miss Leavitt in the smaller Magellanic Cloud, in deriving the period-luminosity curve (solid line, Fig. 226). By means of this curve he was able to determine the distances of those clusters having cepheid variables by the principle discussed in Sec. 443.

467. Second Method. Shapley found that the mean apparent magnitude of the 25 brightest stars in the globular clusters was approximately

1.2 magnitudes brighter than the cluster variables with periods less than 1 day. Since the period-luminosity law gives the absolute magnitude of these variables to be 0.0, it follows that the mean absolute magnitude of the 25 brightest stars is -1.2. From the photographs the apparent magnitude can be found and hence the value of $m - M$ determined. From this the distance can be obtained by the method described in Sec. 410.

468. Third Method. As a final step Shapley examined the relation between the distances of the clusters obtained by the two methods described above and their angular diameters and brought out the significant fact that, with very few exceptions, the globular clusters are of approximately the same linear diameter. It was therefore possible to obtain approximate values of distances directly from photographs—a cluster whose image was twice as large as that of another was very probably only half as far away. This method was by no means as accurate as the first two, but it served in those cases in which the others could not be used.

469. Distances of the Globular Clusters. In Table XVI are given the distances and certain data of a number of globular clusters taken from

TABLE XVI

NGC	Angular diameter	Linear diameter, parsecs	Absolute magnitude	Distance in thousands	
				Parsecs	Light-years
104	53′.6	118	−10.2	7.6	24.8
288	13 .1	55	− 6.8	14.5	47.3
1851	11 .5	47	− 8.1	14.0	45.6
4147	2 .8	16	− 5.5	20.0	65.2
5272	22 .1	78	− 8.2	12.2	39.8
5897	13 .1	53	− 6.5	13.8	45.0
6205	18 .1	50	− 8.1	9.6	31.3
6254	21 .5	52	− 7.6	8.3	27.1
6752	41 .9	71	− 7.4	5.8	18.9
6809	28 .7	48	− 7.7	5.8	18.9
7078	18 .1	60	− 8.3	11.5	37.5
7089	16 .9	68	− 8.5	13.8	45.0

Shapley's most recent work. There are included the largest, the smallest, and a number of the more typical objects.

470. Distribution of the Globular Clusters in Space. An examination of the positions of the globular clusters shows them to be confined almost exclusively to one-half of the celestial sphere as seen from the sun. The center of this hemisphere is in galactic latitude 0° and in galactic longitude

327°.   The distribution of the clusters is approximately uniform north and south of the galactic plane.   From the evidence available the globular clusters are found in a spherical volume of space whose center coincides with the center of the galactic system.   Since the sun is near the outer boundary of the galactic system, it would likewise be near the outer boundary of the system of globular clusters, thus accounting for the apparent localization of the clusters in one-half of the sky.

471. Size and Star Density. Having now obtained a knowledge of the distances of the globular clusters, we may next consider the question of their actual size and star density.   From the relation between apparent diameter and distance we find that the diameter of an average cluster is approximately 180 light-years, or 55 parsecs.   The volume of such a sphere will be approximately 87,000 cubic parsecs.   On the assumption of 100,000 stars in a cluster, the mean star density is approximately 1.15, a value about 11 times the star density in the neighborhood of the sun.   The actual density in a cluster varies, however, being much above the mean at the center and much below near the outer boundary.

472. Spectra and Radial Velocity of the Globular Clusters. In 1909, Fath investigated the spectra of the brighter stars of several clusters and in three following years added some others.   The observations showed that in some clusters the mean spectrum of the brighter stars is of approximately F type, while in others there was evidence of both F and G types. These results were confirmed and much additional work accomplished by V. M. Slipher.   No way has yet been found to determine, with any degree of accuracy, the individual spectral types of the stars in clusters, although such information would be of the greatest value in studying the development of these great aggregations of stars.

The radial velocities of 50 globular clusters are now known.   Most of them were obtained at the Lowell, Mt. Wilson, and Lick Observatories. The velocities range from $+290$ to -360 km per sec with respect to the sun as determined by Mayall.

THE GALACTIC NEBULAE

473. There are scattered about in the sky many objects which appear more or less diffuse in character when looked at through the telescope and they were called *nebulae* by the early observers because of their nebulous appearance.   Later, better telescopes showed that some of these objects were really star clusters, but others resisted every effort at resolution into stars.

474. Classification. We shall follow Hubble in the classification of nebulae.   His subdivisions are as follows:

Galactic nebulae
  A. Planetaries
  B. Diffuse
      1. Predominantly luminous
      2. Predominantly obscure
      3. Conspicuously mixed

This classification refers fundamentally to the apparent form of these objects as shown on photographs taken with large telescopes and not to their physical characteristics. At a later time, when more is known about their actual size, mass, spectra, and physical conditions generally, a different classification may be in order.

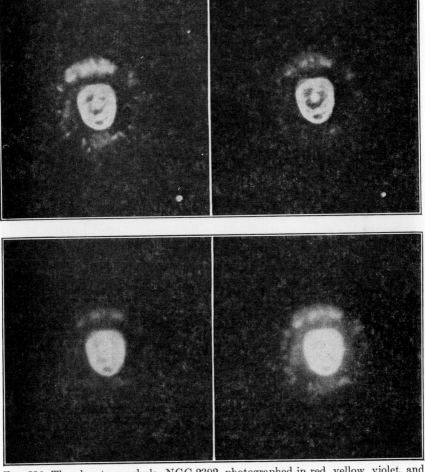

FIG. 236. The planetary nebula, NGC 2392, photographed in red, yellow, violet, and ultraviolet light. (*Mt. Wilson and Palomar Observatories.*)

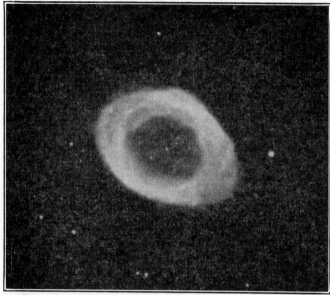

FIG. 237. Ring nebula in Lyra. (*Mt. Wilson Observatory.*)

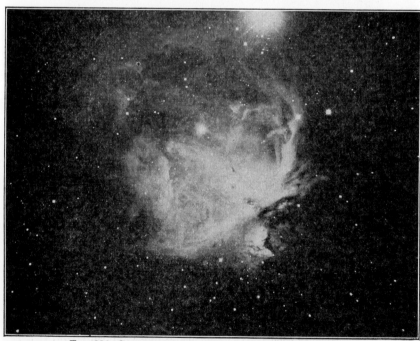

FIG. 238. Great Nebula in Orion. (*Goodsell Observatory.*)

These nebulae are known to belong within the borders of our sidereal system. For the most part they are located in or near the galactic plane. In appearance they vary greatly as may be seen from the photographs. Their composition and physical characteristics will be considered in Secs. 476 and 477.

475. The Planetary Nebulae. These objects were so named by early observers because visually they showed only a small disk with a fairly

Fig. 239. Trifid Nebula in Sagittarius.   (*Mt. Wilson Observatory.*)

well-defined edge. In this they resemble the appearance of Uranus and Neptune. In a considerable number of them a fairly sharp nucleus was also seen. It was not until recent years, when astronomical photography had reached its present high development, that the intricate forms of these small objects became known. Even yet there is much to be desired in their accurate delineation since they are so small that even the great modern reflectors yield only very small images.

Figure 236 shows one of the smaller planetary nebulae in which the brighter parts are very near the nucleus. Another form is shown in

Fig. 237. Here the brighter part is along the boundary with very little nebulosity near the nucleus. From its form this type is often called a *ring nebula,* but there appears to be no essential difference between it and the first.

The nuclei of planetary nebulae are faint but extremely hot stars. The surface temperature of these nuclear stars ranges from 50,000 to 120,-000°K, according to Page. At these high temperatures most of the radiation lies in the ultraviolet part of the spectrum.

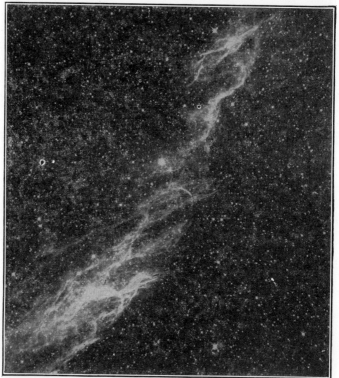

Fig. 240. Network Nebula in Cygnus. (*Mt. Wilson Observatory.*)

The total number of planetary nebulae now known is nearly 400.

476. The Diffuse Nebulae (Luminous). To this group belong some of the most beautiful objects in the sky such as the Great Nebula in Orion (Fig. 238), the Trifid Nebula in Sagittarius (Fig. 239), and the Network Nebula in Cygnus (Fig. 240). Their dimensions are large—so large that they must be expressed in light-years. Thus the bright portion of the Orion nebula in the center of Fig. 238 is about 25 light-years in diameter.

They are not static but the seat of violent currents in great turmoil. In their detailed spectrographic investigation of the Orion nebula, Campbell and Moore obtained radial velocities with respect to the sun ranging from 10 to 23 km (6 to 14 miles) per sec for the central parts. Tremendous streams of nebulous matter are being intermingled in chaotic fashion as no regularity of motion such as rotation of the mass is apparent.

477. Spectra. The spectra of all these various forms of nebulae consist almost exclusively of bright lines (Fig. 241). Because of this characteristic these objects are frequently referred to as *bright-line* or *emission*

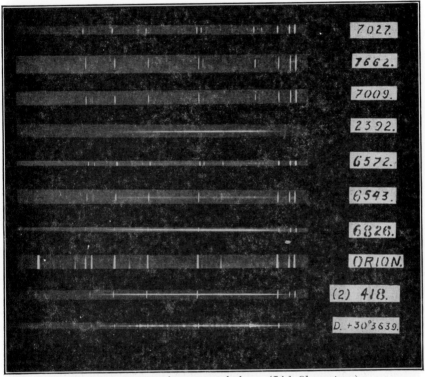

FIG. 241. Spectra of gaseous nebulae. (*Lick Observatory.*)

nebulae. The nuclei of the planetaries are usually O-type stars, and in some cases there is a general continuous background in the spectra.

The first element to be recognized in the nebulae was hydrogen. This was found by Huggins in 1864. Later helium was identified. The two most conspicuous lines in the spectra at λ 5007 and λ 4959 for years defied identification. They were provisionally assigned to a hypothetical element called *nebulium*. Recent advances in our knowledge of atomic radiation, however, now show that the hypothetical nebulium is nothing more than our familiar oxygen radiating under different conditions than can be obtained in the laboratory.

The most complete analysis of the spectra of planetary nebulae was made by Bowen and Wyse at the Lick Observatory. They photographed over 160 bright nebular lines and identified lines belonging to the first 26 elements in the periodic table. A further comparison shows that the relative abundance of these elements in the nebulae is approximately the same as the relative abundance of the same elements in the sun. A list of most of these elements will be found on page 355.

Small objects like the planetary nebulae lend themselves readily to examination by the slitless spectrograph. Accordingly, instead of having merely bright lines (the images of the slit), the spectrum will consist of a series of images of the nebula itself, each image formed by the light of a single wavelength, and, if a reasonable dispersion is used, these images will be separated on the photographic plate (Fig. 242).

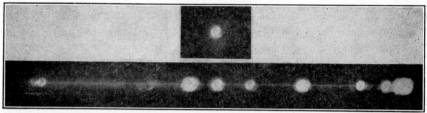

Fig. 242. Slitless spectrogram of the planetary nebula NGC 7662 (below) and direct photograph (above). (*Lick Observatory.*)

The results of the use of the slitless spectrograph on these small objects present many points of interest. For example, it is found that the images will be neither of the same size nor of precisely the same shape. This indicates either a lack of uniformity in the composition of the nebula or, possibly, a variation in the cause of the luminosity. Which of the two is the correct interpretation, or whether both are operative, cannot be decided at the present time.

Another interesting fact concerning the spectra of the bright-line nebulae is that the relative intensities of the lines vary not only from nebula to nebula, but also in some cases in different parts of the same nebula.

478. Rotation, Radial Velocities, etc. In 1918 Campbell and Moore published a very complete spectrographic investigation of 125 emission nebulae which were bright enough to yield results with exposures of 33 hr or less. Three of their results are of especial interest: (1) Most of the planetary nebulae having an elliptical outline are in rotation about the shorter axis; (2) many of the spectral lines were double which indicated expansion of the planetary; (3) the radial velocities with respect to the sun ranged from +309 to −145 km per sec.

479. Distances of Galactic Nebulae. The distances of only a few diffuse nebulae have been measured and even these measures vary considerably. Thus Trumpler found the distance of the Orion nebula to be about 1800 light-years, while Minkowski places it at only a little over half that distance or 980 light-years. The Trifid Nebula is possibly 2000 light-years distant.

Planetary nebulae in general are distant objects; Van Maanen's work on 23 and Anderson's on 33 planetaries agree on a value of $0''.0007$ as the mean parallax of their respective lists. This is the equivalent of a distance of 4700 light-years.

From this mean distance it is possible to get a rough value of mean diameter since we know the angular dimensions of these objects. If we omit the three largest from Anderson's list, we find the mean diameter to be of the order of 1 light-year.

The masses of the planetaries cannot be measured directly, but estimates, based on indirect methods, are possible. Goldberg and Aller find the average mass to be of the order of 0.1 the mass of the sun. This means an exceedingly low mean density, possibly only a few thousand atoms per cubic centimeter.

480. Cause of Luminosity. The primary cause of the luminosity of emission nebulae is the ultraviolet light radiated from nearby stars. Since only the O- and early B-type stars radiate ultraviolet light in sufficient quantities to produce the results, we might say that such stars are a prerequisite for nebular radiation.

There is also a certain amount of continuous background in the spectra of emission nebulae (Fig. 241). Some of it may come from the gaseous materials and some may come by reflection of starlight from dust particles.

481. Obscure or Dark Nebulae. In certain parts of the Milky Way there are found dark lanes such as are shown in Fig. 243. At one time it was thought that these dark regions represented merely the absence of luminous matter. More recent studies, however, show that the lack of stars is due to an obscuring medium—fine dust and gaseous elements (Chap. 19)—which lies between us and the stars of the Milky Way.

Figure 244 shows a nebulous region near ζ Orionis. The illustration tells its own story. It hardly seems possible to look at it and still doubt the existence of a cloud of dark matter lying in front of the bright nebulous masses.

But there is still further evidence of matter in space, aside from the planets, which is not self-luminous. Figure 245 is a reproduction of a photograph of the Pleiades. Around many of the stars great masses of nebulosity are seen. These nebulae look very much like some of the diffuse, bright-line nebulae. In 1912, V. M. Slipher investigated the spectra of the nebulae in the Pleiades and found not a single bright line. By making exposures totaling 21 hr on a single plate he found that these nebulae showed an absorption spectrum which matched, line for line, the

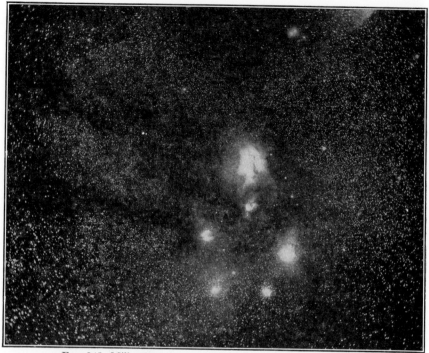

FIG. 243. Milky Way near ρ Ophiuchi. (*Yerkes Observatory.*)

FIG. 244. Region near ζ Orionis. (*Mt. Wilson Observatory.*)

spectra of the stars within their boundaries. The only reasonable explanation of these spectra is that they are produced by starlight reflected from the particles composing the nebulae. We therefore seem justified in holding that if the stars were extinguished, these nebulae would be dark nebulae like the others considered above. Several other objects which show properties similar to the Pleiades nebulae have been found since Slipher's original discovery.

Fig. 245. The Pleiades nebulosity.   (*Goodsell Observatory.*)

482. Changes in Nebulae. Barnard observed variations in brightness in the nucleus of the planetary nebula, NGC 7662, and the central star of the ring nebula in Lyra is likewise known to vary. Until 1918, a few instances of change were also known in other nebulae. In these instances, the nebula appears in the vicinity of, or connected with, a variable star. In one of these nebulae, NGC 2261, whose variability was discovered by Hubble, Slipher has shown that its spectrum is just like that of the variable star with which it is connected, so that we may assume it to be shining by reflected starlight like the Pleiades nebulae. The variation in the brightness of the nebula, however, seems to have no direct connection with the variation of the star. The changes in the nebula are therefore not due merely to variations in the brightness of the star.   Figure 246 is a reproduction of two photographs of this nebula.   It is very evident that marked changes in brightness have occurred in different parts. Changes have been noted in photographs taken only 24 hr apart.

In 1921 Lampland announced that a comparison of Lowell and Mt. Wilson photographs of NGC 1952, the "Crab" nebula (Fig. 247), showed changes in the fine filaments of this object.   Later photographs by Duncan have shown that this nebula is expanding at the rate of 0".21 per year. A study of the spectrum by Mayall showed a radial expansion of 1300

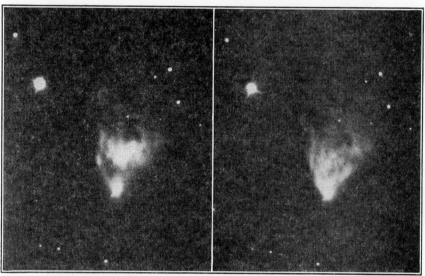

Fig. 246. Hubble's variable nebula, NGC 2261, in Monoceros.   (*Mt. Wilson Observatory, Sept.* 18, 1920, *and Nov.* 1, 1921.)

km/per sec.   Assuming the expansion in the two units to be equivalent, the distance to the nebula is 1250 parsecs (4100 light-years).   The corresponding distance modulus ($m - M$) is 10.5.

If we assume a uniform rate of expansion for the nebula and figure backward, we find it would have been a point image about A.D. 1150.   If the average expansion rate was slightly less than at present, we might assume a point image about A.D. 1050.

In the year 1054 Chinese annals record the appearance of a nova in that region of the sky which was so bright that it was visible by day.   Its apparent magnitude was therefore near −5.

While we cannot be absolutely certain yet, there is reason to believe that the present nebula represents the outer remnants of a star which went through the nova stage and which were given their initial expansive impulse by the outburst.   If this assumption is true, the absolute magnitude of the nova was −15.5, a true supernova.

483. Radio Stars. Visible light represents only a small part of the family of radiation to which it belongs.   This family includes also the very short waves of gamma radiation from radioactive materials; X rays; ultraviolet radiation with wavelengths just shorter than those of visible light; infrared, or heat, waves just longer than visible light; and radio waves.   The various members of the family differ from one another in that each represents a different range of wavelengths.   We might expect

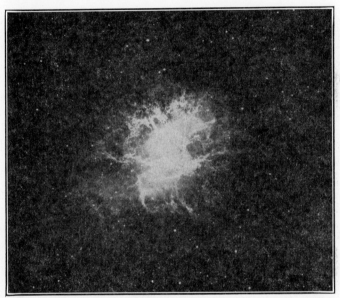

FIG. 247. The "Crab" nebula photographed in red light with the Hale telescope. (*Mt. Wilson and Palomar Observatories.*)

that all members of this family could bring us information about portions of the universe which lie outside the earth.   Such is not the case, however, as the earth's atmosphere serves as a very effective shield against a large portion of the radiations that we might otherwise use in astronomical study.   Two principal ranges of wavelengths are available, however. One range includes visible light, part of the ultraviolet, and some infrared radiation.   It is in this range of wavelengths that astronomical observations prior to 1945 were made.   The other range of wavelengths admitted by the atmosphere includes very short radio waves from 1 to 1000 cm in wavelength.   The discovery of celestial radio signals in this range has opened a new field of astronomy called *radio astronomy*.

Radio waves from space may be gathered in a spherical parabolic mirror just as light waves are gathered (Fig. 248). With such a mirror the resolving power depends, as in the case of visible light, on the ratio of the aperture of the mirror to the wavelength of the radiation. Since the lengths of radio waves are so much longer than light waves, a mirror for radio astronomy would have to be impracticably large to have the same resolution as even the poorest of light telescopes. To achieve better resolving power radiotelescopes have often been built in the form of interferometers (Sec. 415). Thus the telescopes consist of two antennae a

Fig. 248. The 600-in. radiotelescope of the Naval Research Laboratory. (*Official U.S. Navy photograph.*)

considerable distance apart. The combined signal from these two antennae is similar to that which could have been obtained by focusing the radio waves from two widely separated parts of a mirror as large as the distance between the two. When the two antennae are thus used, it is possible to locate various points or regions in the sky from which radio waves are coming.

The sources of astronomical radio waves so far identified are the sun, the radio stars, and the general background of radiation. As seen by radio waves, the sun has approximately twice as great an area as when seen by light waves. This indicates that at least some of the radio waves originate in the solar corona.

Radio stars are point sources of radio waves. Rough measurements of their distance indicates that the brightest is approximately half as far from our solar system as is the nearest visual star, though the determination is not very reliable. Those which have been identified appear to be uniformly distributed in the sky, as are the nearer stars in our galaxy. They appear not to be identified with visual stars, however. The diffuse background of radio noise, on the other hand, fits the general contours of the galaxies (Chap. 21).

These facts suggest that the observed radio stars are distributed similarly to the nearer visual stars in our galaxy, but that they are in such a physical condition that radio waves from them are much more intense than is the case for visual stars, while visible light waves, on the contrary, are much less intense. The new field of radio astronomy promises great advances in the years directly ahead.

EXERCISES

1. The object NGC 5694 was found to be a globular cluster by Lampland and Tombaugh of the Lowell Observatory in 1932. By using the brightest-star method Baade at the Mt. Wilson Observatory finds $m - M = 18$. What is the distance of this cluster?   *Ans.* 39,800 parsecs.

2. If the angular diameter of NGC 5694 is $3'.0$, what is its linear diameter?
                              Ans. 35 parsecs

3. Alcyone, the brightest star of the Pleiades, has an apparent magnitude of 3.0. If its parallax is $0''.01$, what is its absolute magnitude?   *Ans.* -2.0.

CHAPTER 19

INTERSTELLAR MATTER

The various investigations involving star ratios, the period-luminosity law, etc., as considered thus far, have made no mention of any other factor than distance in changing the luminosity of stars. This implies that space is wholly transparent. We must now study some other factors.

484. Gases in Interstellar Space. In 1904 Hartmann of Potsdam was studying the spectrum of the spectroscopic binary, δ Orionis. In this case only one set of lines was found which shifted its position by 170 km per sec in a period of 5.7 days. In addition to these shifting lines, however, he found that the H and K calcium lines did not show these changes in radial velocity but remained stationary. Hartmann interpreted this peculiarity as indicating a cloud of calcium vapor between us and the star, the calcium lines being produced by absorption in the cloud and not by the star's atmosphere. Since that time hundreds of other stars have been found which show similar stationary calcium lines.

In addition to atomic lines of calcium, there have also been found lines of atomic sodium, potassium, titanium, and iron. These lines are now called *interstellar lines* as they show absorption effects of gases which are found in the space between the stars.

The interstellar lines of any element vary in their intensity from star to star. This variation is found to depend on the distance of the star— the greater the distance of the star, the stronger the interstellar lines. This relationship between distance and line intensity is sufficiently exact so that the line intensity can be used as an approximate measure of the distance of a star if no other method is applicable.

A detailed study of the interstellar lines with spectrographs of high revolving power by Beals showed a most interesting structure—some of the lines were double, and later Adams found others with up to six components. The explanation of the multiple character of these lines is comparatively simple. Let us suppose a number of clouds of gas in the path of the ray of light from a star. If these clouds have different radial velocities, their effect on the ray of light will produce a separate absorption line for each cloud. These lines, for any particular gas and region of the spectrum, will fall very close together, but will be separated because of the different radial velocities of the clouds which produce them (Fig. 249). Since these lines have appreciable widths, they may in some cases merge more or less and produce a composite line of varying density.

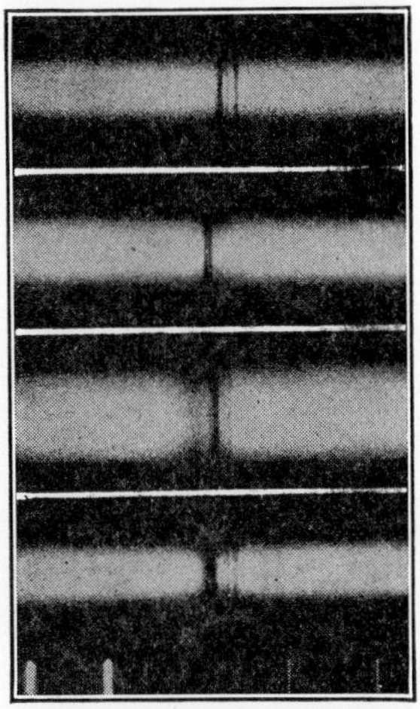

The fact that strong interstellar lines of calcium and sodium are so much in evidence does not exclude the presence of interstellar hydrogen, helium, etc. Under the conditions existing in interstellar space, the atoms of these elements would absorb only in the extreme ultraviolet, a region which cannot be observed.

Struve and Elvey, by means of a specially designed spectrograph, were able to observe faint emission lines of hydrogen in extensive regions of the Milky Way where direct photography does not show any nebulous structure. Thus there is evidence of the existence of hydrogen in interstellar space although no absorption is found.

FIG. 249. Multiple interstellar line, calcium K, with high dispersion. (*Yerkes Observatory.*)

The intensity of the emission lines found by Struve and Elvey varied considerably from region to region, which indicates that the hydrogen, too, is collected into great clouds.

In addition to clouds of atoms, there are also found interstellar lines produced by molecules of CH and CN.

485. Solids in Interstellar Space. Some regions in the sky appear as black or nearly black areas on photographs such as Figs. 239 and Fig. 244. They can be most readily accounted for by assuming them to be clouds of dust, the particles of which cut off the light from stars lying beyond them. In most cases, however, starlight is not entirely intercepted and some stars will be visible although their light will be diminished.

One of these dust clouds is very evident to the unaided eye. The Milky Way from Cygnus to Sagittarius appears to be divided into two parts. This is caused by relatively near dust clouds which stretch along the Milky Way and reduce greatly the number of stars which can be seen.

The effect on starlight is not that of complete blocking off of light but is of a selective character. The phenomenon is called *scattering*, and light of short wavelengths is scattered more than light of long wavelengths. As a result more red than blue light will reach us from the star. A star which, if near, would be white will appear yellowish or reddish, depending on how much of its blue light has been lost by scattering or, in other words, how far away it is—the farther, the redder.

A study of this reddening effect on the light of distant stars indicates that the dust grains responsible for it have an average diameter of the order of 10^{-5} cm (1/250,000 in.). There are about 25 of these grains per cubic kilometer (100 per cubic mile) according to Greenstein.

The grains of interstellar matter, while averaging 10^{-5} cm in diameter, have in all probability a considerable range in size. The range cannot be determined, but it does not seem impossible to assume sizes ranging from coarse gravel to almost molecular proportions.

The composition of these grains cannot be determined directly; but, by indirect methods, Goldberg and Aller are led to suggest glass, silica dust, frozen gases, and ice. In addition we may infer, from the presence of interstellar lines of iron and titanium, that there may also be metallic grains existing in the dust clouds but not in sufficient amount to make their presence known.

486. Arrangement of Interstellar Matter. Photographs show that the dust grains are not uniformly scattered through space but tend to form clouds. The fact that interstellar lines vary in intensity and show differing radial velocities likewise indicates that the gases, too, tend to group themselves into clouds. These clouds of gases and dust are not sharply defined but represent marked condensations in an otherwise continuous medium.

In cases where the condensation is especially marked and where there are stars giving off large quantities of ultraviolet radiation, we find diffuse emission nebulae because of the gases in the cloud; in cases where the nearby stars give relatively little ultraviolet radiation, we have the diffuse reflection nebulae because of reflection from the dust grains.

The mean density of interstellar matter is of the order of 3×10^{-24} g per cm^3. Since this is also the mean density of stars per unit of space, we may say that the total amount of matter in our stellar system can be divided into two approximately equal parts—one half forms the stars, the other half the dispersed matter between the stars.

487. Interstellar Polarization of Light. In 1949 Hiltner and Hall reported that the light of some distant stars is partially plane-polarized. In some cases this polarization amounted to 12 per cent. The cause of the phenomenon is not definitely known but is tentatively assumed to be a magnetic field in space which orients some of the dust particles in such a way as to polarize the starlight passing by. The planes of polarization are essentially parallel over large regions of the Milky Way. This parallelism applies to stars of various spectral types in the same region and is therefore believed to be caused by a condition in space and not by any characteristic of the individual stars. This condition, as stated above, could be a magnetic field which may be caused by the rotation of the galaxy.

488. Source of Interstellar Matter. At one time it was held that interstellar matter was of small import and that, what little there was, had its source in the stars. The sun was found to send out eruptive prominences which carried matter outward beyond its gravitational field and it was dispersed through space. Other stars were assumed to do likewise. The small amount of matter thus dispersed seemed negligble.

More recently, when it developed that interstellar matter and stars divided the available matter more or less equally between them, the question arose as to which is the more important, cosmically, the stars or the clouds of dispersed matter. The question might also be stated: Did the dispersed matter come from the stars, or, did the stars come from the dispersed matter? This question will be considered in more detail in Chap. 23.

489. Absorption of Light in Space. It is evident that the early assumption of the transparency of interstellar space is not justified and that it will be necessary to modify considerably the distances derived by the application of merely the inverse-square law.

The loss of intensity of starlight will depend not only on the distance of the star but also on the energy absorbed by the clouds of gases and the blocking or scattering of the light because of the dust grains. The latter is by far the more important cause of loss of light in space. The gases produce very little general absorption, and the loss caused by the gases in producing absorption lines in the spectra is negligibly small. The big loss occurs by the complete blocking of light by the larger grains and the scattering of the shorter waves of light by the microscopic grains.

Some years ago Trumpler reported that he found an average loss of 0.3 mag per kiloparsec (1000 parsecs) for the visual region of the spectrum, and 0.7 for the photographic region. Since then many others have worked on the problem. The net result shows that the absorbing dust is strongly condensed toward the plane of the Milky Way in a layer about 200 parsecs thick, but the condensation is far from uniform. In some directions the absorption may average $0^m.4$, while in others the average may be $2^m.0$ per kiloparsec. In the direction of the Scorpius-Sagittarius region of the Milky Way the absorption is so great that we can see practically nothing beyond 5 kiloparsecs. It is therefore clear that our study of the structure of the galaxy is greatly hindered by these absorbing dust clouds.

490. Cosmic Rays. The earth is being constantly bombarded by high-energy particles known as cosmic rays, in spite of the fact that they are actually discrete atomic entities. The particles that reach far enough down through the earth's atmosphere for laboratory study consist both of the original particles from outer space, and of rapidly moving fragments of atoms of the earth's upper atmosphere, which have been disintegrated by collision with the bombarding cosmic rays.   The primary cosmic rays, it is generally agreed, consist mostly of nuclei of hydrogen atoms, with the nuclei of some heavier atoms also included.

Only very high-velocity primary particles can penetrate through the earth's magnetic field.   Those which do penetrate are greatly deflected, so that it is difficult to ascertain the direction from which a particle has come from outer space.   Nevertheless, the absence of any day-to-night variation in cosmic-ray intensities suggests that the particles come from all directions in space.   Thus the origin of these particles is somewhat uncertain.   Recent evidence by many investigators suggests that a substantial number of the cosmic rays originate in disturbances in the sun or are, at least, affected by such disturbances.

Two major questions concerning cosmic rays await an adequate answer: (1) Where do the primary particles originate, and (2) how do they acquire their enormous velocities?

Perhaps the cosmic rays pervade all space, galactic and intergalactic. If so, their total energy, judging from the sample taken at the earth, is comparable with that of all of the stars together.   Perhaps the cosmic rays are held within the galaxies by the galactic magnetic fields.   In this case they may originate within stars of the galaxies; they may, for example, have their origin in the supernovae and later be accelerated by passing through streams of ionized matter in magnetic fields, or be accelerated by the magnetic fields of binary stars, which may act as huge alternating-current electric generators.   It is also possible that the cosmic rays originate in the newly discovered radio stars (Sec. 483), quite unexplained in themselves, where conditions are thought to be favorable for the origin of high-speed particles like the cosmic rays.

CHAPTER 20

STRUCTURE OF THE GALAXY

We have found that our galactic system consists of many kinds of objects—stars, galactic clusters, globular star clusters, and clouds of luminous and nonluminous matter. We shall now attempt to study the system as a whole by putting the various parts together in a diagram (Fig. 250).

491. The Stars. From the results of the star counts it was found that the billions of stars which belong to the system are distributed in a volume of space shaped like a very thin convex lens. The diameter of the system is about 30,000 parsecs and its thickness about 3000 parsecs.

The star density is greatest near the center of the system and diminishes as the distance from the center increases. At any particular distance from the center the star density is greatest in the galactic plane and diminishes with increasing distance from the plane. These statements concerning star density apply only when we deal in averages and smooth out irregularities.

In the figure the stars will be indicated by small dots. For reasons which will appear later (Chap. 21) we shall add a few dots around the center so as to produce a bulge there.

492. The Galactic Clusters. The first of the irregularities are small clusters of stars which we call *galactic clusters*. Far more important irregularities are introduced by larger groups of stars which may be illustrated by the star clouds of the Milky Way. These occupy much larger volumes of space than the galactic clusters. There is some evidence that the stars in the neighborhood of the sun form such a larger unit. It is called the *local cluster*. This clustering cannot be shown on the diagram on account of the small scale.

493. The Interstellar Matter. In the space between the stars is found finely divided material: gases and dust. This material consists of atoms of hydrogen, helium, calcium, etc., molecules of CH and CN, as well as larger particles of various sorts which, collectively, are spoken of as *dust*. Both gases and dust are more or less mixed; they are not uniformly distributed and thus give rise to the terms *gas clouds* and *dust clouds*. Under some circumstances the gas clouds reveal themselves as diffuse luminous nebulae, under others as the material producing the interstellar lines in stellar spectra. The dust clouds give rise to reflection nebulae or dark regions in the sky. These clouds are indicated by black irregular areas in the figure.

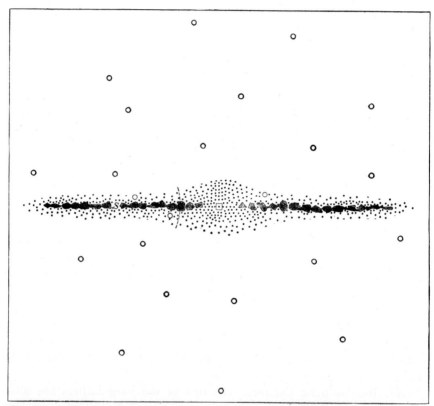

Fig. 250. Schematic cross section of galaxy through sun *S* and center. Stars are dots; small circles are globular clusters; square is center of system; black areas represent clouds of interstellar dust and gases.

494. The Globular Clusters. These clusters were found to fill an approximately spherical space, the center of the sphere being in the galactic equator in the direction of galactic longitude 327°. The diameter of the sphere is of the order of 30,000 parsecs. The globular clusters are represented by small circles in the diagram. Relatively the circles are too large to represent actual sizes to scale.

495. The Star Haze. The lens-shaped surface, which is the general boundary of the stars, represents the volume in which stars are at least moderately numerous. Beyond this boundary, and particularly in a direction perpendicular to the galactic plane, Shapley has found some faint cepheid variables. These may possibly more or less fill the spherical region of the globular clusters. The star density of this intercluster region is very low, possibly less than 1 per cent of that in the lens-shaped region. It might be said that there is a faint haze of stars in the intercluster region. These stars belong to the galactic system but so little is known about them as yet that the most we can do is to acknowledge their existence.

496. Details of Galactic Structure. Thus far we have considered merely the volume of the galaxy when we mentioned the lens-shaped outline. For many years it was evident that the stars were not uniformly distributed within this space; and Easton, in the early part of this century, advocated the idea that the stars were arranged in spirals around the center so that if the galaxy were viewed from a great distance in the direction of a galactic pole, it would look somewhat like NGC 598 (Fig. 258). This idea seemed reasonable, but no direct evidence was available until Morgan of the Yerkes Observatory presented evidence of two spiral arms, an inner arm in which the sun is located and an outer arm at least 6000 light-years farther from the galactic center. Work by Whitford and Cole, of the University of Wisconsin, followed the inner arm in the southern Milky Way to 3000 light-years closer to the center than the sun. Bok, and others, from a study of photographs taken at the Boyden station of the Harvard Observatory in South Africa, have shown marked concentrations of stars in the inner spiral arm.

In Sec. 484 the presence of great clouds of hydrogen in the Milky Way was noted. In 1952 Oort and his collaborators at the Leiden Observatory reported that by a study of the 21-cm radiation of hydrogen by radio methods they had been able to trace a spiral arm of hydrogen clouds almost halfway around the galactic center. Evidence is thus being accumulated that our galaxy has a spiral structure around the mass of stars at the galactic center.

497. Rotation of the Galaxy. The center of the galactic system must be, at least approximately, at its center of mass. If the stars, nebulae, etc., are subject to gravitational attraction toward this center, they should have moved toward it and the system should have collapsed long ago, if they were relatively stationary with respect to the center. In order to maintain itself the system must be in rotation about its center of mass in the same way the planetary system maintains itself by revolving around the sun.

There are two ways to study the problem, by means of proper motions and by means of the radial velocities of the stars. The elementary theory of the second method is the simpler and will be considered here.

In Fig. 251 let M be the center of mass of the system, S the sun, and a . . . h stars revolving around the center in circular orbits. Stars at the same distance from the center will have the same orbital velocity, while stars at different distances will have different velocities; the greater the distance, the less the orbital velocity.

Let us now measure the radial velocities of the stars a . . . h with respect to the sun. Star a is moving around M faster than the sun and therefore its distance from S is increasing—its radial velocity is *positive*. Star b is moving directly across the line of sight from S; hence its radial

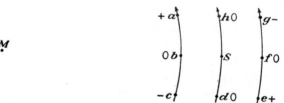

FIG. 251. Relation of the radial velocities of stars with respect to the sun S, and the rotation of the galaxy around its center of mass M.

velocity would be *zero*. Star c is moving around M more rapidly than S, its distance from S is decreasing, and therefore its radial velocity is *negative*. Star d is moving around M at the same velocity as S, the distance Sd remains constant, and the radial velocity is *zero*. Similarly, with reference to S, the radial velocity of star e is *positive*, of star f *zero*, of star g *negative*, and of star h *zero*.

In Chap. 15 we found that stars in general had individual space motions. Therefore the theory cannot be applied to single stars. If, however, we take groups of stars in directions Sa, Sb, etc., and assume that, on the average, the individual space motions cancel each other in each group, then we can study the results.

When the radial velocities of the stars are analyzed, the signs of the velocities are found to change in accordance with theory. If, in addition to the radial velocities, the distances of the stars involved are known, it is evident that we have the data for determining the direction and amount of motion, the direction and distance of the center, and the mass of the system. It so happens, however, that even the best data available for stellar radial velocities leave too great an uncertainty in the sun's orbital velocity and it has been necessary to determine it from work on the globular clusters.

Studies of galactic rotation have been carried out by Lindblad of Stockholm, Oort of Leiden, Plaskett and Pearce of the Dominion Astrophysical, and Joy of the Mt. Wilson Observatories. The results are approximately:

Direction of center at gal. long. . . . . 325°
Distance of sun from center. . . . . 9000 parsecs
Velocity of sun around center. . . . . 275 km per sec*
Time of one revolution of sun. . . . . 224 × 10⁶ years
Probable mass of system. . . . . 16.5 × 10¹⁰ suns
Diameter of system. 30,000 parsecs

Plaskett and Pearce also showed that the interstellar clouds rotate around the galactic center with the stars. A study of the radial velocities of the planetary nebulae by Berman shows that they partake of the rotation. The few large, diffuse nebulae, like the one in Orion, have such low velocities (less than 20 km per sec) with respect to the sun that they, too, must revolve around the galactic center.

Two classes of objects remain to be considered with reference to the problem of galactic rotation—the obscuring dust clouds and the globular clusters. For the present there seems to be no way to study the dust clouds, as they cannot be seen, but there seems no reason to assume that they are different in this instance from the stars with which they are inextricably mixed.

The globular clusters, however, are in a somewhat different situation. As a group they are found far beyond the lens-shaped space in directions perpendicular to the galactic plane. From their apparently symmetrical distribution around the center of the system it is not impossible that they revolve around the center as individuals, in orbits inclined at all possible angles to the plane of the galactic equator. Radial velocities have been determined for about 50 clusters. These velocities range from −360 to +290 km per sec. Since none are equal to the velocity of escape, they are gravitationally a part of the system.

498. Star Drifts. The solutions for rotation of the galaxy must be taken as merely first approximations to the truth. The assumption that the stars are revolving about the center in circular orbits is one case in point. It is more likely that the orbits are more or less elliptical and that different groups of stars have somewhat different orbits which may intersect. Such an assumption explains in a simple manner the star drifts (Sec. 426). Two or more groups of stars in different orbits would pass through each other at points of intersection of the orbits and produce the drift effect.

499. Our Range of Vision. Let us now look again at Fig. 250. The absorbing regions are so distributed that, from the sun's position, S, we cannot see the star clouds at the center. Our observations, therefore, in or near the plane of the galaxy, are limited to one side of the lens-shaped space. Let us then draw the dotted arc as representing the limits of

* Recent work by Mayall on the globular clusters suggests that this value may have to be reduced to about 175 km per sec. If this proves to be correct, the time of revolution of the sun must be correspondingly increased,

observation. We infer that the system is symmetrical and therefore have given it the same structure beyond the center as we have found on our side. In addition the central position has been expanded. The reasons for this will be more easily understood after we have studied the galaxies in Chap. 21.

The range of vision in a direction perpendicular to the plane of the galaxy is not obstructed to any extent by dust clouds, and, in consequence, our vision in that direction is practically unlimited.

CHAPTER 21

OTHER GALAXIES

500. Introduction. The objects to be considered in this chapter are known to lie outside the limits of our galactic system. The evidence on which this statement is based will be presented. Up to the present time these objects have been called *extragalactic* or *anagalactic nebulae*, but the term is no longer appropriate. We shall therefore speak of them as distant *galaxies* since they resemble our own galaxy in size and composition in so far as present evidence goes.

501. Classification. Hubble classifies the distant galaxies as follows:

A. Regular:
  1. Elliptical
  2. Spirals:
    a. Normal spirals
    b. Barred spirals
B. Irregular

This classification, just as in the case of the galactic nebulae, refers only to their apparent form and not to their physical characteristics. At a later time, when more is known about them, a different classification may be in order.

502. Regular Form (Elliptical). The upper four objects shown in Fig. 252 illustrate elliptical types of various degrees of ellipticity. They are brightest near the center and gradually fade out near the boundary. No details of structure are visible in the best photographs obtainable. Their spectra, luminosity, distribution in the sky, etc., are similar to those of the spiral objects.

503. Regular Form (Spiral). The spiral objects may be divided into two groups, the *normal spirals* and the *barred spirals*. Examples of the first group are illustrated in the three objects shown at the left in Fig. 253, while examples of the second group are shown at the right. Additional examples of normal spirals are shown in Figs. 254 and 258.

The *normal* spirals may be further subdivided into three subclasses depending upon the relative proportions between nucleus and spiral arms.

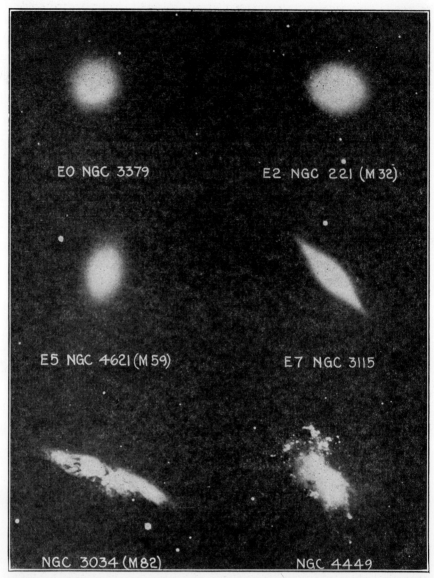

Fig. 252. The upper and middle rows of figures show elliptical galaxies of various degrees of ellipticity. The lower row shows two irregular galaxies. (*Mt. Wilson Observatory.*)

When the nucleus is the dominant portion and the arms but slightly developed, we have an object like *Sa* in Fig. 253. If the nucleus is still prominent but the arms well developed, the form is that of *Sb* in Fig. 253. The third subclass, in which the nucleus is relatively small and the spiral parts are dominant, is illustrated in Fig. 253, *Sc*.

FIG. 253. The three figures at the left illustrate regular spirals. *Sa*, nucleus dominant; *Sb*, nucleus and spiral arms both prominent; *Sc*, spiral arms dominant. The three figures at the right illustrate various types of barred spirals. (*Mt. Wilson Observatory.*)

The *barred* spirals likewise show three subclasses depending upon the relative importance of the nucleus, as shown in Fig. 253 *SBa*, *SBb*, and *SBc*. The special designation of this type of spiral comes from the bright bar crossing the nucleus.

Figures 253 *Sa* and 255 also show another feature which is frequently found in the spirals seen more or less edgewise; namely, the dark rift across the nucleus. Such evidence as we have favors the view that these rifts are not due to absence of nebular material but to occulting matter within or about the object. H. D. Curtis has published photographs of 78 objects, mostly spirals, taken with the Crossley reflector of the Lick Observatory, which show such absorption or occulting effects. It is probable that this absorption effect is similar to that in our own galaxy.

504. Irregular Objects. This group is illustrated by the two lower objects shown in Fig. 252. They have no definite form or structure although they resemble the elliptical and spiral objects in their general spectral characteristics.

505. History. We shall first consider the external galaxies in general. A few were discovered visually by observers with the great 6-ft reflector of Lord Rosse in Ireland in the last quarter of the last century. In the last few years of that time a small photographic reflector in the hands of Sir Isaac Roberts revealed many more. In 1900 Keeler of the Lick Observatory, working with a 36-in. reflector, photographed them in such large numbers that it was evident they were to be counted in tens of thousands, and he further showed that when the images were sufficiently large to show structure, they were of a spiral character.

Up to this time no inkling of their size and distance, and therefore of their nature, had been obtained. Then, in 1908–1910 Fath made the first successful attempt to study their spectra and obtained spectrograms of the bright central parts of 10 of them. Nine showed spectra of the G or K type and one showed bright lines and bands in addition to the absorption lines. On the basis of this evidence he argued that these spirals are composed of myriads of stars. Later, V. M. Slipher of the Lowell Observatory and Wolf at Heidelberg took up the problem. Their results confirmed the first work, and one spiral was found giving an F-type spectrum. Slipher, moreover, succeeded in making a great advance by determining the radial velocities of 39 of these objects. The velocities obtained were large and ranged from −300 to +1800 km per sec. This work was greatly expanded by Humason of the Mt. Wilson Observatory and Mayall of the Lick Observatory. We now have the radial velocities of about 800 of these objects. The values range from −400 to +61,000 km per sec (−250 to +38,000 miles per sec). Only 17 objects are known with negative velocities and these are all of small amount. The great majority of the spirals have very high positive radial velocities.

506. Rotation. Slipher also succeeded in showing that the lines in the spectra of some of the spirals were inclined, which implies that they are in rotation. In some instances the spectral lines are curved in such a way that they indicate greater angular velocities at points near the nucleus than at points farther away. Such objects therefore do not rotate as a unit.

The rotation problem has been more recently attacked by Humason, Babcock, and Mayall at Mt. Wilson and Mt. Hamilton. They have found evidence by the spectrograph of rotation in a considerable number of those extragalactic objects. In the case of two it was found that not only did the absorption lines show tilting, but that in the outer parts there were small areas giving bright-line spectra. It was therefore possible to determine the radial velocity of these emission areas directly.

On the basis of the spectrographic data the evidence shows that a spiral rotates with the convex side of the spiral arms on the forward side.

We shall now examine two of these extragalactic objects in detail in order more nearly to understand their nature.

THE ANDROMEDA SPIRAL

507. Angular Dimensions. Photographs of this spiral (Fig. 254) show an elliptical object with a length of about three degrees and a width of about one degree. On the assumption that it is a flat disk this would indicate that its plane makes an angle of about 20° with the line of sight. A photoelectric study of the general area by Stebbins and Whitford shows that the extent of the object is considerably greater than the photographs show and that the angular length of the major axis is about 7°.5. From the relation between angular diameter and distance this would make its actual diameter about one-eighth of its distance. If it were seen edgewise it might look something like Fig. 255.

508. Distance. In earlier years when the nature of the extragalactic objects was entirely unknown, some efforts were made to determine the distance of the more conspicuous ones by trigonometric methods as well as to determine their proper motion. The results obtained are now known to be entirely illusory and due to errors of measurement of the photographs. The only method which is really satisfactory for determining distances is the application of the period-luminosity law.

In 1924 Hubble announced the discovery of many variable stars, some of them cepheids, in five spirals, one of them being the great one in Andromeda. By 1929 the number of cepheids found in the Andromeda object had increased to 40. The periods of these cepheids ranged from about 17 to 50 days and their magnitudes from 18.3 to 19.4. Using the new values for the absolute magnitudes of the cepheids (broken line,

Fig. 226) places the spiral at a distance of 1,440,000 light-years.[1]   At the new distance the photographic image (angular diameter 3°) gives it a diameter of over 70,000 light-years, a value comparable to our own galaxy.

509. Novae in the Andromeda Spiral. In 1885 Gully discovered a nova in this object.   It rose to the seventh magnitude and then faded to below

FIG. 254. The Andromeda spiral and its two satellite galaxies.   (*Lick Observatory.*)

the seventeenth.   In 1917 to 1920 the observers at the Lick and Mt. Wilson Observatories startled the astronomical world by reporting 17 novae in the Andromeda spiral.   This number has since increased to over 100.   These later novae were very much fainter at maximum than the nova of 1885.   They ranged from magnitude 15.3 downward.   If they

[1] Since the new period-luminosity law has not yet been accurately determined, we shall use the values for distance, diameter, etc., for the extragalactic objects as twice those which have been accepted for some years.   The new values can be accepted only as provisional

were ordinary novae, then the nova of 1885 was a supernova.   The light curves show them to be of the ordinary nova type and spectrographic studies by Humason show their spectra, when they could be obtained, were typical nova spectra.   When the distance of the Andromeda spiral was established, the novae proved to be regular novae of the proper order of absolute magnitude.   The nova of 1885 must therefore have been a supernova.

510. Resolution into Stars. On photographs of the larger extragalactic objects taken early in this century there were found granulations in the

Fig. 255. Spiral galaxy seen edge on.   NGC 4565.   (*Mt. Wilson Observatory.*)

spiral arms which Roberts described as "star-like condensations" or "stars surrounded by nebulosity" and which Ritchey described as "great numbers of soft, star-like condensations." These granulations were studied with great care by Hubble on photographs taken with the 100-in. reflector.   He found that on the best photographs either the granulations were individual star images or the larger granulations broke down into star images.   This meant that at least the spiral arms were composed of myriads of stars.   When the distance to the Andromeda spiral had been determined, these stars were found to be comparable to the brightest stars in our galactic system.

The central parts of the Andromeda spiral cannot be resolved into individual stars by use of the ordinary photographic emulsions as the stars are too numerous to be detected individually. By the use of plates sensitized to the infrared, Baade has succeeded in photographing individual stars, but these are red giants of high luminosity.

511. Spectrum. Early attempts by Huggins in England and Scheiner in Germany showed that the bright nuclear portion of the spiral showed traces of absorption lines on a continuous background. In 1908–1909 Fath succeeded in getting spectra of sufficient intensity to show definite absorption lines which were identical in intensity and position with the absorption lines of the solar spectrum. The conclusion reached on the basis of these spectra was that at least the bright central portion of the great spiral was composed of stars predominately of solar type (Fig. 256).

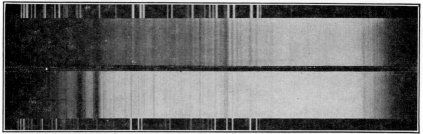

FIG. 256. The spectra of the Andromeda spiral (above) and of the sun (below). (*Lick Observatory.*)

Somewhat later Slipher succeeded in determining the radial velocity of the spiral to be about −300 km per sec (−200 miles per sec).

In recent years various knots or condensations in parts of the spiral have been found to give bright-line spectra analogous to those of the diffuse nebulae of our own system.

512. Rotation. In 1914 Slipher had demonstrated that the central part of the Andromeda spiral was in rotation. This had been accomplished by setting the slit of the spectrograph along the major axis of the telescopic image. The spectra thus obtained showed the spectral lines inclined at a small angle to the normal position. Later investigators confirmed this.

In 1950 Mayall published the radial velocities of 32 emission patches found in the great spiral. When the velocity of the nuclear portion (−267 km per sec) is subtracted from the measured velocities, and the differences in turn corrected for the tilt of the plane of the spiral to the line of sight, we have the radial velocity with respect to the center. Figure 257 shows the results obtained after some smoothing of the data. For distances out to nearly 10,000 parsecs from the center the curve departs but little from a straight line. This leads to the conclusion that the angular rotation is approximately uniform for the greater part of the

system.   The period of rotation of the main mass is approximately 150,-
000,000 years—a period of the same order as that of the sun's revolution
around the center of our own galaxy.

In 1937 and 1938 H. W. Babcock made a detailed study of the spectrum
of the spiral.   For the outer parts he obtained the same results as Mayall,
but within 400 parsecs of the center, where the absorption spectrum is
dominant, he found a rotational period of approximately 25,000,000 years.
This great difference in period requires further study.

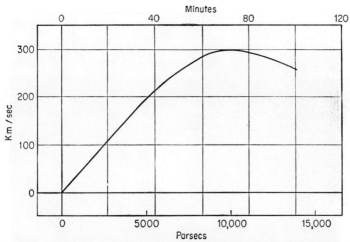

FIG. 257. Rotational velocities of Andromeda spiral.   (*Lick Observatory.*)

513. Mass. Wyse and Mayall made a study of the mass of the Andromeda spiral.   Their starting point was Babcock's rotational velocity
curve.   They found that upon making certain reasonable assumptions
as to the distribution of mass in the general plane of the spiral they were
able to obtain gravitational attractions which would produce the velocities
found in the velocity curve.   The total mass of the spiral was found to be
$1.9 \times 10^{11}\odot$, a quantity comparable to our own galaxy.

514. Star Clusters. In and near the borders of the Andromeda spiral
Hubble has identified 140 objects as globular clusters.   Their distribution
around the spiral is not spherical, as is the case in the galactic system, but
more nearly follows the luminosity of the spiral.   The maximum diameter
of the cluster system is somewhat greater than that of the great spiral
itself.

THE GREAT SPIRAL IN TRIANGULUM, NGC 598

515. Angular Dimensions. Photographs of this spiral (Fig. 258) show
the spiral arms to dominate the structure.   The nucleus is relatively

small. The major axis of this spiral is 62′ and the minor axis 34′ in length on the best photographs. If we assume the material to be within a thin disk-shaped space, then the plane of the spiral makes an angle of about 33° to the line of sight.

516. Distance. This spiral, like the Andromeda spiral, has many cepheid variables. A study of their periods and magnitudes and the application of the period-luminosity law gives a distance of 440,000 parsecs (1,440,-000 light-years). The linear diameter is therefore about 8000 parsecs

FIG. 258. Spiral galaxy, NGC 598. (*Mt. Wilson Observatory.*)

(26,000 light-years). This is about one-third the diameter of the Andromeda spiral if we take only the size of the latter as shown on the photographs.

517. Spectrum. The nucleus resembles a large globular star cluster. Its spectrum is of stellar type F5 and its radial velocity is −167 km per sec. A number of other condensations outside the nucleus give absorption spectra, but there are many more which give bright-line spectra. These emission spectra are similar to those given by the nebulae in the galactic system.

518. Novae. Six apparently normal novae have been recorded, a far smaller number than in the Andromeda spiral. This smaller number is consistent with the probably much smaller mass of the system (Sec. 521).

519. Resolution. The spiral arms, when photographed under the best conditions, show many individual stars. In addition there are what appear to be star clouds as well as globular clusters.

520. Rotation. Mayall and Aller made a determined attack on this problem at the Lick Observatory. They obtained many spectrograms, not only of the nuclear regions but also of condensations in the spiral arms. From these spectrograms, after allowing for the radial velocity of the system as a whole as well as for the inclination of the plane of the spiral to the line of sight, they obtained the rotational velocity curve shown in Fig. 259. This curve shows a gradual increase in rotational velocity

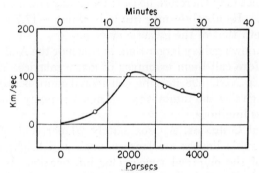

Fig. 259. Rotational velocities of NGC 598. (*Lick Observatory.*)

from zero at the nucleus to about 110 km per sec at a distance of 2000 parsecs from the nucleus. From this point outward to 4000 parsecs the rotational velocity gradually decreases to about 70 km per sec. The rising part of the curve does not depart greatly from a straight line which means that, as in the case of the Andromeda spiral, the angular velocity is approximately uniform. The rotation period of the central portion is about 100 million years.

521. Mass. The probable density distribution of mass and the total mass of NGC 598 have been studied by Wyse and Mayall. By assuming the density practically constant to about 1800 parsecs and then gradually diminishing, the theoretical velocity curve fell very close to the observed curve. The total mass involved is of the order of 3.4×10^9⊙.

522. General Nature. The nature of the extragalactic objects in general is revealed by the study of the two spirals. Since spirals represent the major portion (75 per cent) of all extragalactic objects which can be classified, they may be considered typical.

In the case of the Andromeda spiral we have a great stellar system of the same size as our own galactic system, about 100,000 light-years in diameter. Both are composed of myriads of stars; the total mass is of the same order; there are bright-line nebulae mixed with the stars; there are regions of absorption; there are variable stars, many of them cepheids; there are novae of the normal sort as well as supernovae; and there are many globular star clusters. Both are in rotation and the rotational velocities are comparable. The absolute magnitude of the Andromeda spiral is −19.0.

In the case of NGC 598 we have another stellar system, considerably smaller than our own but still having many points in common. It, too, is composed of great clouds of stars, has absorption areas, has bright-line nebulae, has cepheid and other variable stars, has some novae and some globular clusters. It is also in rotation with moderate rotational velocities. This object may therefore be called a galaxy similar to, but smaller than, our own. Its absolute magnitude is about −17.7 and its mass is about one-fiftieth that of the galactic system.

There is no known galaxy larger than our own or the Andromeda spiral. We may therefore call them examples of giant galaxies. From various lines of evidence NGC 598 may be considered more nearly typical of a galaxy of average size and luminosity. There are many known which are smaller and less luminous.

523. Elliptical Galaxies. Approximately 20 per cent of the galaxies whose photographic images are large enough and bright enough to be classified are of the elliptical type. Our information on these is very limited, for no large one is near which would permit detailed analysis as in the case of the two spirals considered. The two nearest elliptical galaxies are those shown on the borders of the Andromeda spiral (Fig. 254).

Their spectra are similar to that of the central parts of the great spiral and we therefore conclude they are made up of stars. Their total luminosity, however, is so much less, of the order of 1 per cent of the Andromeda spiral, that their masses must be relatively small. Their diameters are less than 4000 light-years. From the evidence available, we have here two examples of dwarf galaxies.

524. The Magellanic Clouds. Most of the work done on the Clouds has been done by Harvard observers, first in Peru and now in South Africa. The principal results of their work are as follows:

1. The Clouds contain many variable stars about 90 per cent of which are cepheids. By use of the period-luminosity law their distances are found to be approximately 170,000 light-years. The diameters are about 22,000 and 12,000 light-years.

2. They contain many gaseous nebulae. One of these, known as 30 Doradus, is over 200 times the size of the Orion Nebula (Fig. 238). Measurement of the radial velocities of a number of these nebulae at the Lick Observatory station at Santiago, Chile, gave the radial velocities of the Clouds with respect to the sun as −276 and −168 km per sec. When the sun's velocity with respect to the galactic center is eliminated, the

radial velocities of the Clouds with respect to the center are small. The actual space velocities with respect to the center are not yet known, but the low radial velocities indicate that the Clouds are probably under the gravitational control of our galaxy.

3. The Clouds contain few globular star clusters but many of the open galactic type such as our Pleiades cluster.

4. On account of the distance of the Clouds we can investigate only the stars which are brighter than the sun. If the sun were placed at the distance of the Clouds it would be too faint to be photographed.

One of the intrinsically brightest stars in the sky is found in the larger Cloud. The star, known as S Doradus, is over one million times as bright as the sun. Its absolute magnitude is about −10.5.

5. The longest diameters of the Clouds as usually photographed are 22,000 and 12,000 light-years respectively. Very long exposures show some faint extensions.

6. Very few novae have been noted in the Clouds. Their absolute magnitudes were about −6.5 and therefore of the ordinary nova type.

7. The larger Cloud has much interstellar dust while the smaller is practically free of it. The larger is made up of stars belonging to population I, while the smaller is predominantly population II.

8. Up to 1954 the Clouds have been considered good examples of irregular galaxies, but in that year Vaucoulers reported on extensive studies made at Canberra and Commonwealth Observatory in Australia which change the classification to barred spirals of a peculiar type in which one spiral arm is predominant. Furthermore he finds evidence of a possible stream of matter connecting the larger Cloud with our galaxy. More work is required before we shall be able properly to understand the structure of the Clouds and their relationship to the galaxy.

525. The Distribution of Extragalactic Objects. The extragalactic objects have been found almost entirely lacking in a broad belt encircling the sky and extending for some degrees on either side of the galactic equator. At first it was thought that their apparent preference for middle and high galactic latitudes represented merely their actual distribution, but in recent years so much evidence of the presence of obscuring matter near the plane of the galaxy has been found that it now seems certain that the reason these distant galaxies cannot be seen in low galactic latitudes is that we cannot see far enough to detect them in such directions.

From the evidence now available we conclude that the distant galaxies are fairly well distributed over the celestial sphere even though we cannot find them near the galactic plane.

In addition to the general distribution there are some regions of the sky where the distant galaxies occur in groups or clusters. Some of these clusters are found in Coma Berenices, Leo, Gemini, and Ursa Major.

Figure 260 shows such a cluster of galaxies in Coma. In addition to these well-marked clusters, Shane and Wirtanen, from a study of the Lick Observatory survey plates, report that their counts "show a strong tendency for clusters to occur in groups of two or more."

Zwicky of the Mt. Wilson and Palomar Observatories has made a special study of the cluster of galaxies in Coma Berenices. He finds the cluster

Fɪɢ. 260. A portion of the cluster of galaxies in Coma Berenices. Most of the small dots are galaxies and not stars. (*Mt. Wilson Observatory.*)

to be about 9,000,000 light-years in diameter and that there are at least 9000 galaxies brighter than the nineteenth photographic magnitude within its boundaries.

526. The Number of Galaxies. No systematic effort has ever been made to solve this problem. It would require many years of work on the part of an observer with a large telescope, and at present there are more pressing problems requiring attention. The figures that have been published from time to time are estimates based on a limited number of plates taken for other purposes, and such results are therefore merely by-products obtained in the course of other investigations. Estimates of this character have been made by a number of observers, but the only one now of value is that of Hubble, based on counts from over 1200 photographs at the Mt. Wilson Observatory.

Taking into consideration only those regions of the sky believed to be comparatively free from occulting or light-absorbing matter, Hubble finds an average of 750 distant galaxies per square degree can be photographed with the 100-in. reflector in 1 hr. Multiplying this number by the number of square degrees in the sky gives a total of about 30,000,000 galaxies.

Hubble also finds that with increased exposure times the number increases regularly according to the principle considered in Sec. 457. He estimates that if we could get rid of all loss of light in space, and the 100-in. reflector could be used for a program of long exposures over the entire sky, about 100,000,000 distant galaxies could be photographed.

Shapley has recently reported (1951) the results of a study of the problem. Assuming the space-penetrating power of the Hale 200-in. reflector as twice that of the 100-in. Hooker instrument, he estimates that there are 2,000,000,000 galaxies within 2,000,000,000 light-years of the sun and therefore within the reach of the Hale telescope.

527. The Local Cluster of Galaxies. The clustering effect among the galaxies is illustrated by those in the immediate neighborhood (within 2,000,000 light-years) of our own galaxy. The two nearest us are the two Magellanic Clouds at distances of about 170,000 light-years. Then come the great Andromeda spiral and NGC 598 at about 1,440,000 light-years. Two others may be seen in Fig. 254, one in the upper right and the other below the center and at the edge of the principal object. From the limited evidence available they are probably close to the Andromeda spiral and not merely seen in the same general direction. They probably bear about the same relation to the great spiral as the Magellanic Clouds do to our own galaxy.

Various types are illustrated in the local cluster. The two near the great Andromeda spiral are relatively small elliptical objects. The great spiral is of the type Sb, NGC 598 is nearly of the type Sc, while the Magellanic Clouds are examples of barred spirals. The classification of our own galaxy is still in doubt but, from the evidence available, it is more nearly Sc than Sb.

Nine other galaxies are considered members of our local cluster which thus numbers 16 if we include our own.

The absolute magnitudes of the members of the local cluster range from $M = -12.5$ to $M = -19$. The mean is $M = -15$ if we exclude our own galactic system. If we assume the brightness of the galactic system equal to that of the Andromeda spiral because of the approximate equality

of the two masses, then the mean value for the local cluster becomes
$M = -15.5$.

528. Dimensions of the Visible Universe. Accepting the theory that
the extragalactic objects are themselves galaxies of the same general order
of size and composition as those near us, it is pertinent to inquire what
conclusions may be reached concerning the depths to which space has
been sounded in our efforts to study the physical universe.

The mean absolute magnitude of the external galaxies for which values
have been determined is about -16.5. The limiting apparent magnitude
for these objects is about $+22.5$ for long exposures with the 200-in.
reflector. Assuming those at the limit of detection to have the same
absolute magnitude as those near enough to be measured, we have for the
value of $(m - M)$ approximately 39. This corresponds to a distance of
about 600,000,000 parsecs or 2,000,000,000 light-years. This is the *radius*
of the visible universe at present. It is sometimes referred to as the
space-penetrating power of the astronomer's most powerful instrument,
the 200-in. reflector of the Mt. Palomar Observatory.

EXERCISES

1. The great spiral galaxy in Andromeda has a photographic angular diameter of
$3°$. What is its linear diameter if its distance is 4.4×10^5 parsecs?
Ans. 23,000 parsecs.

2. If the mean absolute magnitude of distant galaxies were -16.5 and the apparent
magnitude of the faintest which can be photographed with the 200-in. reflector were
$+22.5$, what would be the space-penetrating power of this instrument if no loss of light
occurs in space? *Ans.* 630,000,000 parsecs.

3. If the great galaxy in Andromeda were removed to the limit of the space penetration of the 200-in. reflector, what would be its angular photographic diameter?
Ans. 8″.

CHAPTER 22

THE STRUCTURE OF THE VISIBLE UNIVERSE

529. Nature of the Problem. In considering the relationship between the various units which have been studied thus far, we are approaching one of the great, if not the greatest of astronomical problems. We shall have to attempt to determine the relative importance of stars, star clusters, nebulae, and galaxies, as well as their relations and positions with respect to one another. A complete solution of the problem is not possible. In some instances there is a marked difference of opinion concerning the interpretation of data, but certain general ideas concerning the problem as a whole are gradually emerging and it is these we shall attempt to portray briefly.

530. The Galactic System. In Chap. 17 we learned that by averaging the results of star counts there is evidence that the stars of the Milky Way are more or less confined in a space shaped somewhat like a thin lens. The diameter of this space is of the order of 100,000 light-years and its thickness through the center about one-tenth that amount.

In addition to the stars in general there are those forming the galactic clusters and those in the system of globular clusters.

Intermingled with the stars in the lens-shaped space are the dark obscuring nebulae as well as the luminous nebulae giving bright lines in their spectra.

The diagram, Fig. 250, is an attempt to show the spatial relationship of these units. The figure represents a section through the galactic center perpendicular to the galactic plane and cutting the system through galactic longitude 327°.

531. Structure within the Galactic System. In Fig. 250 no indication of possible details of structure within the lens-shaped space is indicated. Half a century ago Easton advocated a theory that the Milky Way system of stars is a great spiral structure, in some ways resembling a spiral galaxy like NGC 598. On this theory the star clouds of the Milky Way correspond to the coarser details of the spiral, and the division from Cygnus to Scorpio is caused by obscuring matter.

The theory has many points in its favor. It allows for the clustering of the stars, the general appearance of the Milky Way, the main boundaries as indicated by the results of star counts, star drifts due to interpenetration of the members of adjacent clusters, etc.

The problem of the structure of our galaxy is not yet entirely solved but the more recent studies of Seares, Bok, and others strongly favor Easton's theory.

532. Relation of Our Galactic System to Other Galaxies. From the evidence presented in Sec. 525 it seems possible to get some idea of the distribution of the galaxies in space within range of modern instruments. Outward from our galaxy in all directions are found the other galaxies, each separated from its nearest neighbors by a distance averaging approximately 4,000,000 light-years. In a few regions, one of which is our own, there are clusters of galaxies where they are more closely packed.

How far outward this arrangement holds is not known, but there is no evidence of a change in distances up to 2 billion light-years in any direction where our view is not cut off by obscuring matter.

533. The Red Shift. In Sec. 505 we find the statement that of all the radial velocities of other galaxies known only 17 are negative, and these belong to galaxies close to our own. All others, to the number of about 800, are positive. A comparison of the radial velocities with the distances of these galaxies by Hubble and Humason brought out the remarkable fact that the farther away one of these galaxies is from us, the faster it is moving away.

The evidence is illustrated by Fig. 261. These spectra have red to the right. The principal lines of the spectrum which can be measured are the K and H lines of calcium. Their positions are indicated by the arrows. It is evident that the farther away the galaxy, the farther this pair of lines is shifted toward the red end of the spectrum. The phenomenon has therefore been called the *red shift*. The greatest value of the red shift thus far known corresponds to a velocity of 61,000 km per sec belonging to one of a group of external galaxies in the constellation Hydra.

The change in radial velocity with distance amounts to 280 km per sec per 1,000,000 parsecs on the new distance scale, according to Hubble and Humason. This means that the average velocity of the external galaxies is 280 km per sec if at a distance of 1,000,000 parsecs, 1400 km per sec if at a distance of 5,000,000 parsecs, 2800 km per sec if at a distance of 10,000,000 parsecs, etc.

At first the red shift was not interpreted as representing actual motion. Various theories were proposed to explain the shift without assuming such high velocities, but up to the present time no other explanation appears to have any known physical basis even though there are grave objections to it. We are therefore almost compelled to use it as a tentative working hypothesis until something better can be found.

The galaxy for which a velocity of 61,000 km per sec has been obtained is at a distance of 220,000,000 parsecs. This places it at approximately one-third the distance of the space penetration of the 200-in. Hale reflector. If by some means (possibly the electron telescope) it would be possi-

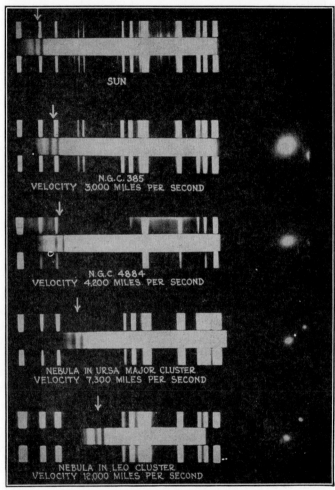

FIG. 261. The red shift of the K and H lines of calcium in the spectra of distant galaxies. The distances of the galaxies range from 46,000,000 to 210,000,000 light-years. The increase of shift with increasing distance is evident. (*Mt. Wilson and Palomar Observatories.*)

ble to obtain the velocity of a galaxy at that limit, the velocity would be about 180,000 km per sec, or considerably over half the velocity of light, provided the speed-distance relationship still holds.

When we deal with such extreme values, it is necessary to use extreme caution. According to the Einstein theory, the velocity of light is the maximum possible velocity of a material object, but, in order to attain this velocity, an infinite force is necessary. Since an infinite force does not seem to be possible, we cannot expect the velocity of a heavenly body to attain the velocity of light. Somewhere short of this limit the velocities of galaxies must no longer increase. It is hoped that the space-penetrating power of the 200-in. telescope may help to clarify this most perplexing problem.

534. The Expanding Universe. The acceptance of the red shift as representing motion leads to some remarkable conclusions concerning the universe. The red shift shows that the external galaxies are moving away from our own galaxy with a velocity which is proportional to their distance from us.

We know of no reason why our galaxy should be shunned in this manner since it does not seem probable that we occupy any unique position in the universe. The alternative explanation is that the universe is expanding in all directions so that the distance between all galaxies is increasing at the same rate. This will produce the result of increase of velocity with distance for each galaxy with respect to all others.

To make this clear consider a chessboard with a piece on each square. Assume the squares to be 2 in. on a side to begin with. Then assume the board to expand until it has doubled its dimensions but leaving the pieces of the same size. This expansion has doubled the distance between any two pieces.

Next consider the velocities between the pieces. During the time involved in the expansion the distance from any one piece to the piece on the adjacent square has increased by 2 in., to a piece on the second square beyond by 4 in., to a piece on the third square beyond by 6 in., etc. Thus the velocity of any piece with respect to any other was proportional to the distance.

In place of the chessboard and pieces consider the universe with its millions of galaxies. If the universe is expanding uniformly in all directions, then the galaxies are separating, and the velocity with which any galaxy is moving away from any other galaxy is proportional to the distance between them.

535. Summary. Essentially all the stars within reach of our present telescopes, the planetary and diffuse nebulae and the globular clusters are organized into a system which we call our galactic system. The diameter of our system is about 100,000 light-years. Outside this system there are similar galaxies at intervals of about 4,000,000 light-years extending outward to the present limits of telescopic penetration, about 2,000,000,-000 light-years.

This universe is expanding in all directions. The rate of expansion is such that two points 1,000,000 parsecs apart will separate with a velocity of 280 km per sec.

CHAPTER 23

COSMOGONY—A STUDY OF ORIGINS

The human mind is limited in perception and experience and it is conceivable that in spite of our best efforts we shall never fathom the history of the universe. Nevertheless, our experience has shown that progress is not impossible and it is this which inspires the scientific worker to gather facts, to study them in the hope of finding the underlying law, and to formulate hypotheses which are to be tested by experiment and observation.

536. The Field of Inquiry. The workers in the physical sciences attempt to study the physical universe. They recognize that they work in a limited field and that physical truth is not the whole of truth. They leave to philosophy and religion the search for the absolute and the explanation of the purpose of all things.

In any scientific consideration of the origin and development of a celestial body or structure one fundamental hypothesis underlies all thinking, namely, *the universe is an orderly universe.* This implies that the laws now governing the universe were in operation in the past and are universal in their application. Some of these laws are the law of gravitation, the law of areas, etc.

The various theories which we shall consider are not to be thought of as dogmatic statements of ultimate truth, but as suggestions put forward to guide mankind in the search for truth. Their authors were or are men who would willingly abandon their theories as soon as their untenability could be shown and who earnestly search for errors in their own theories.

The theories which we shall consider are those relating to the origin and development of galaxies, stars, and the solar system. In no case is there an attempt to account for the origin of matter and energy or the laws governing them. These problems for the present lie beyond the realm of science.

537. The Beginning. It appears reasonable to assume that in the early stages of its history the physical universe consisted of finely divided matter quite uniformly dispersed through space. Whether the matter was organized into atoms and molecules or was composed only of subatomic structures is more or less immaterial.

At a certain time this chaos became "unstable" and broke up into units having masses comparable with the present galaxies. Lemaître holds that this breaking up was of the nature of an explosion, while others believe it was a more orderly process.

Whether the expansion of the universe began at the time of the initial disruption or at a later period is unknown, but it seems reasonable to assume that the dispersive force became operative at an early stage. It may even have been the cause of the disruption.

If we assume that the red shift represents motion and that the speed-distance values have been constant in the past, a result of great interest follows. The radial velocity of a galaxy at a distance of 1,000,000 parsecs is 280 km per sec with reference to our own galaxy. Changing this distance to the proper units and dividing by the velocity, we find that the distant galaxy and ours were in contact 3.5×10^9 years ago. Since this calculation applies to any two galaxies, we may say that the matter in all of them was intermingled that long ago. The time since this "chaos" is the time since the universe gradually acquired its present state of organization, or, we might say, *the age of the visible universe is of the order of* 3.5×10^9 *years.*

The various units after disruption probably differed in size and mass within certain limits, just as their later stages show. Let us follow the history of one of these units.

THE ORIGIN OF SPIRAL GALAXIES

538. Jeans's Theory. Assuming the existence of a gaseous mass, some billions of times the mass of the sun, which is in slow rotation and contracting under its own gravitation, the theory attempts to follow its subsequent history.

At first the form will be that of an oblate spheroid with the shortest axis as the rotation axis. At a certain critical rotation period the equatorial bulge becomes a sharp edge, so that the mass as a whole has the shape of a double-convex lens. At the edge centrifugal force and gravitational force just balance. Owing to the tidal action of other masses in the universe, the matter at the edge will not be left as a ring, but at two opposite points filaments of gas will be given off, the beginning of two arms of the spiral. Continued shrinkage and increased rotational velocity of the nucleus will continue this process of providing the material for the two arms until but little is left in the nucleus. In the meantime, however, the material in the arms is not in equilibrium and these will break up into units of greater or less size, the mean mass of a unit being that of an average star, about 10^{34} g (10^{28} tons).

The next step will be to follow one of the condensations in its further development.

539. The Formation of Stars. In the darker portions of the absorbing clouds of the Milky Way there are found some especially dark spherical globules (Fig. 262) whose mass has been estimated by Bok to average about 2.5 times the mass of the sun. These may be considered typical of the smaller units mentioned in the preceding section. When such a globule begins to contract under its own gravitation, it becomes denser and the central pressure gradually rises. This pressure in turn raises the temperature of the mass until it becomes hot enough to begin radiating

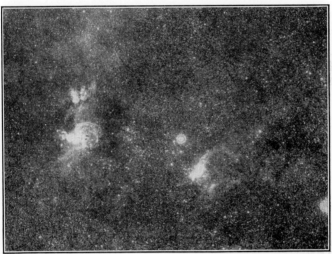

Fig. 262. A portion of southern Milky Way near η Carinae. Note the many small dark regions. (*Harvard Observatory Station, Bloemfontein, South Africa.*)

energy and a luminous star is formed. In the meantime, if the globule has any relative motion with respect to the surrounding cloud, it will collect additional dust and gas and thus increase its mass.

When the contraction has progressed to the point where the globule becomes a luminous star, it takes its place in the H-R diagram. If the mass is small, it becomes a dwarf star in the lower right of the diagram; if the mass happens to be large, it finds a place in the upper part; and, with a mass about that of the sun, it falls near the middle.

It was formerly believed that all stars would first be found in the upper part of the diagram, and, as their mass changed to radiant energy, they would move downward along the main sequence, becoming less massive and less luminous. After the carbon cycle was accepted as the best explanation of the source of stellar radiation, it became evident that the loss of mass was almost negligible and therefore there would be little change in position along the main sequence. The current opinion is that the H-R diagram, in particular the main sequence which contains over 95 per cent of all stars, represents the different kinds of stars which are formed from the interstellar dust and gas—the position in the diagram being determined by the mass of the contracting unit.

540. The White Dwarfs. The existence of the white dwarfs is a problem which does not offer a simple solution. Several hundred are now known. They are abnormal stars. Their abnormality can be best illustrated by an example.

Sirius B, the faint companion of the bright star Sirius A (Sec. 432), was the first of the class to be recognized. From the orbit elements and known distance of the pair it is found that the fainter star has a mass 0.8 that of the sun. Its spectral type as determined by Adams is about A5. This means that, area for area, it is about three times as bright as the sun. Its total light, however, is only about $\frac{1}{400}$ that of the sun and therefore its area can be only about $\frac{1}{1200}$ of the sun's. From this it can be readily calculated that its diameter is about 40,000 km (25,000 miles) and its mean density nearly 50,000 times that of water. A cubic inch of this matter at mean density weighs nearly a ton. The surface gravity is about 1000 times that of the sun or 28,000 times that of the earth.

Other stars of this group are of the same general size and density, some of them even much smaller and with densities as high as about 10^8 times that of water. From theoretical considerations Chandrasekhar finds that white dwarfs are possible only if the mass is not greater than 1.4 times that of the sun.

Since these stars are all very faint, only the very nearest can be detected. If other parts of the galaxy are like our immediate vicinity, Struve estimates there is about one white-dwarf star for every 50 stars in the main sequence. Therefore, as a class, they must be fitted into the H-R diagram. Since their total supply of energy seems almost exhausted, they appear to be end products. When it was held that a star migrated from top to bottom of the main sequence, it was very easy to say that in some way the red dwarfs of the main sequence deteriorated into white dwarfs. Since this view seems no longer tenable, we have to search farther afield. Hoyle suggests that the massive red giants, after going through some intermediate stages, finally become unstable and blow up in a catastrophic flare as a supernova, and then what matter is left assumes the white-dwarf status. This interesting suggestion offers one way out of the difficulty, but there does not appear to be a sufficient supply of red-giant stars to produce the many white dwarfs which probably exist.

541. The Einstein Theory and Sirius B. The comparatively large mass and small radius of Sirius B will result in producing an extraordinarily high value for the surface gravity, many thousands of times that on the earth. The Einstein theory predicted that when a beam of light passes through an intense gravitational field, the vibration frequency will be reduced and therefore the wavelength of a spectral line increased. This will be shown by a shift of the line toward the red end of the spectrum.

Eddington had computed that this shift for lines in the spectrum of Sirius B should correspond to an apparent change in radial velocity of about 20 km per sec. Such a shift was detected by Adams of the Mt. Wilson Observatory in 1924 and was later confirmed by Moore of the Lick Observatory. We accordingly have a confirmation of the high density as well as of the Einstein theory.

542. The Age of the Stars. It cannot be assumed that all stars are of the same age, but there is a reasonable probability that most of the stars were formed at a time when the matter now in the galaxies became sufficiently dense to allow further breakup into masses of stellar magnitude. This may not have been simultaneous in all galaxies nor even simultaneous in any one galaxy. However, the bulk of the stars were probably formed at about the same time when considered on a cosmic time scale. The only stars which we can study with a view to learning their probable age are those in our own galaxy. If we can get some bits of evidence here and draw any conclusions, we may be able to apply these to other galaxies.

The first step will be to consider the sun. If the sun had originally been composed of hydrogen only, we find that it could radiate energy at its present rate not longer than 10^{11} years. Since it could not have been composed only of hydrogen, its age must be less than 10^{11} years. If we consider the amount of helium present as largely produced by the conversion of hydrogen to helium by the carbon cycle, it is found that the sun's present age is of the order of 3×10^9 years. Since there are many stars like the sun, we may assume they are of about the same age.

When we consider the B- and A-type stars, however, we find they are radiating at a far greater rate than the sun, and, after allowing for their greater mass, they are from $\frac{1}{100}$ to $\frac{1}{10}$ the age of the sun. The O-type stars are even younger, possibly not over $\frac{1}{1000}$ the sun's age. It is therefore not impossible that stars are still being formed and that the dark globules in the dust clouds of the Milky Way are the beginnings of stars still to be formed.

The great spiral galaxy in Andromeda shows stars, emission nebulae, and dark clouds resembling our own galaxy. Its age then is probably of the same order. Other galaxies which can be examined in any detail are not very different. We may therefore assume, as a working hypothesis, that the galaxies and therefore the visible universe are of the order of 3×10^9 years old.

THE ORIGIN OF THE SOLAR SYSTEM

From time to time efforts have been made to analyze the present conditions in the solar system in order to read its past history. About the middle of the eighteenth century Wright of England, Kant of Germany, and Buffon of France made such attempts and, in one way or another, contributed ideas toward the solution of the problem. The more recent theories advanced may be divided into two groups which may be called the *single-star* and the *multiple-star* theories, depending on whether it is assumed that the planets, etc., developed from the same mass as the sun or whether it is assumed that the presence of one or more other stars was necessary. They will be discussed chronologically.

543. Laplace's Nebular Hypothesis. This theory was published in 1796 by the great French astronomer and mathematician Laplace. It belongs to the one-star group. He assumed that in the distant past all the matter in the sun and planets was in the form of a hot, rotating mass of gas extending out beyond the outermost planet. As this mass gradually contracted under its own gravitation, it rotated more and more rapidly until at its equator gravity and centrifugal force were exactly balanced. As the general mass continued to contract, the material at the equator would be left behind in the form of a flat ring analogous to the ring of Saturn. With continued contraction another ring would be formed in a manner similar to the first until finally the central mass became our sun and rings had been formed which were spaced approximately as the planets are now.

For a time after its formation a ring would continue to revolve about the central mass and then gradually condense into a single body, a planet. The planet, in turn, would continue to shrink and, because of rotation, leave behind one or more rings which, in turn, would become its satellites.

This theory for many years was generally accepted as giving a reasonable explanation of the mechanical development of our solar system and, with certain modifications, is still accepted by some scientists.

One of the difficulties of the theory is the intermittent action in ring development. It is difficult to see why, when once the process began, it should not be continuous, matter at the equator being continuously left behind as the central mass contracted.

Another difficulty is the assumption that a hot gaseous ring would not disintegrate. It would seem more than likely that the individual molecules, no longer under gravitative control, would, because of their molecular motion, fly off into space and be lost altogether.

Other objections have also been brought forward against the theory and most scientists have abandoned it entirely on the ground that it is inadequate both in its original form and also in the modified forms that have been proposed from time to time.

544. The Planetesimal Hypothesis. This was the first of the multiple-star hypotheses. It was the joint work of Chamberlin and Moulton of the University of Chicago. According to this theory, our sun, at one time in the distant past, was an ordinary star without attendant planets and in a condition much as it is today. In its movements through space it approached another star sufficiently close so that the latter raised huge tides within the body of our sun. These tides, combined with the great disruptive forces within the sun, as evidenced by the eruptive prominences still occurring, caused enormous prominences to be projected from it, not only in the direction of the second star but also on the opposite side. As the two stars swung round their common center of gravity, the eruptions continued for a time, but at any instant the line of eruption was in the line joining the two stars, on the one side toward the second star and on the other side away from it. The final result of the encounter for our sun was that, while on the whole it remained much as it was before, yet it was now attended by the matter thrown out in the prominences, the whole looking like a spiral. The prominence material would cool rapidly.

It is not at all likely that the prominences would be homogeneous throughout, and consequently there would be centers where the material would be more dense than elsewhere. These portions would not only contract under their own gravitation but would also draw in the less organized material in their vicinity. In the meantime, since the material nearer the sun would be revolving around it more rapidly than that farther away, the spiral arms would wind about the sun more and more so that they would become quite intimately mingled.

Thus, in time, the larger nuclei, by their attraction, would gradually clear up most of the matter in the vicinity of their orbits. If a smaller nucleus were to approach close enough to a larger, it would either be drawn in or become a satellite. The larger nuclei developed into the planets and the smaller (called planetesimals) aided in their growth.

545. Other Multiple-star Theories. Jeans, in his "Problems of Cosmogony and Stellar Dynamics," holds that our sun must have been expanded to the diameter of Neptune's orbit, and hence of very low mean density, at the time of the encounter with the second star, and that only one long prominence was shot out on each side, the two prominences later breaking up into various parts. He also suggests that a large proportion of the satellites may have been formed by tidal disruption of the primaries while their orbits were highly eccentric.

Jeffreys advocates the view that there was an actual collision between the two suns, the visitor plowing into our sun to a depth of possibly one-fourth its diameter. As a result of the collision, enough matter was stripped off along the surface of contact to form the planets, satellites, comets, etc.

Barrell follows Chamberlin and Moulton in the main but holds that the geologic evidence requires a fairly rapid fall of planetesimals of a size up to several hundred miles in diameter which, by their impacts, heated the earth until it became a molten mass. Schuchert agrees with Barrell that the geologic evidence favors a molten earth.

The insurmountable objection to all the theories considered is the inability of any of them to supply the necessary moment of momentum to the planets in their movement about the sun. To overcome this difficulty Lyttleton has suggested a three-star theory. He assumes that in the past the sun had a small companion star revolving about it. In the course of time a wandering star came by. The approach was sufficiently close to disrupt the companion star. The fragments which were not drawn away developed into the planets. This theory also has some objections and has not found many adherents.

546. More Recent Theories. Within the last few years the multiple-star theories have gradually been dropped, and astronomical thought is

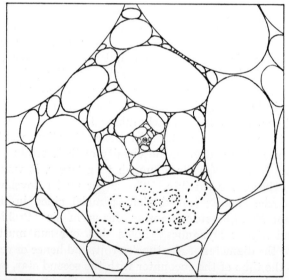

Fig. 263. Schematic representation of Kuiper's theory at the stage where the eddies of dust and gas are most fully developed. (*Yerkes Observatory.*)

returning to a one-star theory. The first to do this was von Weizsäcker in 1944. He was followed by Whipple in 1946, by ter Haar in 1948, and by Kuiper in 1951. We shall give a brief summary of this latest theory.

Kuiper assumes that a globule of interstellar matter condensed to form the sun. While the sun was contracting toward its present size, it had continued drawing in surrounding dust and gas clouds by its gravitational power. This nebulous material, possibly amounting to one-tenth the solar mass, became flattened into a disk and then broke up into eddies of various sizes, in general small near the sun and larger at increasing distances. Figure 263 illustrates this stage. These eddies revolving around the sun in accordance with Kepler's third law would interfere with each other; particularly in regions of contact and interpenetration, some would be destroyed and others increase in mass. This process would continue until a few of the eddies became dominant and finally contracted into the planets. Satellites, in turn, might be formed from some of the smaller eddies. During the process much of the matter in the original nebulous mass would be lost and finally only a small fraction would be found in the planets and satellites.

Urey (1952), attacking the problem of the formation of the planets, accepts the preliminary steps in the development of the planetary system as suggested by Kuiper but attempts to carry the theory still farther by applying ideas based on chemistry. He suggests that the four inner planets, formed from essentially the same materials, developed considerable heat as they formed by coalescence of planetesimals. Then the lighter gases, such as hydrogen and helium, rose to the surface, and, at the temperature existing, the molecular velocities approached the velocity of escape. As a result these gases gradually broke away from their planets and were driven outward by the radiation pressure of the sun. This left the heavier elements and accounts for the higher mean densities of the terrestrial planets.

The major planets, on the other hand, forming at much greater distances from the sun, retained their lighter elements and consequently have much lower mean densities.

547. Conclusion. It is evident, from the material in this chapter, that there is at present no generally accepted theory as to the origin of the solar system. Laplace's theory now has very few adherents. The problem is a very complicated one and its solution depends upon our ability to read the past out of conditions now existing. We believe the problem not insolvable, but it may take many years before mankind acquires the knowledge and the skill necessary for its solution.

The larger questions involving the structure and history of the universe are still farther from solution. It may be that the theories now emerging as working hypotheses are evidences of our ignorance rather than of our knowledge. We do not know whether the universe is a mechanism which is using a limited store of available energy and which will eventually run down, or whether the dissipated energy of the stars is collecting somewhere in space and is to be used again.

The idea of an eternal material universe, forever changing but never reaching stagnation, is a philosophical concept which has a strong appeal to many minds, but the desire for such a condition is not a proof of its reality. The possibility of a cyclical process involving the entire universe of matter and energy must be granted, but we have not, as yet, any definite evidence upon which to base an opinion.

"The subject is new, and we must attend to observations, *and be guided by them*, before we form general opinions" (Sir William Herschel).

APPENDIX

ELEMENTS IDENTIFIED IN THE SUN
(According to Mrs. Charlotte Moore Sitterly, U.S. Bureau of Standards)

Atomic number	Element	Atomic number	Element	Atomic number	Element
1	Hydrogen	26	Iron	58	Cerium
2	Helium	27	Cobalt	59	Praseodymium
3	Lithium	28	Nickel	60	Neodymium
4	Beryllium	29	Copper	62	Samarium
5	Boron	30	Zinc	63	Europium
6	Carbon	31	Gallium	64	Gadolinium
7	Nitrogen	32	Germanium	65	Terbium
8	Oxygen	37	Rubidium	66	Dysprosium
9	Fluorine	38	Strontium	68	Erbium
11	Sodium	39	Yttrium	69	Thulium
12	Magnesium	40	Zirconium	70	Ytterbium
13	Aluminum	41	Columbium	71	Lutecium
14	Silicon	42	Molybdenum	72	Hafnium
15	Phosphorus	44	Ruthenium	73	Tantalum
16	Sulfur	45	Rhodium	74	Tungsten
18	Argon	46	Palladium	76	Osmium
19	Potassium	47	Silver	77	Iridium
20	Calcium	48	Cadmium	78	Platinum
21	Scandium	49	Indium	79	Gold
22	Titanium	50	Tin	82	Lead
23	Vanadium	51	Antimony	90	Thorium
24	Chromium	56	Barium		
25	Manganese	57	Lanthanum		

GREEK ALPHABET
In designating the stars of the constellations the letters of the Greek alphabet are used and are given here for convenience of reference.

α Alpha	ι Iota	ρ Rho
β Beta	κ Kappa	σ Sigma
γ Gamma	λ Lambda	τ Tau
δ Delta	μ Mu	υ Up'-silon
ϵ Eps'-ilon	ν Nu	ϕ Phi
ζ Zeta	ξ Xi	χ Chi
η Eta	o Om'-icron	ψ Psi
θ Theta	π Pi	ω Ome'-ga

PLANETARY DATA, JAN. 0, 1955. ELEMENTS OF ORBITS

Planet	Mean distance	Sidereal period, years	Synodic period, years	Eccentricity	Inclination	Longitude of node	Longitude of perihelion	Mean longitude
Mercury	0.387	0.241	0.317	0.206	7°.0	47°.8	76°.8	305°.8
Venus	0.723	0.615	1.599	0.007	3 .4	76 .3	130 .9	127 .1
Earth	1.000	1.000	.....	0.017	.....	.....	102 .2	99 .4
Mars	1.524	1.881	2.135	0.093	1 .8	49 .2	335 .2	21 .3
Jupiter	5.203	11.862	1.092	0.048	1 .3	100 .0	13 .6	108 .0
Saturn	9.539	29.458	1.035	0.056	2 .5	113 .3	92 .2	219 .5
Uranus	19.182	84.013	1.012	0.047	0 .8	73 .8	169 .9	119 .8
Neptune	30.058	164.794	1.006	0.009	1 .8	131 .3	44 .2	205 .9
Pluto	39.518	248.430	1.004	0.249	17 .1	109 .6	223 .2	137 .6

ASTRONOMICAL CONSTANTS

Solar parallax.. 8″.79
Constant of nutation... 9.21
Constant of aberration.. 20.47
General precession............................... 50″.26 + 0″.000222(t − 1900)
Obliquity of ecliptic............................. 23°27′8″.3 − 0.468(t − 1900)
Equatorial horizontal parallax of moon............................ 57′2″.7
Mean distance earth to moon...................... 384,400 km = 238,860 miles
Mean distance earth to sun................. 149,674,000 km = 93,003,000 miles
Velocity of light......................... 299,774 km = 186,270 miles per sec
Length of tropical year... 365^d.242
Length of sidereal year... 365^d.256
Length of anomalistic year.. 365^d.260
Length of sidereal month.. 27^d.322
Length of synodic month... 29^d.531
Length of sidereal day..................... 23^{h}56^{m}4^s.09 of mean solar time
Length of mean solar day.................... 24^{h}3^{m}56^s.56 of sidereal time
Dimensions of earth:
  Equatorial radius............................. 6378.39 km = 3963.34 miles
  Polar radius.................................. 6356.91 km = 3949.99 miles

CONVERSION FACTORS

1 mile = 1.609 km
1 cm = 0.3937 in.
1 angstrom = 1 × 10^{-8} cm

NAME INDEX

SUBJECT INDEX

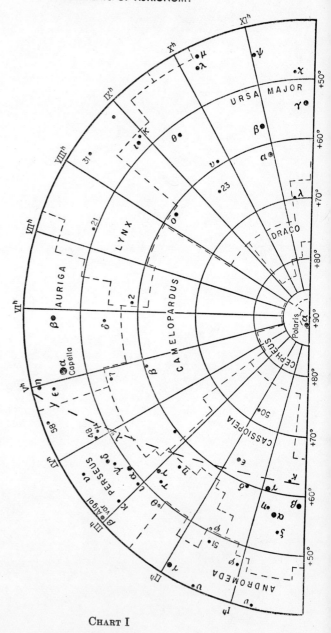

CHART I

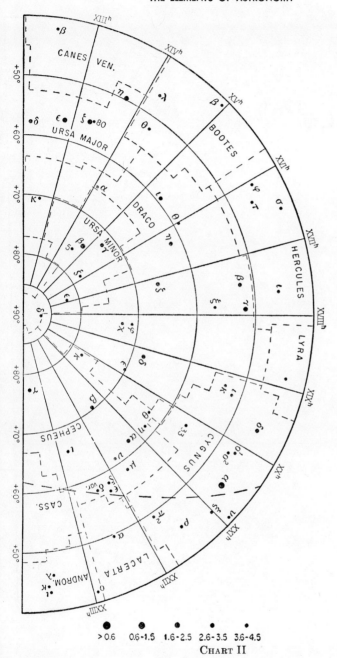

CHART II

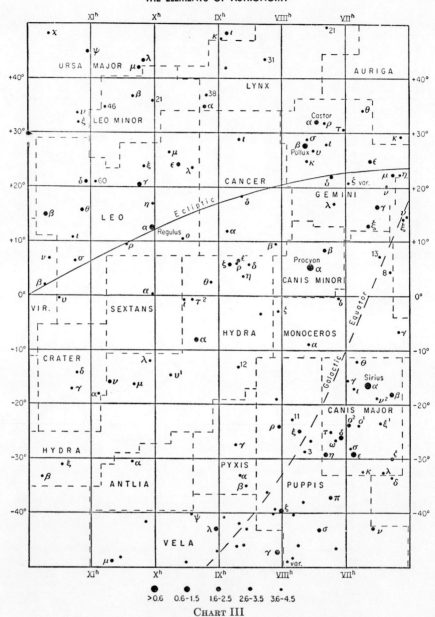

CHART III

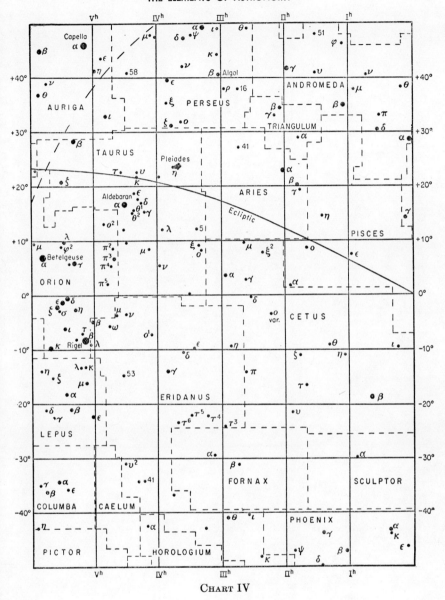

CHART IV

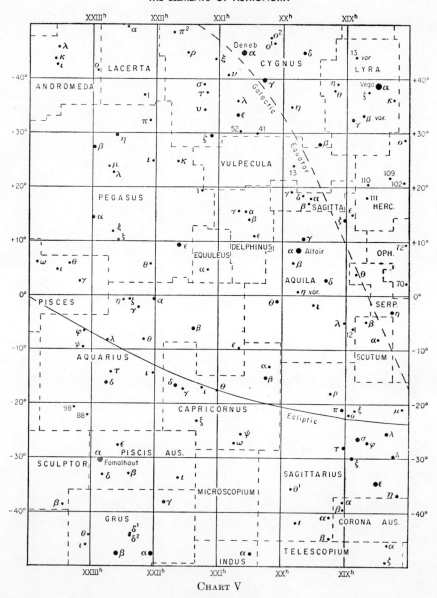

CHART V

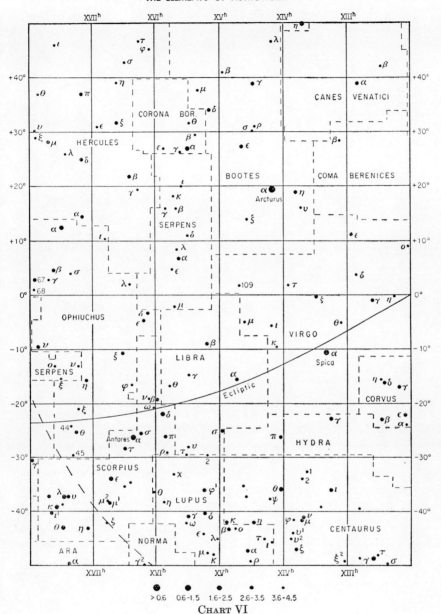

CHART VI

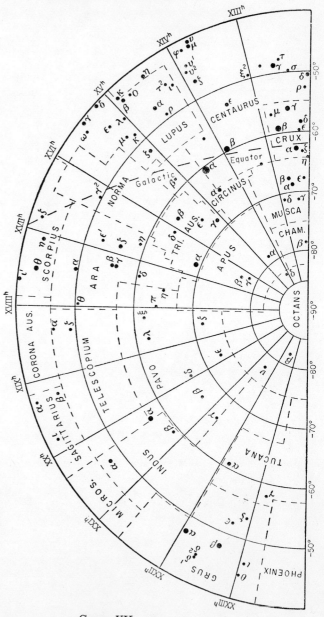

CHART VII

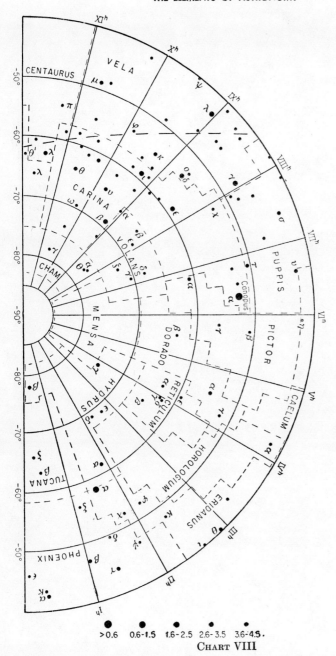

CHART VIII